MW00779270

KINSHIP

KINSHIP

A Story of the Kinneys,

An English/American Family

By

Roger L. Kinney

COPYRIGHT 2009 By Roger L. Kinney
ISBN NUMBER 978-0-615-21250-0

Library of Congress Cataloging-in-Publication Data
Kinney, Roger L.
Kinship A Story of the Kinneys, An English/American Family
Library of Congress Control Number: 2008911194

EDITORIAL ADVISOR, Trina Lambert
DESIGNER, Neal Erickson

Cover Picture
A 16th Century Scene from East Anglia, England
Courtesy of the Kinney Family Collection

Feature Picture
INDEPENDENCE *Wayne City Landing*,
"Start of the Santa Fe Trail" in 1842
By John Stobart
Image©1977 Courtesy of Maritime Heritage Prints
100 Cummings Center, Suite 335J
Beverly, Massachusetts 01915
800-989-3513
www.stobart.com

Limited First Edition, 2009

1 4 6 8 8 4 4
Printed in the United States of America

Contents

Annabelle Fagan Kinney, circa 1902

❧ DEDICATION ❧

This book is dedicated with love, profound respect, and deep appreciation to the wives, mothers, and guardians of the Kinney families throughout the ages:

Birth Dates (circa)

Anna de Kene	1418	Sarah de Kene	1437
Ruth Kynne	1470	Marcia Kynne	1496
Margaret Anne Kynne	1527	Sally Adams Kynne	1547
Martha Eaton Keney	1572	Sarah Cheever Keney	1602
Ann Howard Putnam Keney	1628	Magdaleane Wiggins Keney	1655
Elizabeth Knight Keney	1658	Martha Cox Keney	1685
Mary Starkweather Keney	1710	Martha Gallup Kinne	1756
Lucy Park Kinne	1757	Edith Curtis Kinne	1760
Clarissa Wilson Kinne	1804	Louisa Wells Kinne	1805
Deborah Clark Kinne	1812	Sarah Durfee Kinney	1835
Emeline Kelley Kinney	1858	Ethel Stevens Kinney	1879
Annabelle Fagan Kinney	1884	Mary Louise Springsteen Kinney	1910
Jill Carroll Kinney	1936	Suzanne Olive Peabody Kinney	1938
Barbara Louise Kinney Kall	1939	Nancy Kristin Kinney Holst	1964
Linda Louise Kinney Hantman	1967	Amy Poline Kinney	1968

The Kinne Coat of Arms

Coat of Arms

The Coat of Arms was granted and confirmed to Sir Thomas Kinne and his descendants on October 4, 1618, with the following description:

The crest consists of a cubit arm, erect, vested in red, and cuffed in silver, holding in the hand roll of parchment paper; the whole rising out of an Earl's Coronet. It is believed that this portion of the Coat of Arms was added at a later date, likely to acknowledge the historical records and archival services of the family. The Coronet consists of eight pearls set on as leaves. The mantling behind and around the helmet – of the type assigned to Esquires and Gentlemen – of steel represented in profile with the visor closed – is made to curl to assume fantastic shapes indicating that it has become thus mutilated from service in the field. This being the mantling of a Knight or an Esquire, it is crimson.

The field is charged with three towers or turrets, emblems of solidity, meaning that the original bearer at one time captured or held against attack three towers, turrets, or castles.

The supports are plants, a clan symbol with griffin entwined. The griffin has the head, shoulders, wings, and forefeet of an eagle, the body and hind legs of a lion. These rampant, the ferocious griffin could mean that the first bearer was a fine warrior.

Primary Source: Basil Kinney, circa 1883.

The Family Name

The spelling of the family name has been changed many times over the years. The name appears in various records and documents with over one hundred different spellings. The name is believed to have two distinct origins, Celtic and Norman. Historically, the spelling has changed to adjust the meaning and meet the orthographic needs of the times. Consequently there are many differences in the spelling of the name by various present day families who are descendants of Henry Keney of Salem, Massachusetts.

The Kenny name in Ireland, a Celtic derivation, is believed to have originated from an Irish monk by the name of O'Coinnigh, who is also credited with the town name of Kilkenny.

In the middle ages, surnames, or family names were often derived from an occupation, location, relationship, or some other distinctive characteristic of a family. Since many of the Keney's ancestors came from Normandy, the "de" preceding the name was likely to be of French derivation. The "de" was dropped in the late fifteenth century.

Prior to the eighteenth century, several family members had such irregular penmanship that their signatures resulted in different spellings. In the nineteenth century, several family members changed the spelling for specific reasons. Consequently, what appears to be inaccuracies in spelling are not errors, but derivations of the more common forms used by various families.

Primary Source: Florence Keeney Robertson, 1937

A GENEALOGICAL LINE
OF THE KINNEY FAMILY

I	Robert, Son of Gerald	Knight	1042-1094
II	Gilbert de Kene	Explorer, Confidante	1414-1462
III	Roland de Kene	Farmer, Settler	1435-1487
IV	Charles Kynne	Scholar, Arbitrator	1469-1518
V	Richard Kynne	Merchant, Entrepreneur	1495-1550
VI	John Kynne	Mayor, Merchant, Politician	1525-1573
VII	Sir John Robert Keney	Knight, Shipbuilder	1548-1590
VIII	Sir Thomas Keney	Puritan Baronet	1571-1618
IX	John Keney	Man of God, Builder	1600-1627
X	Henry Keney	Frontiersman, Progenitor, Soldier	1624-1709
XI	Thomas Keney	Frontiersman, Farmer, Militia Man	1655-1687
XII	Thomas (II) Keney	Deacon, Farmer	1678-1756
XIII	Jeremiah Kinne	Farmer, Patriot	1702-1798
XIV	Manuel Kinne	Farmer, Preacher, Patriot	1740-1828
XV	Robert Kinne	Militia Fighter, Farmer, Pioneer	1798-1870
XVI	George Park Kinney	Entrepreneur, Traveler	1834-1902
XVII	Raymond Park Kinney	Printer, Indian Curio Trader	1879-1932
XVIII	Stevens Park Kinney	Lawyer, Businessman	1902-1963
IXX	Stevens Park Kinney II	Colonel, Judge	1933-1993
XX	Douglas Bertram Kinney (Son of Roger L. Kinney)	Businessman, Adventurer	1967-

"He who knows only his own generation remains always a child."

Cicero

"It is difficult to know where you are going if you don't know where you have been."

Author Unknown

"All people should be induced to look back to the days of their forefathers, to be warned of their errors, instructed by their Wisdom and stimulated for a career of Improvements by example of their virtues."

Florence Keeney Robertson

"When you go home, tell them of us and say, for their tomorrow, we gave our today."

John Maxwell Edmonds

"A man doesn't die until he is forgotten."

General George W. Casey

"What we do in life echoes into eternity."

Maximus

Prologue

OPENING SOME
VERY WEIGHTY TRUNKS

When I was a freshman in high school, my parents bought some vacant ground just outside Estes Park, Colorado, a picturesque mountain community in the shadows of Longs Peak. Within a few years, shortly after Dwight D. Eisenhower was elected president, they built a three-bedroom mountain home where they planned to live when my father retired. It was a buy, build, furnish, and expand project from the beginning. The furnishings were essentially hand-me-downs from our primary home in Denver, some sixty miles away. Within several years, a two-car garage and a family room were added. In addition to the disposition of old family furniture, other family relics, including my grandparents' large and very heavy trunks, were gradually taken to Estes Park. They were stored in the garage until my parents presumably would review and dispose of all the contents.

The garage was plumb full with bicycles, garden hoses, snow shovels, and those awkward trunks from my ancestors. The solid trunks had been made with reinforced corners and metal locks to withstand long travels. They were one of those omnipresent things I didn't pay much attention to—I simply went about my business knowing that those mysterious things in those trunks were not to be touched.

Those trunks seemed to take care of themselves until my Aunt Annabelle died in 1961. Unlike most of my aging relatives, Aunt Annabelle was healthy right up to the time of her death when she was seventy-seven years old. Annabelle was congenial, well-liked, and always conversant with small children who were required to accompany their parents for periodic visits. She had live goldfish in the outdoor gardens and lots of delicious chocolate chip cookies to distribute to all her visitors.

Annabelle's pleasant personality and natural attraction seemed to make her trustworthy, and many people, especially the family, confided in her. Unfortunately, I didn't pay much attention at the time, but she would tell wonderful stories about her worldly travels and about the family's history. For some strange reason, she seemed to know all about our family history, including the Dickson & Kinney General Store and how it provided supplies to the Union troops during the Civil War. She had fascinating souvenirs, including a real musket rifle she gave to my older brother. She gave my mother a genuine Indian peace pipe, reportedly from the Narragansett Indian Tribe from Massachusetts. Frankly, at the time, it didn't interest me very much. I was more concerned with the outcome of the National League baseball race. If the Cardinals won, I got to go to St. Louis with my father to see the World Series. But the Cardinals lost that year, and I listened to the World Series on the radio. Before I realized it, several years passed and Annabelle died. I vaguely remember Annabelle's funeral, but I vividly remember helping my brother as we hauled Aunt Annabelle's three very heavy trunks to our garage in Estes Park.

Unfortunately, in 1963, my father had a fatal heart attack before he had an opportunity to retire in Estes Park. He and my mother never opened those trunks to give us directions as to their disposition. Rather, my father who was a good historian and an avid collector, had added to the garage collection by filling two more huge trunks that found their way to Estes Park. Slowly, my brother and I found ourselves moving some of the trunks out of the garage and into the house. They served well for luggage racks, end tables, and, sometimes, for holding table lamps. For many years those trunks just sat there, accumulating dust.

One cold winter weekend in the mid-seventies when I retreated to Estes Park for some mountain hiking, I found it prudent to stay indoors. With a frigid north wind, the chill factor reached minus twenty-four degrees. After two days and beginning to get cabin fever, I decided I had to do something. Just for kicks, I opened one of Aunt Annabelle's trunks.

It was amazing! I began to discover that the contents revealed that time had stood still for some 50 to 100 to 400 years.

Aunt Annabelle was the ultimate collector. She had carefully wrapped everything, including pictures, letters, journals, china, clothing, artwork, uniforms, and firearms. I slowly began to open her parcels. I discovered that opening each new package was more exciting than the last. I couldn't believe my eyes! It was better than Christmas! She had cautiously preserved her mother's eyeglasses, her sewing equipment, and some original artwork. I carefully unwrapped a Union soldier's military uniform and some shattered bullets identified as those from a battle-field at Gettysburg. As I searched further, it became apparent that Aunt Annabelle had been the keeper of the valuables from many generations. There were letters and journals dating from the 1600s and a copy of a will from John Kynne dated 1563. I held some crude medical instruments and some weights and measures, presumably for the valuation of gold and silver. There seemed to be no end to the personal care and preservation she devoted to so many startling discoveries. Meticulously wrapped at the bottom of one trunk, I found another Indian warrior's tomahawk and some assorted arrowheads. There was a package of coins and some paper currency from the Confederacy. My heart pounded as I clutched a small revolver pistol that seemed to fit perfectly in my right hand.

As a youngster, tales of my ancestors meant meaningless family charts and trudging through dreary cemeteries filled with strange grave markers. I paid little attention and quickly forgot those experiences.

But now, touching and holding their personal possessions, my ancestors took on new meaning. After reading some of the letters, I realized that these people, my ancestors, were real people and that they had lived with emotions and feelings just like we have today. All of a sudden, their lives became more than a notation in the family Bible. I was holding my great-great-great-grandfather's pocket knife and his valuable pouch (similar to today's billfold), containing his will, the deed for his farm, and some of his most personal letters.

My casual inquiry into Annabelle's trunk became an all night discovery party. As I opened trunk after trunk, my excitement and adrenalin were flowing as if I were skiing down Vail's Riva Ridge with three inches of powder snow on a crisp winter afternoon. And it just got better and better. Some of the discoveries prompted questions. There was a carefully folded American flag, with forty eight-stars, but without identification as to why it was saved. Was one of my ancestors killed in combat? I found numerous newspaper clippings and copies of crude advertisements from a garden nursery in Nebraska and a perfume factory in Florida.

I opened several other trunks, including one of my father's. Once opened, the musty, dry smell permeated the room, yet the contents were neat and orderly. He, too, had accumulated relics from past generations. The covers of some books were so brittle they broke with the slightest movement. I found six large volumes that, after investigation, I surmised my father's great-grandfather had assembled. In addition to my father's and my great-great-grandfather's papers, there were copies of two publications attributed to the Kinne Historical and Genealogical Society. There was a notation that my great-grandfather, George Kinney, met with other Kinneys when they organized a family society. The Kinne Genealogical Society was incorporated in Connecticut on June 9, 1884. They prepared two publications dealing with Henry Kinne and his descendants in Connecticut.

There were some journals and records from other family members. There were excerpts attributed to Basil Elroy Kinney, most likely from his publication entitled *Kinney Nation*. Some of the correspondence from Julia Geist Kinney dealt with the Old Kinney Burying Grounds of Glasgo (Griswold), Connecticut and related cemeteries. There were reports of Manuel Kinne's vital records and more recent references to the *Keeney Updates* published by Roscoe Keeney of West Virginia.

In time, I learned that other family members had made some remarkable contributions. In 1942, Florence Keeney Robertson compiled and wrote a 183-page book entitled *The Keayne-Keen-Keeney-Kinney-Kenney and Allied Families*. In 1947, she wrote a 231-page book entitled *The Genealogy of Henry and Anne Kinne of Salem, Massachusetts*. I believe this massive work was written to complete her doctoral thesis at the University of Southern California. Her books explained that Henry Kinne was born July 8, 1624 in King's Lynn, England and that he is considered to be the progenitor of the Kinney family in America.

These books are very valuable resources. They identify and describe the lineage of the majority of the family. Upon their discovery, I said to myself, "Thank God and thank Florence Keeney Robertson for her marvelous work." I am so glad that Florence had the patience and dedication to accomplish such a gigantic task. I was especially pleased because my interests lie elsewhere. Without her historical work, my curiosity and research would have always been restricted to other records, which at best, would have been vague and possibly conflicting.

Another major breakthrough occurred when I learned of the ongoing research of Georgia Kinney Bopp. She is the webmaster of a unique project designed to investigate, find, and share accurate information primarily through genetic genealogy. It quickly became evident that by using genetic tests and comparing information available from Georgia's database and the reports of other participants, it is much easier to trace family lines and discern the accuracy of family records. What a nice surprise to find more than a dozen distant cousins – all Kinneys – with a similar Y-DNA match. Several of them, including Rose, a genealogical expert, William Lee, Wayne, Mary, and Captain Bruce were willing to provide additional family information resulting from their own research. Again, I felt grateful that Georgia and other family members have taken on these important projects.

My interest grew. I wanted to know more about the lives of my ancestors. Who were these people and how did they survive through perilous times? What about their character and their successes and failure? What motivated them? Did they merely survive or did they flourish in some generations? Were there common characteristics of family members throughout the ages, and could I identify any of those qualities of kinship that make a difference in the long run? How does the expression, "the more things change, the more they stay the same," apply to a family's history?

I began to make a plan. Could I trace the family's history by following a direct line of genealogy for the past 1,000 years? I realized that much of my curiosity could be met by assembling, connecting, and making historical sense of the records, journals, and books that had already been prepared. With additional research, I could find supporting information and likely expand the historical documentation. Certainly, the great moments and events in history have had a profound effect on the Kinney family and I wanted to know how they dealt with wars, famines, religious movements, and changing economic times. It was important to see, smell, and touch the sites and environments where they lived, worked, and traveled. If there were similarities between the ages, I intended to identify them.

I decided to approach my inquiry in the same manner that I originally discovered the treasures in Aunt Annabelle's trunk. The emotional excitement in each new discovery was a joy in itself. As I made inquiries, traveled to the homes and sites of my relatives, and studied our history, I was determined to make the journey-my quest-as enjoyable as the finished results. I was delighted to find so many friendly relatives and helpful people along the way. What fun it has been to become acquainted with people from four countries, France, the Netherlands,

England, and the United States and many cities and regions including Normandy, Wyke Champflower in Somerset County, King's Lynn, Leyden, Salem, Tolland, Boston, New London, Topsfield, Chicago, Schuyler, and Denver.

The journey brought many new discoveries and disclosures about the Kinney family and how they lived from generation to generation. And now that I am older and retired, I can tell you about those adventures, and, yes, about some of the skeletons in our family's closet.

What would a quest be without a few surprises? I discovered that some of the family's records, especially prior to 1625, were incomplete. In fact, there were questions as to the credibility and accuracy of certain stories passed along to Kinneys throughout the centuries. Some family historians and, perhaps, some professional research consultants have questioned the research of others. Yet, our family's information is probably no different than that of many others that can be reliably traced to the 1600s. It's much harder to find accurate records from earlier times when so few were literate. Handwritten records could be miscopied or destroyed by floods or fires—or even purposely destroyed to protect a family which faced religious persecution.

Consequently, I have encountered conflicting facts, names, and dates. For example, in John Kynne's will of 1563, he refers to his wife as Margaret and later as Anne—and the family name is spelled four ways. When faced with such circumstances, I have taken what I consider the easiest and most logical routes, relying to some extent upon my intuition. In this case, I gave her both names, called her Margaret Anne Kynne, and then proceeded with her story. Rather than bicker or get hung up on details I cannot prove, I chose to focus on the prominent, essential characteristics of the family. Thus, when records were sparse or incomplete, I recounted historical events from other family members with similar circumstances. I tried to determined how a person would have reacted to the circumstances of a particular time, period, and location. Yes, such passages are fiction, but they are based upon whatever details we do know. After 1675, the family records improve greatly in scope and accuracy, making it much easier to be factual about the history and content of each story.

In the end, my journey's goal is to have captured the essence of the Kinney family history over the years. No doubt I will occasionally miss the precision of historical accuracy, either by omission or error, so I ask for forgiveness in advance. I don't profess to be a master genealogist, but simply a man who went on a quest to discover what he could about the men and women who came before me–and learned quite a bit about himself in the process. My greatest hope is that this story will enrich the lives of others and touch the hearts of my grandchildren and future generations, and thus serve as an inspiration for them to excel in whatever their passions may be throughout their lives.

Now please join me in an exploration of the contents of our family's dry, musty, and very heavy old trunks that have divulged so much that is so rare and valuable to me.

INDEPENDENCE *Wayne City Landing*
"Start of the Santa Fe Trail" in 1842 By John Stobart
Path of the Kinneys moving westward

William the Conqueror

Chapter 1

Robert, Son of Gerald
Circa, 1042 – 1094
Knight

AFTER THE CONQUEST

The knight, Robert, son of Gerald, tilted his head in awe under the high vaulted ceiling of Westminster Abbey. Around him, the excited flutter of both Normans and Anglo-Saxons, each in their own languages, filled the cold, stone cathedral with anticipation. For two years, Robert, serving in the cavalry unit, had accompanied Duke William of Normandy. The decisive Norman victory in the Battle of Hastings nearly three months ago had brought Robert to this spectacular place at a moment in history that would live forever. It was a proud and exhilarating time for the successful troops from Normandy. They had fought hard, killing King Harold and had won the decisive battle. They knew that in due time, the rewards of the victory would be theirs, and that from that day forward, their leader William no longer would be called "William the Bastard," but he had gained a new name, "William the Conqueror." Today, Christmas Day, Year of our Lord, 1066, William the Conqueror would be crowned King of England.

The terms of surrender had been completed. The Anglo-Saxon forces agreed to hand over all arms and demobilize all troops. Without hesitation, any violations encountered by the Normans would be met with

harsh penalties, including death. However, William issued some conces-
sions by maintaining English social customs, including common rights
and privileges for law-abiding citizens, in order to appease much of the
Anglo-Saxon's anxiety.

Robert and the Norman troops triumphantly marched northward
from Hastings, across the River Thames, toward London. They spread
word of the conquest to the people in the farms and villages along the
way, taking supplies only as needed. Despite encountering some resistance from King Harold's loyalists, they moved forward with persistent
determination. William needed to reach London to seal the victory and
claim his and England's destiny.

When the advance party arrived in London, it announced the terms
of surrender, including the most important term: William the Conqueror
would assume full control of the government. In light of King Harold's
death and the collapse of his troops, the officials from the city of London
reluctantly agreed to all terms. As preparations for the coronation of
William unfolded, Robert and the rest of the Norman troops moved to
keep order. They continued to combat the insurgents and establish the
ground work for the new government.

Robert knew that England and Normandy would never be the
same—and that his own life was turning in a new direction. He sent news
home by messenger in the last fortnight of the great victory in the Battle
of Hastings and the upcoming coronation. His father had wholeheart-
edly supported his decision to join Duke William's forces and the push
to conquer England. They agreed that success over the Anglo-Saxons
could bring new opportunities, social status, and land to Robert–maybe
even to other family members. No doubt his father would be pleased.

His family lived in Normandy and in a rich, agricultural area
called Champfleury, southeast of Normandy. Family legends told that
his forefathers had arrived with the Vikings from Norway in the early
seventh century. Robert's ancestors passed stories about the proud
family's history from one generation to the next. For over 400 years,

since about 625, they had flourished within the Norman feudal society, tilling the land, growing families, and uniting with the feudal domain's master in defending and protecting their families and the castles of their lords. Many of the men received special training to become warriors and knights within the ranks of Duke William of Normandy. Robert and his brothers were pleased to continue that tradition. Robert excelled in his military training and was chosen to accompany Duke William for the attack on England.

Now Robert's decisive role and success in the Battle of Hastings meant he was changing his family's homeland, and, if things went as planned, he would continue to be part of a bigger destiny, that of a new ruling class in England. Robert had proven his loyalty and he had fought hard these past years. He extended his commitment to serve in the military and to assist with the establishment of the new government and the dismantling of the old courts. Robert, now twenty-five, planned to take advantage of his new opportunities, including his association and friendship with the barons who had accompanied William to England.

Many of the powerful leaders from Normandy were sitting in Westminster Abbey with Robert waiting for the coronation to begin. A hush descended as the ceremony began. But as tradition dictated, those in attendance were asked whether or not they accepted their new ruler. Robert and the other Normans shouted their acceptance in their native French tongue, while the Anglo-Saxons responded in their native English. Their voices joined in unison. The future of these two proud peoples came together, growing louder with the exultant sounds rising to the very top of the high walls and spires of the great cathedral. Inside, the people had expressed their unity for their new ruler. But outside, the uncertain crowd had mistaken the noise and unsupported rumors as an assassination attempt. Within a few minutes, smoke from unidentified sources drifted into the church and some of the people fled outside. As the disturbance spread, Robert joined other soldiers to extinguish the small fires and keep order.

Despite the melee outside the cathedral, William the Conqueror was crowned monarch of England. Order was restored within the boundaries of London and King William moved quickly to establish control with his new government.

Within several months, King William announced plans for a complete inventory of all the assets of the country. The results of this massive project would become known as the *Domesday Book*. The information gained from this inventory was very valuable for King William and was used for many years to come. Shortly thereafter in 1067 work began on the historic Bayeux Tapestry and Norman architecture began to spread throughout England.

Robert assisted with the new administration, helping to set up a system to obtain information and enforce accurate accountability, even in remote areas of the country. The Anglo-Saxons were surprised with the swiftness and decisive manner with which the Norman troops moved to obtain control and retrieve the inventory records.

Robert's diligence during the conquest and bravery in the Battle of Hastings, as well as his continued loyalty and obedience as a member of the King's staff, led to some substantial rewards, just as he expected. He was awarded two Knight's fees, which meant two substantial parcels of land in Somerset County. This grant would be kept in his family's ancestral estate name, eventually passing to his son John de Kene. Robert dispatched by messenger this good news to his family in Normandy. With his land grant and his position with King William in place, Robert returned to Normandy to marry his childhood sweetheart, Caroline.

In Normandy, Robert had a joyful reunion with his family and friends. He spent hours telling his father and brothers of the Battle of Hastings and the ongoing skirmishes to establish order throughout the land. He told them of the new lands in Somerset County and he invited some relatives and friends to join them there. Robert and Caroline had a glorious wedding, and soon, they grew anxious to move to their new home. Robert had a keen sense that this might be his last trip to his homeland, and parting, especially from his mother, father, and brothers, was difficult.

The journey northward by coach through Normandy to Calais was long and tiring, especially for Caroline, who had never been more than a few miles away from her home. The ocean crossing to Dover was smooth and they were thankful for warm weather and calm seas. Robert grew eager to show Caroline their new home. He had been traveling for years and was ready to settle down, at least in a manner where they could establish a family and he could perform his knightly obligations for King William. Once on English ground, they were accompanied by a military convoy and traveled by coach to Canterbury, then westward through London, then Bath, and on to Glastonbury. Along the way they heard reports of progress resulting from King William's progressive policies. Plans were underway and construction would begin in 1078 for a great tower in London.

At last, they began the final leg of their journey east from Glastonbury. One can imagine that Caroline sighed, "It's beautiful here but I miss home and Campfleury so very much."

Robert replied, "Please be patient, wait until you see what is ahead, Caroline."

The coach moved on, over a stone bridge across the River Cary and toward the rolling hills of Somerset County. Some native deer came into view, and they also saw some pheasants along the road, scampering and quacking to get out of the way. Some beautiful large oak, elm, and cottonwood trees grew along a meandering stream.

Robert said, "All these years, I didn't know if you would wait for me. But once I saw this country, I knew it would be a beautiful place to live and raise a family with you. Look, Caroline, see the site of our new house. And down toward the River Brue, I will build a barn."

Carolyn opened her eyes wide. "Robert, you are right, it's not so different. What do you call it?"

"Home," he responded, "and you will know it as Champfleury, or

Wyke Champflower as they say in the Anglo-Saxon language."

Robert watched as Caroline surveyed the rich, agricultural land that was very similar in color and texture to their native land in Normandy. After peeking at the small cottage, she gathered some native flowers. Her smile and growing enthusiasm told him that she believed him and that she was happy. Life would indeed be good here for Caroline and Robert de Kene, as he would come to be known throughout Somerset County.

There was much work to be done to establish their manor estate, which was the common way to live and to work with farmers and laborers under the existing feudal system. They cleared much of the land planting hay, wheat, and alfalfa. The wheat was excellent for baking bread and it came to be known as the best in the region. The rains and clear streams provided ideal conditions for fishing and hunting. The nearby hills were filled with wild game, including deer and some elk. Dairy cattle flourished in the meadows. Caroline and Robert prospered on their estate at Wyke Champflower. They had four children and the estate passed on to their son, John de Kene, in later years.

For the next 350 years or so, the de Kene family lived on the estate, enjoying a reputation for "high antiquity." Although the details of the genealogical progression have been significantly lost during the period, it is believed that the various families' lifestyles continued much as they had on the family feudal estate. The Normandy history about Robert de Kene was passed on through the centuries and he was credited with gallant and heroic efforts in the Battle of Hastings and for moving the family to Somerset County. Over the years, there were reports of some members of the de Kene family serving in the military during the Crusades and the Hundred Years' War. Other members of the family remained in Somerset County, sowing the land, growing new generations, and remaining dutiful to the feudal lords, even during the dark days of the Black Death and dreadful Plague.

With the decline of the feudal system in the late fourteenth century and early into the 1400s, some family members realized their way of life was disappearing. They grew apprehensive, especially as massive sickness and the Plague spread across the land. One member of the family was determined not to sit back and watch the world change without his reaction and attempts to find a better life.

Young Gilbert de Kene ran away from home in the spring of 1428, firmly setting the family in a new direction: a direction that would mark a new destiny not only for himself, but also for the de Kene family members who would follow.

The road leading to Wyke Champflower and Castle Cary

Neptune Captain Millard Hobbs

Chapter 2

Gilbert de Kene
1414 – 1462
Explorer, Confidante

EXPANDING HORIZONS

Gilbert was naturally adventuresome. He had an innate tendency to be the first one in most every undertaking he took. Even when he was hiking with his best friend Matthias, who he called Matt, he had an inclination to move quickly, staying far ahead of him. Matt was likely struggling behind and calling, "Gilbert, wait up, I wish I had your energy, but I don't."

Gilbert, as a boy of fourteen was not tall, but he was energetic and even with all his gear, he moved through the trees in the Isham Woods with ease, his wiry body pushing aside branches with force. As he came to a clearing, he stopped to wait for Matt. The sun shone on his brown, curly hair, highlighting the copper tint. His piercing blue eyes looked back at Matt, who was slight and pale. Matt seemed to be holding his chest and breathing hard. The boys had grown quite a bit this summer while many of their childhood friends had succumbed to the constant illnesses that embraced the country. His friends, John, Vincent, and Eloise, were in the church's graveyard, while his mother's face grew more drawn with every passing day and more funerals. Now the leaves in the Batcomb Woods were ready to fall, and Gilbert knew that death would come for more of his friends in the months ahead, even if the Plague might take a winter's rest.

"Matt, let's climb the Castle Rock on Horse Hill. We can eat something there, before the cold sets in, and we have to return to our homes."

"OK," said Matt, "I'll catch up, but take your time-I don't seem to have much speed today."

As Gilbert bounded to the top of the flat rock, he heard Matt's breath quicken. No, no, no, he thought. Not Matt's health, too. Too much disease and too little good food these days. Shrugging off those thoughts, he threw the pack off his back, dropped his bow and quiver, and flopped down on the ground. Matt joined him, grinning at his bold friend with a tepid smile.

After unpacking hard-crusted bread and some cheese, Gilbert pulled the knife from his belt and divided some tasty portions between them. Gilbert asked, "Don't you ever want to get out of here? I am so tired of all the sickness and the funeral masses. I am so tired of people who know nothing about what is happening outside of Somerset. I want to get out of this rut and find out what is happening in London and the rest of the world, maybe even travel on the high seas."

Matt responded, "Gil, the sickness is everywhere–and it is worse in the big cities. You cannot run from it. Death will find you wherever you are if that is God's plan. Why do you think Father Jones talks about the ashes at every mass?"

"Matt, you spend too much time inside helping the Father. God lives outdoors too, and he will follow us to Bath and wherever we go. Sometimes, I wonder why he does this to us-Matt, don't you ever get mad? Besides, what are you going to do inside a chapel? You need to get outside, relax, and get some healthy color back into your skin."

Matt stared at the hard crust awhile and looked straight into Gilbert's eyes. "I'm not sure that is going to happen. I've been talking a lot to Father Jones since my mum has been gone. Next spring I'm beginning my studies at the abbey in Glastonbury. I've heard my calling–I'm planning to join the order."

Gilbert jumped up and began pacing around Matt. "Matt, you are not really going to stick yourself inside away from this world? So much is happening right now. My uncle tells me that times are changing–the world as we know it is breaking down, and we have the chance, and hopefully, the freedom to find out what is out there. You can't run away from the sickness in the abbey."

Matt calmly looked up at his friend, his eyes following him as he moved back and forth. "I'm not like you, Gil. I don't have your strength. Besides, God needs me. Our time here is short–the cart comes for people most every day. People are in need–if they don't get their last rites from people like me, what will happen to their souls? Priests are in more danger from the spots than most people because they enter the homes with the dreaded mark."

Gilbert shook his head and grabbed his hunting gear and his backpack. "You are right, my time here in Somerset is short. Winter is coming–let's head for home before the sun goes down."

Matt gathered the remaining bits of food, and followed his friend down the rocks and back onto the trail toward home. Within an hour, they reached the junction where they parted, Matt heading toward Bruton, and Gilbert toward Wyke Champflower.

Gilbert was the third son in a family of six siblings, numerous cousins, and many playmates. He had two sisters, one older and one younger. He had watched helplessly as his younger sister and two older brothers became sick and died from the dreaded disease. He considered himself and his younger brother Curtis to be as healthy as possible, but he constantly worried about their health.

Over the winter, Gilbert had plenty of time to ponder his future. He was determined to make the most of his humble beginnings. He had an inquisitive mind, especially about nature and animals. He watched the habits of the farm animals and he studied their functions as they related to the anatomy of people. When he was twelve, he had dissected a chicken and then reconstructed all of the bones back into their working positions. The skeleton of the chicken sat atop the shelf in Gilbert's room, serving as a constant reminder of God's intricate creations and the family of life.

Gilbert's family lived close to the ancestral estate in the traditional feudal system. Because of his family's lineage, Gilbert inherited the status of a freeman. The family was considered to be in the gentry class. They were largely dependent upon the farm and the agricultural products-primarily sheep-that they raised.

On occasion, the family would travel to Glastonbury to attend services in the Great Abbey or St. John's Church. Legends say the first Christian church in England was in Glastonbury. The family was Catholic and Gilbert was raised in an environment requiring strict enforcement of the Church's dogma. There was a small Catholic chapel on the grounds of the family estate. In recent years, Gilbert was deeply troubled about his faith and he had many questions about Father Jones and what he considered to be the Church's naive response to combating the spread of disease throughout the region.

There was a market and sometimes fairs and public events in Glastonbury. For very special occasions, the family would visit the famous George Inn. For most of the common necessities, the family traded in the small villages of Bruton, Castle Cary, Yeovil, and Shepton Mallet. Gilbert had traveled to the city of Bath with his father when he was ten and again when he was twelve. There, he liked the excitement of the market-place and the bristling activities on the docks.

In the spring, Gilbert and his brother Curtis, who had been busy for weeks helping with the lambing, were eager to see their friends. Gilbert had not seen any of his good pals, including Matt, for several months. Finally, when the birthing was finished, his father consented and sent both boys to town to pick up some supplies.

Gilbert and Curtis almost galloped as they took to the road with their bags swinging and a frisky spring in their steps. Over the winter, they had both grown stronger, and Gilbert, now fifteen, looked more like a man than a boy. He hoped to see Matt before his friend left to join the abbey.

As they approached town, they ran into another friend named James who had grown up with Matt and Gilbert. James announced, "You won't be visiting Matt today. They put a mark on his door. Not much longer now, Father Jones has already gone to do the rites."

Gilbert and Curtis barely answered, but turned quickly to continue on their way. As they passed by Matt's home, they stopped to visit with a neighbor. She said, "Pity both of them like that. Might as well tear down the whole house with Matt and his Mum both gone. The cart will come soon."

Gilbert turned to look at Curtis. "That's it. I am not going to stay here any longer. If death personified is going to come for me, he will have to find me first."

Curtis was startled and responded, "But Mum and Dad won't let you go—you are supposed to take over the operation of the farm after Dad."

Gilbert shook his head and replied, "You can have it, Curtis, with my blessing. I have other plans."

With that, Gilbert turned and strode toward the market. The boys made sure to get everything their parents had marked on the list. They remained silent for most of their visit in town, knowing better than to circulate among the townsfolk. They did not want their casual comments to provide material for the nosy women to create any gossip. With their supplies in hand, they left town and headed for home.

On the road, Gilbert formulated his plan. He began to explain his plan to Curtis, appealing for his help. Gilbert would squirrel away some food, his traveling clothes and some coins he had saved. By the next full moon—Holy Week—he would be ready to run away from home. Gilbert pleaded to Curtis and Curtis agreed to remain silent until he was long gone.

Following Good Friday Mass at the chapel, the family returned home and retired for the night. Gilbert pretended to fall asleep, but as the home filled with silence, he crept from his bed and slipped outdoors. He stopped by the barn to put on his clothes and tie his boots. He took his backpack which contained some food, a water pouch, a knife, a small amount of money, and a few clothes which made-up his provisions for his trip.

The moonlight pointed his way toward the main road that would lead him to the main intersection and the road to Bath. He knew that Bath was a flourishing city with an extensive market and a busy seaport. He walked cautiously, not to arouse the farm animals. As he left the family estate, he turned and whispered, "Goodbye, my dear family, goodbye Wyke Champflower."

He followed the path and some of the old trails that the Romans had used many years before. He traveled all night and when the sun began to rise, he slept in the forest. He was very worried about being caught by authorities who would send him back home to the wrath of his parents- back to waiting for his own death. With extreme caution he continued on his way, generally traveling in the early morning and evening time.

He met strangers and learned to visit with farmers and peasants along the way. To obtain food, he worked doing odd jobs and occasion- ally he stayed with farmers for several days. He was naturally inquisitive and he asked many questions about directions, about people, and about faraway places. He always enjoyed listening to stories of adventure and discovery.

He seemed to thrive when talking to new friends and he wondered how some people knew so much and were so opinionated about strange subjects. As he traveled he talked with an old soldier about the British monarchy and the affairs of the State. He heard stories about Henry V who had died and about his son Henry VI, who was to succeed his father when he came of age. Gilbert was fascinated with the Monarchy's power and rule over the country. He was told that King Henry V believed that he was predestined by God to conquer and rule France and England. Gilbert began to wonder about God's influence upon the King. Did Christians have the right to question God's (or the King's) authority? There seemed to be more questions than answers. Gilbert hoped that in the course of his travels he would come to understand more about such worldly affairs.

Gilbert arrived in the city of Bath in the early summer. He remembered where to find the market from his earlier trips with his father. He toured the city and discovered many historic buildings. He realized that the city was perhaps the largest, the oldest, and best preserved in Britain. He visited the mineral springs and the Great Abbey. He began to develop an appreciation for the architecture when he saw the distinctive stone buildings and the magnificent Borough Walls.

The market in Bath attracted traders from throughout the region. Gilbert wandered about the market, seeking food, provisions, and help with passage to one of the seafaring ports. Just as in the country, he performed odd jobs in return for food and shelter.

He made friends with a sailor named Nathanial Spencer from Portsmouth. When Gilbert asked about his travels, he told him of the wondrous cities of Portsmouth, London, Paris, and Amsterdam. Gilbert was fascinated with Nathanial's stories about the uprising of the Lollards and their leader Sir John Oldcastle. He heard the story about the escape of Sir John from the Tower of London and how he was recaptured and hanged as a traitor. The tales of adventure motivated Gilbert to travel and learn more about the world.

Nathanial arranged for Gilbert to work for his passage on a small cargo boat going south on the Avon River toward Bournemouth or Portsmouth. Aboard the small boat, Gilbert made repairs and learned the basics for the ship's navigation. He helped load and unload the cargo and the ship's supplies. He proved to be a good worker and the boat's captain felt confident in recommending Gilbert when the opportunity eventually arose for him to move to a larger vessel.

Gilbert spent some time exploring in the cities of Portsmouth and Dorchester. He saw the castle of Henry VI and was fascinated with the fort which was built to protect the town. The large, round tower was a striking landmark in the harbor. He developed a personal habit of identifying and remembering key landmarks in major cities.

Gilbert did not have to wait long for an opportunity to move to a larger vessel. When the small cargo boat docked at Portsmouth, he found several large vessels already there, preparing to set sail north toward London and Calais. With the recommendation of the cargo boat's captain, Gilbert was hired as a seaman on the *Neptune*.

The *Neptune* was a majestic, forty-ton, three-masted schooner. It had a crew of ten to fourteen men. It transported and traded merchandise as directed by the owner and sailed by Captain Millard Hobbs. It sailed between Portsmouth, Brighton, Calais, London, Bishop's Lynn, ports of the Netherlands, Hamburg, Edinburgh, and several small ports in between. Gilbert was put to work in preparation for sailing north for their first stop in Brighton. If he performed well, he would likely serve a five-year obligation.

Gilbert was sixteen years old when he began sailing the northern seas, including the Mediterranean Sea and the English Channel. He was a quick learner, not only for navigating through shipping lanes, but also for performing other seaman's duties. He could read maps well, and he had a good sense of weather conditions. He learned to repair lines and he was an excellent forward observer. He was physically fit, with a strong and agile body. He seemed to thrive in the outdoors, with healthy sea breezes and variable water conditions. His endurance in difficult circumstances was noted by his shipmates and his superiors. In a short time, he became a trusted member of the ship's crew.

On one occasion, when the *Neptune* was carrying precious cargo bound from Calais to Portsmouth, the *Neptune* was followed out of port and attacked by a mysterious, unidentified ship. Sailing through the Straits of Dover in bad weather could be very difficult. It was especially dangerous with an enemy ship trying to overtake and seize the *Neptune*. Gilbert navigated the ship through the turbulent storm, staying on duty, primarily at the helm for thirty-two hours. The unidentified ship finally gave up and turned away. The incident could have been a disaster. The captain and the crew all recognized Gilbert's courage and tenacity. He was naturally modest and he became respected as a valued shipmate who always seemed to be in a crucial place whenever danger arose.

Gilbert developed a good friendship with Captain Hobbs. He was a good teacher who taught Gilbert how to read and write in English. Gilbert was fluent in French and he could speak some English, but until then his vocabulary and grammar had been limited. Gilbert began to keep a log, primarily in English, of his personal activities, including some special events and a record of the ship's sailing dates and their destinations.

The success of the *Neptune* depended upon the value of the cargo and successfully delivering the cargo to buyers willing to pay the appropriate prices. The owner of the ship acted as the buyer and seller of the merchandise. Captain Hobbs was the communications link between the owner and the ship's crew. The ship's crew grew to anticipate the directions they would be taking. The ship normally sailed to northern ports during the spring, summer, and fall, and stayed in southern ports in the winter. Wherever they sailed, Gilbert sought out learned men who could share stories and tell him about foreign ports.

Gilbert's inquisitive nature kept him aware of worldly events. He heard stories about Joan of Arc who was burned on the cross in 1431. A sailor told him of a Portuguese man known as Prince Henry the Navigator, who sailed south and discovered parts of Africa. Members of Prince Henry's family, Antao Goncalves and Nuno Tristao reportedly brought the first captives from the Sahara back to Portugal, and thus began the capture and trading of slaves.

In the summer of 1433, the *Neptune* sailed north, bound for Yarmouth and Bishop's Lynn in East Anglia. East Anglia was a region known for salt preserves and rich agricultural land. The ship was scheduled to transport a load of salt, corn, wheat, and barley to London. The ship broke its rudder coming into port at Bishop's Lynn. The repairs took time, and the ship remained at the dock for an extra two weeks. During that time, Gilbert explored Norwich County, including a visit to the Abbey at Castle Rising, the city of Bishop's Lynn, and the vast farming area in East Anglia. He was impressed with the beautiful coast, the salt deposits, and the potential to profit from shipping the bountiful agricultural products.

Although the ship lost time to repairing the broken rudder, the agricultural products from Bishop's Lynn were sold at a relatively high price in London. Consequently, that portion of the voyage was still considered successful. Gilbert recorded the results of the sales along with his personal observations of the area. He vowed to return to East Anglia someday.

Gilbert sailed as far north as Edinburgh and across the North Sea, east to Hamburg and ports of the Netherlands. If permitted, when the ship was in port, Gilbert would explore the villages and countryside. He had a deep respect for the sea, but his love and passion would always be for the rolling hills, forests, and country streams. As time passed, he realized that his native homeland in Somerset County was his favorite place to live. He gradually developed a yearning to return home.

Calais and Dieppe were common ports for delivering supplies to the troops in France. When the ship docked in Calais in 1434, Gilbert met some of the soldiers who had been fighting in Normandy. They told him about past years of combat with the French forces. In recent years, even though the fighting had diminished, there seemed to be a period of dissention and unrest within the country. The soldiers' plight made a lasting impression on Gilbert. He felt sorry for the soldiers who were committed to serve in the King's army without neither personal freedom nor ability to choose their life's destiny.

After Gilbert fulfilled his initial five-year commitment, he stayed another six years on the *Neptune*. By then, he had sailed to all the major shipping ports in the North Sea and he was ready to return home. He left the ship, Captain Hobbs, and his friends serving on the crew in the summer of 1441. He gathered his personal belongings as well as some navigational equipment and the maps he had drawn. When the *Neptune* was docked in Portsmouth, there was a going away party for Gilbert. He left the ship in the good graces of the Captain Hobbs, who offered tenure and a place on the ship's crew if he ever decided to return.

Gilbert was ready and eager to go home to see his family. He had saved a considerable amount of his earnings. He had grown in stature and maturity and was now literate in French and English. After an emotional parting with Captain Hobbs and his friends, he departed for his new home. He traveled north to Salisbury, then to Warminster, and westward to Wyke Champflower.

Gilbert's homecoming was met with mixed emotions. His mother cried with happiness to see her son, but his father had died three years earlier. His brother, Curtis, now twenty-seven, had assumed the leadership of the family. But Curtis was in bad health and it was becoming difficult for him to supervise the manor estate. Curtis had married a kind woman named Anna and had three children, Harry, seven, Roland, six, and Elizabeth, three.

Curtis and Gilbert renewed their strong bond as brothers and both were pleased that they could address the family's needs together. Their brotherly friendship mended quickly as if they had never been parted. Under difficult circumstances, Curtis had done a miraculous job in maintaining the estate. There had been three successful growing seasons for their crops. The past two winters were mild and there was sufficient water and feed for their farm animals. The peasants had cultivated a new field. In Bruton, four new housing structures were built for the workers and a schoolhouse had been built for the children.

Gilbert immersed himself in the family circle. He delighted in Curtis and Anna's children, spending hours telling young Harry, Roland, and

Elizabeth about his travels. Young Elizabeth had difficulty pronouncing "Uncle Gilbert," so she called him "Gibby," and that proved to be a good nickname to be used by all the family. Gilbert had a strong affection for the children and he taught them many things, including how to read and write. They never tired of asking questions and listening to Gilbert's stories about faraway places. They in turn grew to love and emulate their Uncle Gibby.

In 1443, the Duke of Somerset (Cardinal Beaufort's uncle) and his traveling party moved through Somerset County seeking support for his troops. The Duke appealed to Curtis and Gilbert for their support. They discussed their appropriate role and agreed to provide limited support. Although they wanted to stay out of the government's civil disagreements, they agreed to supply some food and supplies. They sensed a growing concern for further confrontations of the royal families. They would resist sending their workers and sons into battle for the respective armies. As some consolation, Gilbert offered his personal assistance, including his regional diplomacy with local citizens, as a trusted representative of the Duke.

Curtis' health continued to decline. In 1445, he contracted pneumonia and died. At his deathbed, Gilbert promised Curtis that he would care for Anna and help raise his children. He and Gilbert had spent four years together since Gilbert had returned from the seas. Their solid relationship—their kinship—since early childhood meant everything to Gilbert and he lived the rest of his life ever mindful of his solemn oath to Curtis. Curtis was buried in the family cemetery at Wyke Champflower. Gilbert, who never married, became the surrogate father for Curtis' children. He was a loyal and compassionate brother-in-law for Anna.

Gilbert assumed the leadership of the family's manorial estate. He was well liked by the workers who were loyal to him. He prepared Harry, the oldest son, to assume the family estate at the appropriate time. Gilbert's friendship with the royal Duke of Somerset increased and he often attended parties and special events of the royal family when they visited Somerset County.

Under Gilbert's guidance and instruction, Harry and Roland became well educated young men for their time. They learned the basics for farming, geography, and some seamanship. Harry was well prepared to inherit the family estate and Gilbert made the transition smooth for him when Harry reached full maturity.

Roland was adventuresome and inquisitive, somewhat similar to Gilbert. He always wanted to expand his travels and discover new lands. He persisted in asking Gilbert about the exotic places that he had visited in his younger days. He considered Gilbert to be a wise and respected man and as he grew older, he looked to Gilbert for advice and counsel.

As Roland matured, he often asked Gilbert, "What is to become of me? I know that Harry will assume the family estate and I will need to move on. But before I settle, I want to see new lands and explore the treasures throughout this land. Gilbert, will you help me discover my dreams?"

Gilbert responded and assured Roland saying, "Your opportunities are coming-be patient and be prepared-for you will be well tested in due time." When the time came, Gilbert directed Roland toward some promising opportunities in East Anglia knowing that Roland's travels and new life would bring further changes for the family.

Gilbert's final days were spent at Wyke Champflower. Occasionally, he traveled to Glastonbury and Bath where he enjoyed the heated spring waters and the abundance of the open markets. He recorded his travels and became an accomplished artist, even though his modest nature prevented him from showing and selling his work to the public. His greatest pleasures in old age were the moments he shared with Curtis and Anna's children and their young friends on the family estate.

He died in 1462 and was buried in the family cemetery, near the burial plots for Anna and Curtis de Kene.

Family Cemetery, Wyke Champflower

Chapter 3

Roland Kene
1435 – 1487
Farmer, Settler

MOVING AWAY FROM
FEUDAL TIMES

On a bright and sunny Saturday afternoon in the spring of 1452, Roland was visiting with the family blacksmith, reviewing the condition of some of the horses in the stable. He was planning to take a ride in the afternoon to the market in nearby Bruton. While he was examining one of the horses, two children came running toward the stables, yelling for help.

One of the guests, young Sharon Miller who was there visiting Roland's sister Elizabeth, had tears in her eyes as she cried, "Sarah lost the reins and that wild horse named Thunder has run away with her. She can't stop."

Another young visitor, her twin sister Karen Miller pleaded for help, "Please come help, Sarah doesn't know what to do."

Sarah's horse was running out of control and racing toward the southern meadow and the River Brue. Her horse had been startled by an errant gunshot and Sarah dropped the reins. Roland quickly mounted his favorite horse, a startling bronze stallion named Blaze, and dashed off after the young lady. Across a wheat field and toward the south meadow, Roland finally caught the runaway horse Thunder as he was about to enter the thistle patch by the area known as Skunk's Corner. Roland gradually brought Thunder under control. It took about fifteen minutes to calm the horses and begin the return trip to the Kene's barn.

The frightened young lady was speechless. Without Roland's gallant rescue, what might have happened could have been disastrous.

Roland tried to be modest about the affair, saying "Thank goodness you held on and were not thrown off by Thunder. And I am really glad I didn't have to go into the skunk patch. Can you imagine what we would smell like if those skunks would have let loose with a blast?"

With Thunder calmed, Roland continued to hold the reins so that both horses easily walked back to the barn side by side. He dismounted and then led Thunder next to a small stump so Sarah could dismount easily.

Back on steady ground, the frightened young girl regained her composure and thanked Roland in her deep voice saying, "I didn't know what to do. Thunder ran so fast, I just held on to the saddle horn and prayed for help. I couldn't have lasted much longer. When I saw you riding toward me in the meadow, I knew my prayers were answered."

Roland arranged some comfortable chairs for all the guests. He brought cold drinks and refreshments, and he suggested that the girls rest and recuperate. As Roland retreated, he couldn't help but watch his sister as she visited with her friends. The grace and beauty of the young lady he had just rescued surprised and shocked him.

Sarah Clarke, a charming fifteen-year old lass from Glastonbury, was visiting her cousins in the neighboring village of Cheddar. She was obviously well mannered and polite. She stood about five foot three inches tall with deep blue eyes and a clear complexion. Her deep voice and an infectious smile drew Roland despite her young age. Once again, he was awestruck with her beauty and her sincere empathy and thought-fulness for her friends.

Sarah, too, was in awe of Roland, not only for saving her when her horse ran away, but also for his kind and gentle behavior in the aftermath. She noticed Roland's broad smile and prominent western teeth, as well as the blush that crept across his face every time she glanced at him.

Roland was seventeen years old, tall at six foot one inch, muscular, and stalwart from the strenuous physical work in the fields on the family estate at Wyke Champflower. He had brown hair, a wide forehead, and a well proportioned body. He was naturally shy and sometimes seemed awkward with newcomers and company.

Roland's father Curtis had died when he was just ten years old. Roland's mother had devoted her life to raising his older brother, Harry, himself, and his younger sister, Elizabeth. His Uncle Gilbert became the guiding influence in Roland's life. He was his teacher and his confident. He taught him to read and write in French and English, some history, geography, horticulture, and agriculture. All of the children learned to work on the farm and to share family responsibilities at an early age.

Gilbert took the children on trips to the neighboring counties, including Cornwall, Suffolk, and Dorset and they visited the ports of Plymouth, Southampton, Bristol, and Cardiff. At an early age, Roland developed a liking for travel and adventure. Although he was well schooled and trained for farming, he had an air of independence and exploration. He was fascinated with the stories his Uncle Gilbert told him about his travels when was aboard the ship, the *Neptune*.

Over the next two years, Roland continued to visit with Sarah whenever she came to Cheddar to visit her cousins, and, more often, to Wyke Champflower. He, in turn, traveled to Glastonbury to extend their courtship. Over time, they fell in love, destined to be together forever. They were married in 1454 at the Kene family chapel called St. Michael's on the grounds of Wyke Champflower.

At that time, there was a growing feeling of uncertainty and insta-bility within the country, especially on the farms and the feudal estates. Ever since King Henry IV issued a new constitution, there seemed to be a gradual deterioration of the feudal system. Some farm workers were moving into towns to work on the docks and in the markets. Shipping and regional trade were increasing. The new economic system seemed to favor merchants, traders, and independent business operations. Skilled workers were becoming specialized and joining recognized guilds.

In addition, skirmishes were leading to a civil war that would come to be known as the Wars of the Roses and were beginning to threaten the country. Scattered violence erupted in the Midlands. Troops from York battled those from Lancaster and both sides were recruiting large numbers of troops.

Roland and Sarah were living on the family estate at Wyke Champflower. Roland felt restless about his future, knowing that his brother Harry would assume the estate and that warring conditions were threatening his family. Roland's apprehensions were evident as he spoke with Sarah and Gilbert about the future.

"What opportunity do we have here in Somerset County? The Wars constantly engage our neighbors and our workers and the military forces persist in confiscating our crops. The tenant farmers are restricted to their acreage, which makes some of them want to leave to find other work before they are compelled to work in the service of the Crown. What are other people doing–what must we do-to tolerate these changing times?"

Gilbert was perplexed too, but he was sympathetic and he wanted to be helpful. "Roland," he said, "I know you and Sarah want to find a place where you can build a home and raise a family of your own. You are right. These are changing times, and where there are problems such as you have identified, there are also bound to be some good opportunities if you have the persistence to find them."

Sarah intervened, "Let's find them. We are young enough to accept any necessary changes now. Roland and I want to have a family and build our own estate."

With their pleading, Gilbert brought out his traveling records and maps, including the descriptions of some of the areas he had visited years ago. He said, "Roland, I think you are right. Maybe it is time for you and me to take a trip and investigate some new areas."

As he pointed to new locations, he told Roland about possible trading opportunities near the ports of Plymouth, Calais, and London. He also suggested they visit the agricultural fields in Suffolk, Canterbury, and possibly Norwich County.

Gilbert exclaimed, "You know Roland, Norwich County might be the place. One of my favorite areas in East Anglia, near the city of Bishop's Lynn, is full of rich agricultural lands and some valuable salt deposits. What do you say?"

Roland answered, "I say I trust my Uncle Gilbert. Why I seem to remember that he was the one suggesting I court a beautiful young lady on a runaway horse and that was the best decision of my life."

As they planned the trip, Roland grew excited for an adventure and for the opportunity to find a better life for his beloved Sarah and any children that would bless their union. In the summer of 1456, Roland and Gilbert set off on an exploratory trip. They traveled east to London where they stayed for five nights. They sailed on the River Thames, visited Westminster and the London markets, and mingled with merchants and traders. They collected information about the most productive areas, fishing habitats, and trading routes. Then they traveled north, stopping in Cambridge and then to the great seaport of Yarmouth.

When they arrived in Yarmouth, the ship, the *Neptune* was in dock. Gilbert hurried to see Captain Hobbs and some of his old friends. After a friendly reunion, Gilbert told Captain Hobbs about Roland and the possibility of his relocating in East Anglia. The captain agreed, suggesting they visit the rich farming area near Bishop's Lynn. The area was known for vast salt deposits, good fishing, and the agricultural land, which was believed to be ideal for wine, wheat, corn, and barley production. Some sheep and cattle were raised in the area. Captain Hobbs sent them off with the names of his trading friends, the merchants who lived in Bishop's Lynn. Roland was ecstatic that his Uncle Gilbert had the good fortune of running into his respected friend, the well-traveled captain.

According to Captain Hobbs, the merchants in Bishop's Lynn were improving the ship yards and dock facilities. Several new warehouses

had been built on the River Nar. Agricultural production was consistently increasing and traders could buy and sell commodities for three
neighboring counties using the navigable rivers and sea routes to the
North Sea. Direct routes were possible to Scotland, across the North
Sea to the Netherlands and Calais, and southward to London. From the
captain's description, it appeared that the area in East Anglia was primed
for future development.

Gilbert and Roland traveled northeast along the coast until they
reached Norwich and Bishop's Lynn. From there they surveyed the
surrounding farm lands. They encountered Henry Grave, one of the
merchants Captain Hobbs identified as a friend and trusted merchant.
His opinions of the opportunities in the area were consistent with those
of Captain Hobbs. He suggested that the change from simply local
farming to the production of crops and animals would be valuable to
merchants and traders on a regional basis and that the wool and clothing
industry looked promising. Shipping to neighboring counties would give
added value to the other important resources within Norwich County.
Roland and Gilbert asked Henry Grave to inform them if he found a
farm in the area that might suit Roland's needs.

After several days in East Anglia, Gilbert and Roland traveled
southward through Peterborough, Oxford, the city of Bath, and then
home to Wyke Champflower. The trip was informative, enlightening,
and a bold incentive for Roland to pursue his dreams. He was developing an expanding vision of his country. Each day, his confidence grew
along with his passion to build a new and better life for Sarah and
himself. Gilbert, now forty-one years old, was gratified to share his heart
warming experience with Roland. He reveled in Roland's excitement in
each new discovery. He had a keen sense, that if directed properly, the
youth and vitality of Roland pointed toward financial success and a very
happy family. Although Gilbert had opened new horizons for Roland,
he accepted his responsibility to stay in Wyke Champflower with Harry
and the rest of the family.

It was a joyous homecoming for the men. Roland was brimming with exciting news he wanted to share with Sarah. Sarah too, had good news for Roland-she was expecting their first child to be born in the fall. Their dreams seemed to be falling into place. Their daughter Judy was born in October as they continued making plans for a new home somewhere in East Anglia. In the meantime Roland continued to correspond with Henry Grave and prepared to move his family.

Shortly after the first of the year, Henry Grave responded with a letter containing some good news.

Dear Roland,

There is a farm estate along the Nar River that you may like. It's about twelve kilometers outside of Bishop's Lynn. The farm has about forty acres and some undeveloped forest land on its west side. Some of the land used to be worked by unsuccessful farmers who have left the area. It would need considerable work. But some of the ground appears to be fertile, and water is plentiful. It has abundant grazing land adjoining the farm for common cattle and sheep grazing. If you are interested, I suggest you come inspect the property at your earliest convenience.

Respectfully yours,

Henry Grave

Sarah quickly asked, "Roland, do you trust this man, Henry Grave?"

Roland responded, "Yes, Gilbert and I agreed that he was honest and trustworthy."

Then Sarah added, "Then you must go inspect the property as soon as possible." Roland agreed. He responded to Henry Grave, thanking him and telling him about his new plan to visit him and survey the proposed farm. Although the winter cold weather still covered the land, Roland took ample provisions and traveled on horseback in late February to Bishop's Lynn. His enthusiasm and anticipation for his new home kept him safe and warm as well as did his overnight accommodations in some friendly inns along the way.

Roland inspected the proposed farm and found it to be precisely what Henry Grave had described. It needed substantial work, which didn't seem to discourage Roland. He identified a site for a new farmhouse and he created a preliminary plan for some gardens. He met some of the neighbors and other friends of Henry Grave. They convinced Roland that this area could thrive in the next fifty years. With trading routes along the Nar River and using the North Sea, there would be many enterprising merchants looking for good crops to sell on the outbound vessels.

Upon Roland's return home, Gilbert and Harry agreed to use family funds for the initial investment. Roland agreed to assume the complete responsibilities for the new farm. He would repay them when the farm operations became profitable.

Shortly after Roland returned to Wyke Champflower, he and Sarah began to assemble their belongings in preparation for their move to Norwich County in the spring. It was difficult leaving his brother, Harry, and his wife, as well as his sister, Elizabeth. Uncle Gilbert agreed to go with Roland and Sarah for a short time to help them get settled. They all agreed to visit Roland and Sarah when they were settled in their new home.

About this time, Roland decided to drop the "de" from the family name. When he signed the title for the new farm, he dropped the "de" and spelled his name Kynne. Over the years, the spelling of the family name changed many times. But this was the first time that the French components had been altered.

By late spring, Roland, Gilbert, Sarah, and their baby arrived at the farm outside Bishop's Lynn. While the family stayed in temporary quarters, Roland, Gilbert, and a small crew of laborers worked feverishly to construct a new farmhouse, a small barn, and some outbuildings for the chickens and pigs. Sarah planted the original family garden with some vegetables, several fruit trees, and an area on a distant hill reserved for a flower garden. The vegetable garden grew larger each year to accommodate the appetites and expanding needs of the family.

In the flower garden, Sarah started modestly with a few daffodils, lavender, and some wild flowers. Taking one summer at a time and taking one step at a time, she doubled the planting each year until she created the most colorful garden with radiant colors. For the newcomer, the sweet aromas and magnificent sight were breath-taking. She had planted the flowers in majestic, swirling patterns with great ribbons and swaths of deep purple, orange, white, lemon, salmon pink, and butter yellow. Each different color was confined to its natural pattern, leaving a flowing sensation that moved with the sunshine and the gentle breezes. After twelve years, the whole hillside, about one and a half acre, had been overtaken by the beauty of Sarah's flower garden. Roland tantalized her about such an extravagant pursuit but he knew that her flowers fed the big, healthy bees that provided honey and roamed about his crops.

Roland concentrated on improving the farm. He purchased a few cows, chickens, and pigs. He cleared more land and purchased feed and supplies from his neighbors. His major investment was made for a small flock of "top-quality" sheep because he intended to produce a premier quality of wool. With a modest beginning, he planned to consistently improve his line of sheep.

They worked hard to establish a modest home and make the farm productive as quickly as possible. It was a "dream come true" for the young and happy couple. The experience and knowledge they had gained from Wyke Champflower was indispensible for their success as they worked from dawn to dusk, six days a week. Sundays were spent in accordance with their Catholic traditions.

As time passed, the family traveled to Bishop's Lynn where they attended All Saints' Church. The priest, John Capgrave, served the Austin Friars at the Lynn Friary on Austin Street at that time. Roland took communion, broke bread, and shared company with other members of the church.

During the next thirty-one years, Roland and Sarah lived happily together on their farm. After repaying their loan to Gilbert and Harry, they acquired more property and expanded their crops. By focusing on improving the breeding of their sheep, the valuable wool brought premium prices. His crops, including the wheat and barley, were premium quality, allowing Roland to become a steady supplier to the brewers in the region. The regional markets, including Ely, St. John, and Norwich, fulfilled their buying needs. Roland associated with the traders and merchants at St. George's and the Guildhall in Bishop's Lynn. The family made friends, primarily with their neighbors, but directed the majority of their time and work to the creation of their successful farm and the steady growth of their family.

Their lives became routine in a farming sense, but were far from dull as they had nine children over the years. Oldest was Judy, who was born in Wake Champflower, then Gilbert, who was named after Uncle Gilbert, and Nicholas. Oliver died in childbirth and Virginia died when she was two years old. Then came Marcia, followed by sons Michael, Ted, and Charles. Charles, the youngest, followed his older brothers closely and, at times, he was inseparable from the older Michael and Ted. All the children began at an early age to help with the chores and operations of the farm.

About the time that Italian Leonardo da Vinci was drawing extraordinary pictures and diagrams about human anatomy and flying machines, Roland began selling a modest amount of wool and some sheep to the government forces of the House of York. He quickly became an important supplier for the troops of King Edward IV. As King Edward IV won important battles in the Wars of the Roses, he sequestered estates and lands of the defeated Lancasters. The grateful king gave or made those lands available to the loyal nobles of the House of York and to his prominent supporters, including Roland. Roland was thrifty and he acquired some of the available lands, primarily to increase his farming operations. In addition, he acquired some raw lands in Lincoln County. The property in Lincoln County was believed to be valuable, but Roland never examined nor developed the ground.

Gilbert, the oldest son, was well trained by Roland for farming and he assumed his responsibilities for the operations of the original farm upon his maturity.

Four sons, Nicholas, Michael, Ted, and Charles volunteered for service in support of the House of York for King Edward IV. Although Charles was too young for warfare, his commitment and dedication to the monarchy would serve him well in future years.

Ted survived the war and eventually returned to live near the family farm in Norwich. Michael was killed in combat. Nicholas returned to Norwich for a short time and then traveled to Ireland with several of his military friends. Nicholas visited several areas, including Waterford, Dubie, and Kilologher, and eventually settled in County Cork. Nicolas married an Irish lady named Anne Neville from Wexford. Their family of eight children flourished in Counties Cork, Kent, and Kilkenny. Although the genealogical lines were muddled, their oldest son Nicholas II reportedly had several sons, establishing a large family of Keneys throughout the Emerald Isle.

Charles' brothers' military experiences had a profound impact on him, which helped to motivate him to become an accomplished student, professor, and justice of the peace in the King's service. After extensive self examination, Charles would conclude that he and the family should address their patriotic responsibilities at a time when turmoil was likely to consume the entire country.

Charles was inclined to move away from the agricultural and trading interests of his family. With an advanced education for his time, he moved toward administrative and civic endeavors. Paving the way for his children to succeed, he was eager to expand educational opportunities for many young people.

Roland and Sarah remained on their farm during their elder years.

Their oldest son Gilbert assumed the management of their original farm. Their holdings had expanded so that sufficient lands were available for their other remaining sons, Ted and Charles.

Roland and Sarah took great pride in their children and their accomplishments. Their steadfast dedication to the success of their family farm led to considerable wealth for the times. Using the family's wealth and sound moral teachings, the children moved on to establish their own distinguished careers. The success of their children provided a mutual contentment for Roland and Sarah in their later years.

While still living on the family farm, Roland died in 1487 and Sarah died in 1491. Both were buried in the family cemetery plot next to All Saints' Church in Bishop's Lynn in Norwich County.

The sign leading to Wyke Champflower and Castle Cary

Roland and Sarah Kene Descendants

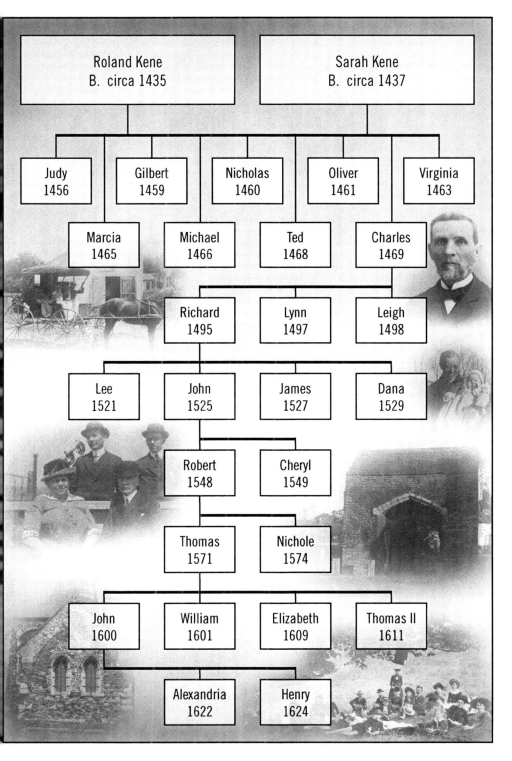

Roland Kene
B. circa 1435

Sarah Kene
B. circa 1437

| Judy 1456 | Gilbert 1459 | Nicholas 1460 | Oliver 1461 | Virginia 1463 |

| Marcia 1465 | Michael 1466 | Ted 1468 | Charles 1469 |

| Richard 1495 | Lynn 1497 | Leigh 1498 |

| Lee 1521 | John 1525 | James 1527 | Dana 1529 |

| Robert 1548 | Cheryl 1549 |

| Thomas 1571 | Nichole 1574 |

| John 1600 | William 1601 | Elizabeth 1609 | Thomas II 1611 |

| Alexandria 1622 | Henry 1624 |

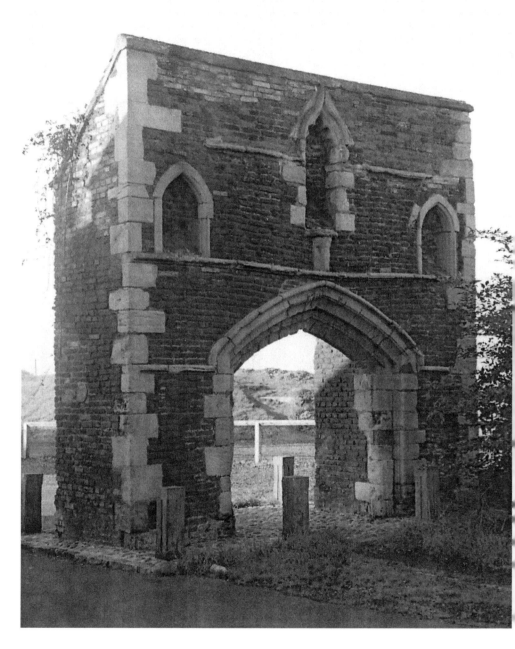

Gate of the White Friars, King's Lynn

Chapter 4

Charles Kynne
1469 – 1518
Scholar, Arbitrator

SOWING PEACE
IN THE FARMLANDS

Charles, the youngest of nine children, was curious and inquisitive with a natural inclination toward personal independence. Even at an early age, he seemed to find happiness with his freedom and unrestricted ability to satisfy his own curiosity and instincts. One of his favorite things to do was to follow his brother Ted, tagging along whether or not he was wanted or included.

One time Charles and his brother Ted learned an important lesson about kinship when they disobeyed their mother's instructions. Ted returned home one evening to find his mother waiting at the front door. Early that morning his mother Sarah had sent Ted on a few errands and she had given him permission to stay and play with his friend Jerry Townsend until supper time. When he left home that morning, his younger brother Charles, or Chuck as he was called, followed him out of their house. But shortly Ted confronted Chuck and told him to go home. Chuck refused. When Chuck wasn't watching, Ted made a quick turn through the trees and lost his pesky little brother.

"Ted," his mother called out as she saw him. She had that look in her eye, stopping his whistle and cheerful song in midstream.

"Yes, Mum," Ted half whispered. "I've done just what you asked. You did say I could stay and play with Jerry after I delivered your packages. Remember?"

"And what about Chuck?" she inquired. "Did you know that your brothers and sisters spent half the day looking for him?"

"Mum, you didn't give him permission to come with me. How was I supposed to know that he was following me?"

"Perhaps because he's done it before. You ought to look out for your little brother since he tends to wander away. He's your kin—you need to take care of him. That's the way kinship works. Remember the Bible—remember in Genesis when Cain asked, 'Am I my brother's keeper?' The answer was 'yes you are' and that means we take care of each other. Your sister Judy takes good care of him, but you and your brothers let him wander anywhere."

Ted glared at his red-haired baby brother who appeared, grinning behind his mother.

Chuck said, "It's okay, Mum. I wasn't lost. I told Ted I wanted to go over to my friend Dave Hollingsworth's house. I know the way, and I know the marks on the trail, including the tree that was struck by lightning. You want to see the map I made? I'll go get it if you want to see it."

Sarah shook her head and said, "No, Charles, just make sure you have permission and let me know where you are going before you leave. We were all sick with worry. Not to mention that you neglected your gardening duties while you were gone. There will be extra weeding and pruning for you tomorrow."

"Yes, Mum, may I go now?"

Sarah continued, "It's almost time to eat, you and your brother should go wash up." She left the boys alone as they moved outside.

Ted stared hard at Chuck one more time, then relaxed into a wide smile before he reached out to tousle his kid brother's hair. "We'll play together tomorrow, after you finish your chores."

"I hate gardening. You know that, Ted. I'm not spending my whole life tilling the soil. There are lots of other things to do that are more fun."

"Is that so? Well, what did you do today for fun after I left you?"

"Dave and I played a game called 'hoops' in the morning."

"Hoops? What is that?"

"It's a new game that Dave taught me. Each player has ten hoops and he throws them around a peg about twenty feet away. The one with the most hoops around the peg wins the game. Then we went back to his house for snacks. Dave's father asked us to go to his village shop, so we went there to help him for awhile. I swept the floor, loaded supplies for some customers, and then old Mrs. Cadle came in. She bought all kinds of things, but you know, she is so old and feeble and half blind, I felt so sorry for her. Anyway, Dave and I carried her supplies home and she wanted to pay us, but Dave and I refused. You know, she has six cats, three dogs, and two ponies in her back yard."

Ted said, "You sure are nosey. Did you see her trophy room?"

"No," said Chuck, "but I did meet her housekeeper Tillie and I saw a room in the back of her house with over fifty books in it. She said she had been collecting them since her father died, but now she can hardly read, so she loans them to friends. Most of the primers and religious books were hand-written by the friars at church. She let me borrow one and I told her I would return it next week. Do you think father would read it to us?"

"It's worth a try," said Ted.

Chuck's father, who was generally eager to see new books and expand his awareness of new ideas, began to read the borrowed book that evening. Such experiences always tested his father's limited ability to read and translate Latin. Like many of the religious books at that time, it dealt with passages from the Bible and expounded the four cardinal virtues of the period. They were first, **prudence** and good judgment, next **temperance** and self-control, followed by **fortitude**, and finally **justice**. Charles was captivated by the messages. The next day when he was alone, he studied the words in the book and attempted to memorize some of the passages. Reading from books, for Chuck, opened a whole new arena for learning and understanding the world beyond the family farm and daily life in Bishop's Lynn.

Charles never did like gardening, but he became a good student and a quick learner. His parents conducted home school classes for all their children. Just as with clothing, Chuck was the recipient of all the "hand me down" primer books, lessons, and instructions since he was the youngest child. He could find answers to most of his questions and additional instruction from his father and older brothers and sisters. His initial education included lessons in good manners, some arithmetic, French, and Latin. In addition, he attended classes at St. Nicholas Catholic Church where he had an introduction to religious history. The family attended mass regularly and occasionally visited the great cathedral in Norwich.

In 1474, William Caxton printed the first book in England and, in 1477, he printed the first edition of Chaucer's *Canterbury Tales*. Charles continued to borrow primers and instructions from Mrs. Cadle and spent many evenings with his father reading scriptures from the Bible and sometimes from one of the classics of the time. At an early age, he became an exceptional reader. He read Chaucer when he was thirteen. The Catholic friars were so impressed with his scholastic progress that they recommended him for advanced studies. When Charles turned sixteen, the friars and his father arranged for him to spend a school year at Cambridge studying religious history, morality, and the basic laws of conduct involving local justice and England's justice of the peace system. Thus, Charles became the first member of the family to have an advanced education, an experience he cherished throughout his life. His education paved the way for his family's recorded history.

By then, Charles had grown tall. Like his father he stood six feet one inch. With his strength, quickness, and agility, he became an accomplished outdoorsman. Charles liked to climb mountains and often went for long walks along the coastlines or river beds. Although an excellent marksman, he did not shoot wild game just for sport. Rather, he hunted only to provide food for his family, and he insisted upon proper cleaning and disposition of all game and fish. For times of meditation and personal solitude, he preferred to explore wilderness areas just for fun and good exercise.

In the summer of 1485, Henry Tudor and his troops defeated Richard III at the Battle of Bosworth. With the victory and the crowning of Henry VII, the Tudor Age emerged in England, signaling a change in government authority. Within a year, rebels again challenged the Crown. King Henry VII moved his army into the Midlands and defeated the rebels at the Battle of Stoke in 1487, which is considered by some to be the last battle in the Wars of the Roses.

During these turbulent times, Charles completed his studies at Cambridge. At seventeen, he volunteered to serve with several other students in King Henry's guard. Charles served with his comrades in support of the fighting troops as the fighting continued against the renegades for three more years. He completed his obligation and returned to Bishop's Lynn in 1490, after gaining considerable maturity and experience in the service of King Henry VII. The friends and valuable allies he made in the King's service would serve him well the rest of his life. He returned home with a strong sense of loyalty and patriotism for his country. Initially he considered a teaching career, largely because he enjoyed the friendship and association with his academic friends from Cambridge. But he changed his mind shortly after arriving home when he became aware of other opportunities associated with the family's properties.

While Charles was away, his father had died. His oldest brother, Gilbert, inherited the original family estate and assumed the management of the family farm. Charles and his other brothers inherited other properties from his father. Charles received two tracts, one a remote property to the north in Lincoln County that was reported to have limestone deposits and another property, a small farm located on the River Nar, closer to the town of Bishop's Lynn. Tenant farmers lived on the farm property and were growing barley and wheat. They called it the Nar River Farm. Rents from the farm would provide a small but adequate income for Charles.

Charles had also been eager to return home to reacquaint himself with Ruth, his childhood sweetheart. Ruth was cheerful, outgoing, and popular with her many friends. Ruth's warm personality made her attractive to young children, who seemed to follow her wherever she went. Using her unique ability to tell enchanting stories, Ruth sometimes gathered young people in a group to share her tales and make-believe fantasies. Ruth's family came to Bishop's Lynn from Gronigon, Holland in the Netherlands. Her family attended St. Nicholas Church which is where Charles met Ruth. Their courtship and wedding in 1492 was a blissful success from the very beginning and their mutual devotion lasted throughout their lives. Their first home was a cottage on Thomas Street in the southern part of Bishop's Lynn.

Ruth was a dedicated homemaker. With a practical knowledge of how to do most anything and everything around their home, Ruth could cook, sew, and assemble most anything needed around the house. Using wool from the sheep, she made warm blankets for all the members of her family and some of the neighbors. When the fruit trees were harvested in the fall, she made apple and cherry cobbler that attracted friends and neighbors throughout Bishop's Lynn. To the delight of the small children, Ruth could make toys and games out of the simplest ingredients. Taking excess wool fragments from the sheep, she made singular rope strands, which she tied together to make jump ropes for the children. With a cheerful countenance, Ruth brought joy to Charles and their mutual friends.

Charles turned his attention to the properties he had inherited and to other possibilities to advance his career. He consulted with a mining expert to determine the extent of the stone quarries on their property near Ancaster in Lincoln County. The expert identified the quarries, but he could not explain with certainty how deep nor how extensive the valuable deposits were situated.

Charles thought the initial estimate of the costs for mining were too vague and too expensive. Consequently, he chose to postpone any mining until he had sufficient funds and was more certain of the value of the deposits.

The Nar River Farms had been operated by the tenant farmers and some of their families had lived on the property for over thirty years. After careful observation, Charles did not want to interfere with the working agreement since the farmers were relatively successful and had been loyal to his family. His father had helped some of the families through difficult times. However, the farmers and some of their neighbors asked Charles to become involved in another way. They suggested that he serve as their merchant, assisting with the transportation and sale of their wheat, barley, and oats to various buyers. Charles agreed and began arranging the sale and transportation of their products, primarily to the breweries in the area.

In 1494, another opportunity presented itself to Charles. The fighting in the Midlands had subsided and King Henry VII was determined to stabilize the government. The King was building his treasury and making a comprehensive effort to collect all revenue owed to the Crown. The King's Council hired men versed in the law to help collect the taxes and settle local disputes. With recognition for his service to the Crown and his brief legal education, Charles was asked to serve as a representative for the King's Court in Norwich County where he would have the title of Justice of the Peace. He accepted the offer which would assure him of an ongoing association with members of the King's court and some of his former comrades from the King's Guard.

Charles quickly learned that serving in the King's Court, with the responsibility for collecting taxes, was not necessarily a popular occupation. The reaction and ongoing resentment from many citizens startled him. He soon realized that soothing ruffled taxpayers required a firm, yet tactful approach. Determined to be fair and equitable, Charles expanded his philosophy that incorporated his religious and moral beliefs into a practical code of conduct for everyday living, including tax collecting.

Within a short time, Charles and Ruth would be parents of Richard, their first child, born in 1495. He was followed by two girls, Lynn in 1497 and Leigh in 1498. Following his own father's example, Charles was devoted to raising and educating his children. As his son grew, Charles personally tutored him in English, Latin, and mathematics, sharing his own enthusiasm for learning.

Nonetheless, Richard preferred physical activities, but also showed an early interest in sailing and shipbuilding. Sensing his son's fascination for ships, Charles fostered this interest by taking him often to the ocean shores and to the docks to see the oceangoing vessels. Richard responded by carving model ships out of wood. Over time, he would be able to identify the major ships sailing in and out of the harbor. Consequently, he learned a great deal about shapes and sailing capabilities of the merchant ships.

As Charles aged, he continued to serve as the Justice of the Peace. But he also continued to be fascinated by the ships coming into and leaving the harbor near Bishop's Lynn. He enjoyed visiting with sailors, their captains, and the merchants at the port authority office. In 1495, news reached Bishop's Lynn that a Spanish Ship, the *Pinta*, and an explorer named Cristobal Colón (Columbus) had discovered a new land and likely a new shipping route to the Far East. Another report claimed that Portuguese explorers were trading on African shores. Although these discoveries might not have an immediate impact on Bishop's Lynn, Charles thought that, in time, they would have an impact on shipping and future exploration for England and all major European countries. Spain and Portugal appeared to be the leading countries in the international race for exploration, but he hoped that England would join the race soon.

When King Henry VII announced a new policy calling for expanded trade and commerce, Charles took note and began to take a more active interest in the shipping facilities in the neighboring harbors. He reasoned that if products from East Anglia were to be sold to larger markets, larger ships and better facilities would need to be built.

As trade and commerce grew, the trade associations and guilds expanded. At that time, there were five active guilds in Bishop's Lynn. Charles had several friends who were guild members and they invited Charles to join the Trinity Guild. He enjoyed socializing with the merchants and he felt honored when he was asked to become a member. He considered this to be the "great guild," for its members consisted of the most successful merchants and traders in the county. But he declined, sighting his preference to remain independent in service to the Crown as a justice of the peace.

In 1498, King Henry VII visited Bishop's Lynn. Charles and Ruth attended the welcoming party. As proud citizens, they would talk the rest of their lives about the celebration at the Duke's Head Tavern and the King's attendance at an evening theatrical performance at St. George's Guildhall.

At that time, many farmers were building enclosures and crude fences to limit access to their properties. Farmers wanted to keep intruders, including other farmers' cattle and sheep out of their private lands. Some of the tenant farmers objected and some heated arguments ensued. In his role as a representative of the King's government, Charles was asked to mediate some of the disputes. Using his law background and his aptitude for good common sense, Charles attempted to reach satisfactory solutions.

To establish the proper decorum in the court and to put the parties in the proper frame of mind, Charles would open the proceedings by announcing, "Gentlemen, we are here to study the facts of this case and to reach a solution. Unfortunately, neither one of you is likely to be pleased with the solution if it is left for the court to determine the verdict. But if both of you have an understanding of the rights and concerns of one another and are willing to compromise in the interest of fairness to each other, then, I believe a fair and equitable solution can be reached." Once opposing parties began to compromise, they often settled their disputes without further interference.

Over the years, Charles heard many unusual cases. In addition to boundary and land disputes, he often dealt with tax cases and offenses against the King. He had a keen knack for identifying merchants making exorbitant profits and swindlers taking advantage of poor farmers and peasants. If a defendant was found guilty, Charles did not hesitate to punish him by sending him to the stocks and sometimes placing guilty parties in shackles on exhibit in the public square.

Over time, Charles developed a reputation as a justice of the peace with a fair and equitable disposition. He advocated "a fair day's pay for a fair day's work." He believed that for the economic system to work and if people were to get along with each other, any agreement needed to be fair for all the parties and all the parties would need to respect each other.

As the years passed, Charles developed a friendship with Thomas Thoresby, a wealthy merchant who built a college in Bishop's Lynn. The college was established to support the Church and provide an educational institution for the area. At that time, wealthy men contributed money to provide for the monks, who in turn conducted worship services for the souls of the prominent men. In support of Thomas Thoresby and his college, Charles contacted his friends and the leading merchants throughout Norwich County to appeal for their cooperation. Friends responded from as far away as Ely, London, and Cambridge. The construction for the school was completed in 1510, and it soon opened to serve the community. Charles was proud to be part of the expansion of education in Bishop's Lynn.

In his later years, Charles returned to his academic pursuits and spent much of his time in study, research, and contemplation of the Church's doctrine. He studied the Bible and expanded upon the four "cardinal virtues" he had adapted as a young man. In addition to prudence, temperance, fortitude, and justice, he advocated three "theological" virtues. They were **faith, hope** (often viewed as **charity**), and **love**. At All Saints'

Church, Charles expounded upon these virtues and their relationship to a man's kinship with his spouse, his children, his family, and his friends.

Charles never developed the property in Lincoln County where the limestone deposits were located. That property and the Nar River Farm would be left to his son, Richard, in the same condition as he had received it from his father.

Richard grew to idolize his parents. He learned well the value of kinship, and in time, he would make good use of his father's advice and his inheritance to build a sizeable estate. He would begin the family's inquiry into the religious changes of the times.

To the end, Charles excelled in scholastic and literary pursuits, including a philosophic inquiry about the relationship between the court system and the Crown. His thoughtful style instilled a deep and lasting impression upon his children which carried forward in their pursuits to study, to learn, and to pursue their dreams.

Ruth was a superb influence, although in completely different ways. She had become an accomplished gardener lining the entrance and the yard near their home with colorful plants. She nurtured the girls as they grew to attract the attention of all the eligible boys in town. Ruth continued her delightful ways of telling stories and in time, she expanded her repertoire by including the travels of Uncle Gilbert and the heroic military campaigns of Uncles Ted and Nicholas. Both daughters, Lynn and Leigh, came to tell compelling stories just as their mother did.

Charles and Ruth's greatest hope was that their example of respectable Christian living exemplified by their integrity, discipline, and moral righteousness would be indelible to their children and serve as the most valuable gift a parent can give a child. Their children, Richard, Lynn, and Leigh, all married and rewarded Charles and Ruth with eight grandchildren.

Charles died of natural causes in the winter of 1518. Ruth passed away in 1521. They are buried on the grounds of All Saints' Church in Bishop's Lynn.

All Saints' Church, King's Lynn

Chapter 5

Richard Kynne
1495 – 1550
Merchant, Entrepreneur

NAVIGATING THROUGH PERILOUS TIMES

The small and enthusiastic boy named Richard looked down at the new paddleboat tethered to the dock on the River Nar. Richard had watched, and helped as he could, while his father Charles had built his requested birthday present. Finally, the morning of his sixth birthday arrived and there they were, his dad already in the boat. Richard, whose front teeth had yet to grow in, grinned a big toothless smile as he got ready to jump into the six-foot paddle boat.

Perhaps the launching went something like this:

Charles hollered, "Hold on there, Richard. Don't you think the maiden voyage should go beyond the dock?" Charles pointed to the rope still tied on the dock beside Richard.

"I was so excited, I forgot that," Richard yelled as he grabbed the rope, untied, and released it as he dropped down into the boat. "I can't believe I did that!"

"I can't either, because I think you already know more than some of the sailors I've seen in Bishop Lynn's Harbor who are three times older than you."

Richard smiled with glowing approval.

"Happy Birthday, mate," said his father.

"Yes sir. Thanks, Dad. This is the best present ever—but I can't wait until I am old enough to sail on the great River Ouse and in the ocean."

"I'm sure that will come soon enough," said Charles.

Two years passed while Richard's infatuation with ships and sailing in the ocean steadily increased. On his eighth birthday, his parents gave him a ten-foot rowboat with an attached sail. Together, Richard and his father rowed about the harbor and then they began sailing near the mouth of the River Nar and the inland waterways near Bishop's Lynn. Charles taught the boy how to steer by adjusting the sails according to the wind currents, by moving the rudder, and by working with the tide. Richard learned how to communicate with other ships and the harbor patrol, using flags, bells, and whistles. Onshore, he threw himself into studying maps and navigational charts. Charles played games with Richard, testing his math skills so that he learned different ways to solve navigational problems. In time, Richard knew how to calculate his position at sea or within the inland waterways so that he could accurately predict his arrival time. As he grew older, he gained a healthy respect for weather conditions and knew what precautions to take in case of a severe storm.

Although he was an early reader, Richard preferred sailing and other athletic activities to the academic pursuits so favored by his father. At the same time, his father's business of selling and transporting barley, wheat, and oats from regional farms to the breweries drew him in at an early age. He accompanied his father to the Merchant's Exchange, the docks, and the city hall. On these trips, Richard heard his father and his acquaintances discuss local shipping, warehouse, and sales news and exchange reports of explorations and discoveries around the world.

Richard was fascinated with stories about Cristobal Colón (Columbus) who reportedly discovered Española and some remote islands in 1492. In 1498, Colón set sail again on his third voyage to the New World during which he would discover what would be South America, and, eventually, Martinique, Honduras, and Costa Rica. Colón was followed by an Italian from Florence named Amerigo Vespucci, who was credited by a geographer Martin Waldseemuller for identifying the New World, which he called the "forth part of the known world." Accordingly, the New World became known as "America."

Richard heard many other stories on the docks. He was exposed at an early age to the expanding world of merchants, new markets, trade routes, and business opportunities. He studied well and vowed that one day he would be a successful entrepreneur. He often listened to the conversations of his father with other loyal friends of the Crown, including many who had served under King Henry VII. Often, their talks turned to military affairs of the King and his son, who would later be called Henry VIII, who was born only a few years before Richard.

Richard was the only son and oldest child in his family. He had two younger sisters, Lynn and Leigh, and many cousins and playmates with similar ages. The family was Catholic and they attended church on a regular basis at All Saints' Church. Many of their family activities were spent with other parishioners and most all of their daily activities were influenced by the church's religious schedule.

Richard was proud that his father Charles was a respected merchant and a member of the inner circle of the King's legal system when he served as Justice of the Peace in Norwich County. Richard never doubted that Charles was a devoted supporter of King Henry VII, and noted how he was loyal to the troops he had served with when he was in the service of the King.

Following family tradition, when he was sixteen, Richard fulfilled the family commitment and joined the King's forces. At that time, King Henry VIII was preparing a crusade against France. The English Parliament provided a grant, and in the spring of 1513 the troops, including Richard, sailed to Calais. They overtook the town of Therouanne, in what came to be known as the Battle of Spurs. When they captured the City of Tournai, reports of a great victory returned to the homeland and news quickly spread throughout the kingdom. King Henry VIII made a triumphant return to London. Richard served with distinction during the French campaign and, shortly thereafter, he and his regiment returned to England where he moved to a post near London. A peace treaty with France was officially signed in 1514.

In London, Richard met Marcia Shay, a bright, popular, and engaging young lady who caught Richard's eye from the moment they met. With exceptional domestic training from her mother, Marcia was a classic homemaker with many attributes similar to Richard's mother, Ruth. Marcia made many of her own clothes and could sew and repair most anything made of cloth. Everyone loved her cooking, especially her muffins and fresh bread. She had a simple yet comfortable way of decorating and arranging the kitchen and the common areas of the home. Although many compliments came her way, she modestly acknowledged them and continued on her generous way of caring for others. Knowledgeable about basic medical care, she often cared for sick and injured children. Everyone who knew Marcia agreed that she would be an ideal wife and Richard thoroughly agreed.

After a courtship throughout the summer, they were married in London in the fall of 1515. Richard and Marcia shared many common interests and what would be a successful marriage that reflected their love and devotion to each other from the very beginning.

London was an expanding city in 1515. John Colet was the Dean of St. Paul's Cathedral and there were ominous signs of corruption within the Church. Erasmus of Rotterdam, who taught at Cambridge, had written a book entitled *In Praise of Folly* which marked the abuses of the Church. Richard, who was inquisitive by nature, obtained one of the books and without divulging his interest for fear of reprisal by Church officials, he began to study the history and the interplay of the Church and its critics.

Dick and Marcia made many friends during his tenure in the military, especially when they were living near London. A friend named Lester Brand came from a family of miners from Nottinghamshire County.

Richard told Lester about the his family's land with the limestone quarries in Lincoln County near Ancaster and, on special leave, they traveled to survey the property. They reached the property on a very bright and sunny afternoon, shortly after a heavy rainstorm. There was a distinctive rainbow in the distance. The sunshine reflected against the majestic hills, and the fragrant scent of wildflowers permeated the air. It was such a memorable scene that thereafter, the property was called the Sunshine Mine. After a comprehensive inspection and accumulation of rock samples, Lester and Richard returned to London, with hopes that someday they might develop the area.

When Richard completed his military obligation, he and Marcia returned to Bishop's Lynn. At that time, business conditions were difficult throughout the entire East Anglia region. Under normal conditions, farming was difficult, but when there were droughts and extended natural calamities, farming was subject to even more hardships. With poor crops for the past two seasons, the tenant farmers were suffering. Many of them could not pay their land fees to landlords. The dreadful disease, commonly called the Plague, was spreading and some members of the families of the tenant farmers had contracted it.

Although Richard's father's age and health curtailed his activities, he was eager to welcome him home. He was determined to provide as much assistance as possible for Richard. He discussed the economic challenges, advising him about possible steps to withstand a prolonged depression, including the association of some reliable business partners and the possibility of beginning other business ventures.

Charles had arranged for Richard to become a member of the Trinity Guild, but in light of the uncertain economic times, Richard wanted to consider other options. In addition to managing the currently non-producing farm, he began investigating other businesses such as the Sunshine Mine. He also made plans for an animal tanning and processing plant as well as a shipbuilding operation.

Richard visited with his friends in London, including some government authorities, attempting to learn from their experiences and hoping for positive prognostications about the future. He found that many people were confused by the ongoing distractions between King Henry VIII and the Church. He concluded that he would need to make some important decisions on his own to persevere through this perilous time.

During the next three years, Richard traveled extensively to visit his relatives and friends whose primary livelihoods involved farming in Norwich County. He studied the farmers' routines, exploring ways to improve their livelihood. Richard concluded that the farmers needed to generate additional income and they needed to improve working conditions to achieve better health and welfare for their families.

Shortly after his father died in 1518, Richard began to take some aggressive business actions. First, he made an agreement with Lester Brand. He sold the Brand family a fifty percent interest in the Sunshine Mine, with the agreement that they would begin excavation operations. Lester would be the mine superintendant and Richard would act as the merchant responsible for the sale and distribution of the limestone. Profits from the operations of the mine would be shared evenly between the two. Richard and Lester were working partners and their success would extend beyond their business operations to that of loyal and compassionate friends for the rest of their lives. Both Richard and Lester built small homes on the property. After a few years, the Sunshine Mine became profitable and it grew to provide a stable income for Lester and Richard.

Next, Richard made an agreement with his cousin, Albert Kynne, a sheep farmer near Peterborough on the Nene River. They built a tanning and processing business for animal hides, naming the business the Farmers Tanning Company. Each partner owned one half of the business and would share profits evenly. Albert would supply sheep from his farm and work with other farmers to acquire other animal products. Richard provided some initial cash investment to build an operations building and a warehouse. He acted as the company's merchant to sell and transport the hides to the markets. He also arranged for two families, who previously worked as tenant farmers on the Nar River Farms, to go to work for the Farmers Tanning Company. Cousin Albert proved to be a conscientious worker and a good partner. The business grew steadily and soon became profitable for the men. They reinvested their profits into the expansion of their business for about five years, purchasing new equipment, paying their employees above standard wages, and solidifying their relationships with farmers and other suppliers. After about seven years, the business was well established and the future looked bright for the company.

Richard's next venture was a dream-come-true, as he had been infatuated with boats since he was a small boy. The shipbuilding docks on the Nar River had been a relatively small scale operation for many years. He was familiar with several family operations since he and his father helped plan, build, and purchase small boats from the shipbuilders for hauling various grains from the farms to the breweries. Since the Plague and ensuing depression, shipbuilding on the Nar had fallen stagnant.

Richard agreed to a fifty percent investment in the Nar River Shipbuilding Company with his friend, Oliver Swan, a notable shipbuilder with a fine reputation. Although known for his high quality craftsmanship, Oliver's shipbuilding operations were limited and relatively small. He needed capital to expand his operations, so he could begin building larger ships. The agreement between Richard and Oliver was made on a handshake. It called for Oliver and his son Brainard to oversee the assembly operations. Richard agreed to supply some initial capital and act as the sales merchant. Three more tenant farmers who were out of work at the time agreed to work at the shipyard. Oliver trained the men. Together the partners agreed to specialize in building larger boats, capable of moving native grains and products throughout East Anglia via the inland rivers and waterways. They would produce custom-made boats, with storage features and onboard facilities specifically designed for the needs of the boat's crew.

During the first year of operations, the Nar River Shipbuilding Company built six boats and had agreements to build four other boats in the next year. Oliver spent many hours teaching his carpentry skills to the young workmen. Their pride in craftsmanship and the satisfaction of accomplishment was very gratifying to Richard and Oliver. With patience and persistence, they built steady and durable boats and the company's reputation for high quality workmanship began to spread further throughout the region.

In 1522, Richard traveled to Cambridge to meet with Don Larkin and a group of friends. Don, who knew of Richard's studious nature and his having already read several hand bills about the book *In Praise of Folly*, invited him to a town meeting. When Richard hesitated, Don became demanding in requesting his attendance. The conversation likely went something like this.

"Richard, I'm sure you will want to hear this fellow, William Tyndale. He is a graduate of Oxford and he is translating the Bible into English."

Richard replied, "That sounds interesting. But I've heard that the Pope and the Church would like to silence this Tyndale fellow. What has he done to irritate them?"

Don responded, "I understand that he emphasizes the Word of God and that his translation of the Bible examines the relationship between the Church and the state. Tyndale argues that all Englishmen, regardless of status in life, have a right to read the Bible."

Richard's curiosity was aroused, "That sounds like another indication that times are changing. I would like to hear this man, Tyndale. Let's go see what he has to say."

Richard listened intently to Tyndale's talk and was intrigued with his message. Tyndale spoke of salvation for all people if they lived according to the living Word of God, regardless of their penance to the Church. When Tyndale was finished, Richard stood to ask Mr. Tyndale a question.

"Mr. Tyndale, based upon the Bible as stated in your translation, who is the ultimate Papal authority?"

Tyndale replied, "Christian living is a life of service according to the New Testament and not according to the Church." His answer brought a muffled gasp from the crowd. He continued with a quote from the Bible, Matt: 16:18, saying, "That thou are Peter, and upon this rock, I will build my congregation." After a pause, he added, "Congregation is the key word on which to build the head of the Church, not the friars, priests, nor even the Pope."

Richard and Don left the meeting thinking about the meaning and long-range implications of what Tyndale had said. They agreed that the leaders of the Catholic Church would not agree with Tyndale and that he could face condemnation by the Church and the King if he preached to the public. Consequently, Richard and Don agreed to keep that meeting and their personal opinions a secret from everyone, even their colleagues and friends. If trouble would come, Tyndale's followers could be punished for supporting his startling, new translation of the Bible. Richard put this experience in the back of his head, with plans to think about it at a later date. Several months later, he acquired some hand bills about Tyndale's work, the content of which likely led to his book entitled, *The Obedience of a Christian Man*. Richard kept a small collection of these handbills, books, and records with his family Bible and other family papers.

Richard's involvement in his business ventures changed with the times, but his commitment of time and support for his family never wavered. He was completely devoted to Marcia and their four children. Their oldest son, Lee, was born in 1521. Their next son, John, followed in 1525, and another son, James, was born in 1527. Their Daughter, Dana, was born in 1529.

The children grew up in a beautiful country environment, near the mines where they were largely secluded from heavily populated areas. They were homeschooled, with the majority of their primary education provided by Marcia and Richard and a hired mistress. There was major emphasis upon proper manners and fundamental reading and writing. The mistress used a "hornbook," which was a wooden tablet with a handle. On the tablet there was a printed sheet with the alphabet prominently featured. Following the alphabet were about two dozen combinations of letters using the vowels. Then there was a copy of the Lord's Prayer, which became a constant reminder for children to say their daily prayers. Additional attention to Bible stories and studies was given to the children to build their strong moral characters.

On occasion, the family would travel to Bishop's Lynn or to Norwich to visit the markets and the great Cathedral. In the course of their travels, the family heard many rumors about the King's wives and his tirades with Church officials. Richard paid little attention to the flamatory stories, concentrating on his business activities. He directed his family to disregard the rumors and simply care for their personal affairs.

From 1515 to 1526, there were no crops on the Nar River Farms. The ground lay fallow for over ten years. Then Richard, with the advice of a Norwich County agent, began to allow some of the tenant farmers gradually to plant rye or wheat for one year, followed by another fallow year. Then planting beans, barley, or hemp for a year. This pattern continued, allowing the ground to rejuvenate over a period of years.

Richard changed another common practice of grazing his stock in a common pasture. He kept his herd separated in a private grazing area, thus protecting his cattle from the diseases and improving the breeding characteristics of his herd. Gradually, over a period of about twenty-five years, the farms were restored and some of the tenant farmers began returning to work on the farm.

In 1536, Richard and Marcia moved back to Bishop's Lynn to a home on Chase Street where Richard also conducted his business affairs. An entry in the records of the Bishop Lynn's City Council recorded the transaction as follows: "grant by S. Peper and others to Richard Kynne of Lyn for the tenement on the north part now held by Andrew Brandelyng, the tenement on the south part, and the gardens to the east of John Davy."

The family quickly adjusted to living in the city. The children were old enough for advanced schooling and they enrolled in classes at St. Margaret's Church. Marcia soon made new friends and joined a sewing club. With Richard's financial success and the expansion of his business interests, the family became relatively wealthy for the times. Richard joined the Trinity Guild. He enjoyed spending more time with his friends at the Market and the Trinity Guild Hall.

In 1534, King Henry VIII's official decree called the Act of Supremacy was passed by the English Parliament and circulated throughout the country. The decree stated that the English National Church would effectively replace the Pope and the Roman Catholic Church. This decree was followed in 1536 by "Six Articles of Prescribed Beliefs" for everyone throughout the kingdom. In time, the town of "Bishop's Lynn" would change its name and officially become "King's Lynn." The church clergy and all officials were to convert and abide by the English Church or face dismissal and possible banishment. The Reformation was underway and the Church in England was primed for major upheaval.

Wherever Richard went, he was confronted with more tales and warnings of imminent changes throughout the country. He tried to stay focused on his business activities continuing to direct his family to concentrate on their personal affairs. Privately, he remembered the stirring talk and warning from William Tyndale and the scathing book of *In Praise and Folly* which foretold the corruption of the Church. Richard felt that in the long run, the Act of Supremacy would change almost everything in the entire country. He realized that the state of affairs was far from settled, so he withdrew from further involvement in both Church and State directives and concentrated on local affairs. His intention was to consolidate his business affairs and safeguard his wife and children.

Another reason for family consolidation came from an unfortunate accident. Richard's oldest son, Lee, was killed in a boating accident when he was eighteen years old. Attempting to save a young girl, Lee was caught in a rapid current and could not free himself. Marcia and Richard consoled each other and the remaining children in those dark days following Lee's death.

By his fifteenth birthday, their son, John, showed promise as a builder. With a natural aptitude for carpentry, he enjoyed working on several projects for the city. In addition, he was a good salesman and an aspiring merchant. He felt compelled to further his family's good name, especially since his brother Lee would not have that opportunity. He planned to retain his father's agricultural accounts, including the sales generated by the Nar River Farms and the Farmers Tanning Company. With recognition of his interests in carpentry and his experience with the city's building projects, Richard suggested to John that he consider a future in public office.

Richard and Marcia's youngest son, James, turned his interest to farming and horticulture. Richard frequently took him to the Nar River Farms where he spent some time as a youth working at the Farmers Tanning Company. Bit by bit, he grew to understand the fundamentals of the family's agricultural businesses. In time, he would work with his brother John, who acted as the sales merchant for their products.

Their daughter, Dana, was musically talented and enjoyed playing the harpsichord. A sociable young lady, Dana married Lester Brand's son and moved with him to Lincoln County, close to the Sunshine Mines. One day they would become full owners of the mine, inheriting through both of their fathers.

In 1547, King Henry VIII died. He had maneuvered the country through perilous times and left a legacy that would change England forever. In his later years, he had consolidated the military power of the country for the safety of the kingdom. Following the Treaty of Toledo, whereby the French King François joined forces with the Holy Roman Empire, King Henry built strong defensive outposts at the major port cities in anticipation of foreign attacks. He set the stage for the intensification of the Protestant Reformation. More changes within the Church would follow, including the elimination of some bishops and other church officials. There would be widespread distribution of the Church's property throughout the country. Any backlash would be met with stern discipline and often violence.

Richard warned his children to be prepared for additional changes and to adjust to meet the requirements of the new Church's demands. It was a perilous time and Richard's constant message was to adapt and seek new opportunities.

Richard and Marcia spent their elder years with their children and their families in King's Lynn. Richard continued to advise and counsel John and James. He was delighted with their success as young entrepreneurs and felt sure that John's civic contributions might lead to public office one day.

Richard died in 1550. He and Marcia were buried in the graveyard at All Saints' Church in King's Lynn.

Anna Lyon (Springsteen Kinney), circa 1850

Chapter 6

John Kynne
1525 – 1573
Mayor, Merchant, Politician

BUILDING THE COMMUNITY
WITH PUBLIC SERVICE

John Kynne and his friends stood on a dock in the harbor of King's Lynn. The River Great Ouse wandered before them. Even after leaving the Tudor Rose where they had enjoyed a pint, these merchants continued to discuss the curious matters of doing business in their town, and the conversation no doubt went something like this:

"The Ouse is ripe today, isn't it?" asked Petre Morse.

"Sure is. Smells like something the cat brought home," replied his friend, William Judye, commonly called Will.

Petre responded, "Kind of makes a fella want to have a stout pint before he leaves for home."

Petre continued, "Thank goodness our friend John here started the cleanup along the shoreline, north of the docks. Not even five years ago, it was much worse when the garbage piled up outside the fishing village. Most days, you wouldn't think so many people lived here in Lynn, but you sure couldn't tell by the ship's debris and the trash along the docks."

Although John started a cleanup campaign along the north waterfront when he built the new water line into town, the cleanup was never completed.

Another friend, William Kemp, spoke with words of conviction, "My Lizzie sure appreciates the water being piped into our neighborhood."

Petre responded, "Nothing like good water. As for me, there's no doubt that the fresh water has improved the ale from all of our breweries. You know a fella needs a good drink once in a while."

Will continued, "My Annie wouldn't have consented to moving to Queen Street if we hadn't improved on the stench, that's for sure. Definitely not fit for the health of ladies and small children, it wasn't."

"But there is so much more to be done," John replied. "Sometimes, after dinner, I walk back over here and think about all we still have to do. Look around at these buildings made of old wood and thatched roofs. I keep telling the aldermen and the city's building committee that we are just waiting for a big fire to tear through here."

"So, John, what are you suggesting?" asked Petre.

It was obvious that John had thought about this, and he replied, "I'd get the city council to pass some laws to make the city safer and I'd ask builders to use bricks and reinforced timbers to reduce the risk of fire. Today, builders can use many different products like tiles, plaster walls, and good solid doors and window frames. The new warehouses should be made of bricks or stone, with preventive fire passages. If we want our prominent buildings like the Trinity Guildhall, the Tudor Rose, the White Swan, and St. Nicholas Church to last, we'll simply have to improve our building standards."

Will looked at John and laughed. "John, if you were in charge, this town would definitely become the finest port on the North Sea. I, for one, would not protest if your improvements came to be and those Germans, Swedes, and Dutchmen couldn't get here fast enough to do even more business with me–and every other merchant in town. Just last month, two Germans, I believe their names were Delbert Ritchhart and Frederic Schmidt, were here to select warehouse locations and advance their trading quotas. I can just picture the Hanseatic League warehouses built right next to where we are standing. And you, John, you will be our constable or alderman—even mayor? Why not? Have you thought about it?"

"I used to discuss that very thing with my father, God bless his soul. My mum wanted me to be mayor. At first, I thought they were just dreaming. I just wanted to be a carpenter and build new projects in Lynn. Now I know that people with authority can do much more with support from city council and the townsfolk. With my kids growing up, it's much easier for me to work on the city's projects and keep my family and the merchants happy at the same time."

Will Judye replied, "Well, what do you say, fellows? Let's keep John's mum happy and get behind him with our political support. With the merchants' endorsement, John will build a bigger and better city and our business will be better than ever."

Cheers rang out from the men. John smiled with approval as they began walking away from the pub. Petre looked at the sun, low in the sky over the river in the west, and said, "John, tomorrow we'll start on your campaign. You can count on our support from the Guild."

Will said, "I'll drink to that." With that, they parted company for their homes.

John won the next election in 1556, serving as a constable and then as alderman. With ongoing support from the merchants, he was elected twice as mayor, first in 1562 and again in 1572. He served many years on the city council. The aldermen of Lynn so respected him that on March 15, 1572, they elected him to represent Lynn and County Norwich in the House of Commons. These elections marked the crowning events of a distinguished career in business, politics, and public service.

John's remarkable accomplishments came at a time when distant events in the known world were dramatically changing the path of history. About that time, when French explorer Jacques Cartier was seeking a northwest passage in America and when Francisco Vásquez de Coronado was exploring in what became Colorado and Arizona, John Kynne was living admidst religious upheaval in England.

The Reformation began in force in Europe in 1517, and, by 1550, Protestantism was established across half of the continent. King Henry VIII had assumed the crown of England in 1509, and as the affairs of state and as his personal life evolved, the King reacted with important decisions and policies that would impact the country forever. People were confronted with conflicting religious philosophies. Either they declared allegiance to the Church of England or were threatened with excommunication and possible retaliation. Most people had lived for centuries believing that conformance with the Roman Catholic faith would lead to eternal salvation. Consequently, many were confused and uncertain about the future.

The Church was not only the center of religious activities, but it also embraced the social and educational activities of most families. As the decree spread across the country, there were reports of rejection and retaliation by those loyal to the Church of Rome. Also, there were reports that King Henry VIII would not recapitulate, and with force and decisive action, the Church of England would prevail, thus eliminating the influence of the pope and the Church of Rome from England forever.

Indeed, it was a time of substantial changes which began when John was still living with his parents and then continued throughout his lifetime. Under the tutelage of his father, an avid student of religious history, John foresaw the resistance of the Roman Church. He had studied the writings of John Wycliffe and read from his father's copy of William Tyndale's *Obedience of a Christian Man*. John's father prepared his children well, and as time passed, they learned to accept many of the conflicts between the Church of England and the Roman Catholic Church.

On a personal level, John Kynne's family responded with allegiance to the Church of England. They were pragmatic and chose to adapt to changing influences following the example of John's father. They had seen the abuses of the Roman Church and felt hopeful that the King and his successors would return to a religious position supporting the authentic word of God, as expressed in the New Testament in the Bible.

They were pleased that the Church of England would conduct services in English and that the Bible would be translated into English and be available to all Englishmen.

As time passed, John and his family did their best to follow the primary religious practices of the times. John kept their older religious books locked in his father's trunk. The family began afresh by attending St. Margaret's Church, the recognized Church of England. By avoiding distractions on the religious front, John focused his attention on the family's stability, as well as his business life and public service.

John's ability to focus on his personal affairs would not have been possible without good training and strict discipline that he encountered as a child. He learned to work independently and concentrate on his personal projects. He was especially adept at working with his hands. He enjoyed building wooden toys and games as well as repairing furniture. He made birdhouses and wooden tops for a spinning game. Under his father's instructions, he built a chicken coop, and soon he had more chickens than the family could accommodate. His business career started when he sold chickens and eggs at the Saturday market in Lynn. He quickly developed a good sense for a profitable business and recognized the importance of producing good products to be sold at fair prices. This simple philosophy would serve him well as he grew to become a successful merchant.

John's interest in building expanded with time. At the Nar River Shipbuilding Company, he watched master craftsmen, such as Richard Galylye and Reginald Wright, work on ships. After learning to distinguish between different kinds of lumber, he experimented to determine the strength and durability of various types of timber. He learned to read building plans and, as work on projects was completed, he recorded the results, sometimes with uncanny descriptions of the job. He expanded his interest in other kinds of construction by recording the progress of a number of community projects, including the great wall, the gates to the city, and an addition to the Town Hall. In the course of his work, he developed friendships with some of the city planners. After work, he often spent his leisure time discussing the future of Lynn with friends and associates.

In addition to his interest in construction, John spent considerable time with his father learning his business as a merchant. He would accompany his father as he made his rounds to the markets, the shipping docks, and to his customers. John's father kept abreast of the regional shipping and trading activities, primarily to support the sales of his customers' products to the breweries and other buyers in East Anglia.

In 1541, John began a two-year period studying as a merchant apprentice at the Merchant Taylor's School in London. Although the apprenticeship was demanding, John grew to enjoy the excitement in London and there he met many new friends and future business associates. As he learned the proper protocol for business, he spent the majority of his time working at the markets and docks along the River Thames. On a daily basis, he met associates at Billingsgate to exchange information about ships arriving and departing. Although he developed a careful eye watching for ships traveling the North Sea to King's Lynn, he gained a healthy appreciation for the large number of merchant ships traveling to other ports.

John developed a personal interest in exploration and discovery. Using the Thames River as his pathway, John floated past the palaces of the royalty to view Greenwich, Paul's Wharf, the Blackfriars, and the Essex House. Occasionally he walked across London Bridge to visit Southwark to watch the wild animal fights and other traditional entertainments.

John wandered about London, sometimes going beyond the city walls. He visited the famous houses of Hampton Court, Northumberland, Westminster, St. James Park, the famous Royal Exchange, and Covent Gardens. He studied the magnificent architecture of the churches, the city walls, the gates, and the Tower of London. He made records and drawings of the buildings, the warehouses, streets, and parks. With thoughts for Lynn in his mind, he envisioned improvements to the buildings, parks, water, and sanitation systems.

At that time, London was the center for many of the confrontations between King Henry VIII and the Church of Rome. The executions of nobility, including those for Margaret Pole, Anne Boleyn, and Thomas Cromwell, were generally held in privacy. But word quickly spread when the executions were completed. Executions for common traitors and criminals were held in public on Tower Hill. John watched the proceedings and understood the power and decisiveness of the King. When the announcement came forth calling for the execution of Catherine Howard, another of the King's wives who had been charged with adultery, John wondered if the violence would ever end. Catherine's lady-in-waiting was also implicated, found guilty, and executed with Catherine.

John was well aware of the danger and potential guilt by association with followers of the Church of Rome. He was careful as to who he associated with and he became deliberate with his religious commitments. He attended Sunday services at St. Paul's Cathedral where he met Dean William May. In time, John rededicated his allegiance and his loyalty to the Church of England.

When his apprenticeship in London was completed, John was ready and eager to return to Lynn. With enthusiasm and many new ideas, he returned home to learn that the city was considering improvements to its water and sanitation system. John was asked to help with the planning, including the initial presentation to the city council. The plan called for the diversion of sewage that accumulated in the north section of town. Additional water conduits for channeling water into town were planned. As waste and debris accumulated along the Ouse River, the shoreline was constantly changing. Consequently, there was a need to reclaim and establish a functional shoreline. The plan submitted by John and his associates was accepted and the initial work for the water channels was completed over a four-year period.

John worked hard and liked his work, but there was something missing in his life. He had not found his special lady. That is, not until one evening when he was visiting with friends at the Guild House of St. George. There, he recognized an attractive girl who had grown into womanhood during the period he was away from Lynn serving his apprenticeship. She was a young widow who had lost her husband in a fishing accident. He likely recognized her as someone he admired in his youth, but had lost contact with over a period of time. Years ago, she was in a class with his sister, Dana, at St. Margaret's Church. John suspected, as he glanced at her, that she might be looking at him too and he decided to take a chance.

"Excuse me, ma'am, but I think you were in a class at church with my sister, Dana."

"Ah, Dana Kynne, yes. I have known her for several years. She loves music and she plays the harpsichord. And you must be…."

"John Kynne," he finished for her. "And your name is?"

"Margaret, Margaret Anne Barbor."

"Well, Margaret Anne, I think I've seen your father and your little boy out in his boat. Your father is a fisherman, right? You live north of town in the fisherman's village, don't you?"

"Yes, now I live with my father and my son, Roger Barbor."

John replied, "When I was away in London, I heard about your husband's accident. I am so sorry and wish to convey my condolences."

Margaret Anne responded, "Thank you for your kind words. Please call me Anne. You are right. Now we live just north of town with my father in the fisherman's village. We came from Amsterdam when I was very young, but I learned to speak English at school. Do you think I have a Dutch accent?"

"No," replied John. "I can tell you speak very proper English and I can tell you have very good manners. Would it be all right for me to call on you?"

"Yes, although you'll have to speak with my father when you stop by. Just be gentle with him, because he does have a Dutch accent."

"Sure, I'll be gentle with him, and I hope he is agreeable toward me. No doubt, I would like to meet your son and visit with your father."

John and Margaret Anne courted for about two years and they were married at St. Margaret's Church in 1547. Their grand reception was held at the Lattice House. In attendance were many friends and towns- folk, including young Roger Barbor. This would not be their last social function, but just the beginning of an exciting and glamorous social life for the happy couple. They enjoyed dances, the theater, and parties with their friends. Often, they joined with political acquaintances, other merchants, and friends to celebrate special occasions in Lynn.

On the national scene, this was a time of great unrest in the country since King Henry VIII died in 1547 and Prince Edward succumbed in 1553. He was followed by Queen Mary who became the first woman to succeed to the throne. She was followed by Lady Jane Grey and, finally, Queen Elizabeth who brought stability to the country in the spring of 1559.

The ships coming and going from Lynn provided the main commu- nications link with the rest of the known world. News was slow to reach Lynn. John and other merchants would meet with the ships' captains to exchange information. Gruesome news of torture, beheadings, and humiliation continued to come from London. This was followed by reports of mercenaries moving throughout the country to enforce the government's rule.

The ship captains also told stories of great travels, discoveries, and exploration-including those to the New World. Since Columbus, who discovered the Canary Islands, had died in 1509, Spain had sent other explorers sailing in search of new lands. Ponce de Leon sailed north of the Canary Islands and landed in North America. Pizarro had discov- ered Peru and Cortez had sailed southwestwardly to Mexico. A Portu- guese explorer, Magellan, discovered the straits off the Cape of Good Hope and sailed on to South America. A French man, Cartier, sailed north and discovered the Gulf of St. Lawrence. Merchants throughout England listened and watched with anticipation that English ships would join the western paths of discovery to the New World. The merchants in Lynn knew that if England were to defend its shores from foreign invaders, and if it were to compete with foreign exploration, England must dramatically improve its shipbuilding and naval capabilities.

As business improved and trading increased, the merchants of Lynn increased their political power. John grew wealthy for his time as his merchant business grew steadily with additional trading accounts. He, too, joined the Trinity Guild. Reginald Wright was hired to be the captain of his personal ship. Although his friend, Brainard Swan, managed the Nar River Shipbuilding Company, John maintained a partial ownership position. His wealth increased as he helped Brainard with the company's sales.

John and Margaret Anne moved to a new home, which included a warehouse and small yard on Queen Street in Lynn. The family had a servant named Agnes Lockenton to help run the business and assist with family affairs. John's construction experience and building acumen-especially with the municipal projects-made him a valuable member of the city's administration. However, his greatest asset was his popularity among his friends and loyal followers at the Trinity Guild. They trusted John and, with a fraternal kinship, they became his most important political allies.

At that time, Lynn was one of many English towns experiencing physical decline of buildings, docks, and roads. Although the city had made progress with the water and sewage system, there was more community work to be done. Much more. Old structures needed to be torn down and replaced. The threat of fires was a constant danger. The roads needed repairs and some bridges needed to be replaced. Additional improvements would decrease the deplorable stench from unsightly garbage that was still left at undesirable sites near the city.

As alderman, John led a movement to make major building improvements. New brick kilns were built in West Lynn, Peterborough, and Ely. The city council, with the support of several aldermen, passed an ordinance forbidding thatching, primarily to reduce the fire danger. Other new products were introduced, including tiles, plaster walls, and oak and elm doors and windows. In 1559, glass windows replaced wooden shutters at St. Nicholas Church.

Slowly, Lynn became energized and revitalized. Employment steadily increased. Improved buildings and sanitary conditions had a positive impact on other commercial ventures. New homes were built extending the city's boundary beyond the city's gates enhancing the improved exterior roads. Foreign merchants, including the Germans, Swedish, and Dutch representing the Hanseatic League, built new warehouses on the Ouse River. The demand for agricultural products increased and local farmers gradually increased their production and their sales to new markets. More visitors came to the Lynn markets to make their purchases.

At that time, John's younger brother, James, was working at the Farmers Tanning Company and the Nar River Farms. His sister, Dana, and her husband owned and worked the Sunshine Mine. John continued to serve as a merchant for those businesses.

While John's business prospered, he and Anne shared the ongoing growth and progress of their family. Together, they raised Roger Barbor, Anne's son by her first marriage. In time, Roger became an accomplished fisherman. In addition, they had two other adventuresome children, John Robert, whom they called Robert, born in 1548, and Cheryl, born in 1549. The children were blessed with good health and they enjoyed a happy childhood amidst an unpretentious environment in King's Lynn raised by their prominent and adoring parents. As the children grew up, Margaret Anne taught them to be good readers. Both Robert and Cheryl excelled in English grammar and literature, leading them to become competent scholars in their own rights.

On one occasion, when Robert was twelve, they visited Cambridge and Ely, traveling on the inland water passage. Robert was so impressed with the maneuverability of the small craft that he developed an interest in sailing. John soon introduced him to other boats and he encouraged Robert to paddle with him around the bays and inlets, similar to the sailing he enjoyed as a small boy with his father.

John's popularity continued to grow as public improvements were completed. The gates to the city were updated and the town hall was enlarged to accommodate public meetings. More improvements to the water system made it possible for additional fresh water to flow to neighboring homes and to the breweries. The local taverns became popular sites for social gatherings. There was a gradual conversion of the monasteries and some other church properties to other uses. The Greyfriar's Tower was saved, protected as a historical site, and used as a watchtower for navigation. The friar's quarters next to St. Margaret's Church were eventually converted to public housing. As improvements were made, citizens developed a renewed pride in their city.

During John's second term as mayor and while he was serving on the city council, he had a unique opportunity to extend his community influence. At that time, Queen Elizabeth was in her sixth year as reigning Monarch of England. She was popular in Lynn. Citizens were devoted to the Queen and they openly expressed their loyalty. John directed that the Arms of Elizabeth I be embedded above the door of Trinity Guildhall. This pleased the Queen and extended good relations between the Monarchy and her subjects in Lynn.

John's administration created a plan for the land along the waterfront of the Ouse River, calling for the diversion of water, deposit of the silt and debris, and security in case of flooding. In addition, new building in the area would be subject to strict rules for public use, including the dock area for the ferries, and access locations for other boats. Any new building along the waterfront would be required to have sufficient landfill and durable building foundations. John created a study to determine the dangerous water currents. He studied how the flow of the

Ouse River would affect the dock facilities over time. If flooding were to occur, it would be beneficial to predict the movement of the water, with procedures in place to minimize the potential damages.

With numerous building projects underway, Lynn was strained to meet the cash requirements for running the city's government. It became necessary for the city to borrow or obtain additional funds by other means. John agreed to loan the city 300 pounds and he duly recorded the loan in the records of city council in 1572.

In addition to his ambitious building programs for Lynn, John encouraged additional economic development for Norwich County. The sheep population was growing rapidly and the woolen mills were capable of expanding to accommodate the growing needs. The fertile agricultural lands were producing record crops of wheat, oats, and barley. Traders continued to come to Lynn to acquire salt for the preservation of meats and poultry. With the urging of the merchants, John encouraged new trading partners and expanded the regional markets to accommodate international sales to Amsterdam, Calais, and London.

Lynn was one of the 100 English boroughs that elected representatives to sit in the British Parliament. Wealthy landowners and prominent national politicians were anxious to be elected to the House of Commons so that they could represent important areas such as Lynn. They campaigned vigorously, sometimes with indignant overtones. But the Lynn townspeople and aldermen grew to be cautious. They objected to interference from "outside" politicians.

There was an altercation involving national politicians in the election of 1572, and after it was settled, John was elected to the House of Commons to serve with Sir Robert Bell. Thus, John was elected mayor and representative to serve in Parliament at the same time. Parliament was expected to be convened by Queen Elizabeth in the spring of 1573.

John prepared to become a knowledgeable and contributing member of Parliament during the winter of 1572. He studied the minutes and reports of the previous sessions of Parliament. He was aware of some religious overtones, especially those coming from the Puritans in County Lincolnshire. But he did not dwell on religious matters. He directed his preparations toward issues dealing with finances, taxes, government institutions, and the defenses for the country. John met with Edwin Sandys, the Chaplain for the Parliament, and Sir Robert Bell, who would also represent Lynn and who was a likely candidate to be the Speaker for the House of Commons. Sir Robert was well experienced, gracious, and helpful to John in preparing for the next session of Parliament.

John's reputation for building municipal projects and political ingenuity preceded him. In the fall, John traveled to London to meet with government officials and share information about government building programs, the danger of foreign intruders, and several other issues likely to come before the next Parliament.

John was also asked to help prepare citizens in East Anglia for the defense of the country. The Crown was concerned about attacks from French and Spanish troops. East Anglia was especially vulnerable with its proximity to Holland and coastal cities across the North Sea. John responded with his renewed loyalty to the Crown and his unwavering devotion to his Country. He pledged to serve the Queen in whatever circumstances lay ahead.

John returned home to Lynn and spent a joyful St. Nicholas season with Anne and their children and grandchildren. It was a wonderful holiday season, with caroling, sleigh rides, and winter festivities throughout the city.

John told many stories about the Kynne family, including those about reunions and past holidays with Grandfather Richard and Grandmother Marcia. He unlocked his storage chest to share some of the family relics with his children. He encouraged his children, Roger Barbor, John Robert, and Cheryl, to expand their horizons and set lofty personal goals.

John Robert had taken his keen interest in seamanship to work at the family's shipyard on the Nar River and would eventually become a master shipbuilder. At a time of his country's need, he would provide ships to the Royal Navy and be prepared to defend the monarchy with his life. His loyalty to the Crown would bring special recognition to the family.

Cheryl had a charming, outgoing personality, much like her mother. She was a brilliant student, earning recognition as an honor student and a popular teacher. She married a gentleman from Ely and had two children. Unfortunately, she contracted a cancerous disease when she was twenty-six years old and died after a short illness.

Shortly after the first of the year, John suffered from what was believed to be a heart attack. Although he fought hard, his condition worsened with complications and he died in February 1573.

Even though John's life was cut short with his untimely death, he left an impressive record of accomplishments, including many years of public service for his beloved city of King's Lynn. John's philosophy of not allowing himself to be distracted by uncontrollable outside influences and focusing on accomplishing realistic goals served him well during difficult times. His generosity and timely gift to the city of King's Lynn marked him as one of the first philanthropists in the country. His vision for civic improvements served his community well into the future.

Funeral services for John were held at St. Margaret's Church and a public resolution was read at the Guildhall. His will, which was recorded in the minutes of the city council reflected his generosity for his beloved city. His will specified bequeaths to his wife, Anne, his sons, John (Robert) Kynne and Roger Barbor, his loyal servant, Agnes Lockenton, the Master of his Ship, Reginald Wright, and other friends.

There were so many friends of John attending the services that the crowd extended outside the church into the nearby streets. Standing on the steps of St. Margaret's Church, John's friend Robert Morse gave a parting farewell toast to his comrade, that went something like this:

"Here's to our friend and loyal companion, John. May God rest his soul. He served us well. He gave us clean water when we needed to bathe and he gave us fresh air when we needed to breathe. When our docks were full of trash, he showed us how to clean up and bring the fish back to our shores. Thank God he saved our Golden Brewing Company by bringing fresh water directly to our distilleries because any normal fella needs a stout drink every once in awhile. So, let's head to the Tudor Rose after we praise the Lord for the life of our beloved friend, John. God rest his soul."

William Kemp likely responded, "Right on, brother Morse. John was a good man and he will be missed. We will not forget our kinship with him. I'll drink to that."

With that, the merchants and brothers of the Trinity Guild, with their wives and families, strolled over to the Tudor Rose for a pint in loving memory of their friend John Kynne.

John was laid to a well-deserved rest in the cemetery grounds of St. Margaret's Church.

The Jail at Castle Cary

From St. Elizabeth's Church & Graveyard
Looking to The Guildhall and City Hall, King's Lynn

Activity on the Docks, East Anglia

Chapter 7
Sir John Robert Keney (Kynne)
1548 – 1590
Knight, Shipbuilder

DEFENDING THE HOMELAND

John Robert Kynne stood on the deck as the supply ship, *Little Annie*, pulled away from the Lynn dock heading toward the open sea. Captain Jeremy Swan was at the helm. The ship, loaded with corn, barley, some salt, and various animal hides was en route to the North Sea and the ports of Yarmouth, Aldeburgh, and London. Like most inhabitants of King's Lynn, Robert found it easier to travel to London by the North Sea rather than taking the much less developed land routes.

A shipbuilder by trade, Robert glanced around at many ships in the harbor, noting a few that had been crafted by his own company. In fact, just last year in 1585, he had delivered a supply vessel to Sir Humphrey Davey, Captain of the Queen's Admiralty. Ever since he had heard reports of Spanish warships attacking British merchant ships, he was prepared to do anything to help the Crown defend the country, including recruiting troops and sending a supply ship to the Royal Navy.

Robert hadn't known it, but Captain Davey had notified the Queen's Court of his contribution to the British fleet. He was now on his way to the formal ceremony where he would be knighted for "a gift of ships for the sea." Though he had missed his father many times in the past few years, he was acutely aware of his absence at this time. Members of his family had long provided support to the Crown, including his own father who had been elected to Parliament. He had heard family stories about his ancestors from his father who had heard them from his father, as had many past generations. They told of Robert, the Knight, who arrived in England during the Norman Conquest. Yet no one had received knighthood since his namesake, who had been knighted by William the Conqueror back in 1066. Yes, indeed, he thought to himself, I am very proud to receive this honor.

Not that he would have time to rest on his laurels. He had already been busy organizing the militia in Norwich County. When he came back as Sir Robert, he would return to recruiting and training militia members. Many of his longtime friends and business associates had already shown their loyalty by joining the cause. He continued to put his shipping experience into service for the Crown by gathering guns and other supplies. Plus, he planned to finish a transportation program he was devising in case it was needed for replenishing supplies to the troops throughout East Anglia.

Robert looked out again at the sturdy ships within his view in the harbor. He was angry and fed up with good English ships being attacked by Spanish ships just for doing trade in the Netherlands. He was determined–when those Spanish ships sailed to the English coasts-that he and the militia would be ready to keep those tyrants from landing. But for now, he was off to receive this honor for himself and his ancestors. It might be tense out on the North Sea, but once they reached the Thames, he could readily focus on the festivities ahead in the great city of London. This honor and this break would do him good, and would serve as a symbol of loyalty and patriotism for himself and hopefully for future generations.

Robert had been born some thirty-eight years ago on July 31, 1548, first child of John and Margaret Anne Kynne. His sister Cheryl followed a year later. A healthy child with a solid and well proportioned frame, Robert had a strong constitution that provided him with ample stamina to participate in vigorous activities. He would grow to become a handsome young man standing five foot ten inches tall. Using his native instincts well, he spent many hours outdoors with his father, often fishing on the nearby rivers and streams including the Nar River and the Gay and Wissey tributaries.

Robert's mother, Anne, was a strong disciplinarian. He grew up in an orderly environment demanding strong family values with strict adherence to Christian teaching. Robert's parents were devoted members of St. Margaret's Church. Many of the family's social activities centered around the church's activities. Robert's father was a church alderman and many of his business associates had similar affiliations, even through all the changes within the Church of England during these times.

He adapted well socially and gravitated toward academic endeavors. With a special interest in shipbuilding, he and his friends would take model ships to the streams and nearby lakes for sailing. He was fascinated with the design and maneuverability of the small crafts. In the course of his father's work, Robert would accompany him to the shipyard on the River Nar where he visited with sailors and shipbuilders, some who worked for his father.

As the children of a prominent family, Robert, his older stepbrother Roger Barbor, and his sister Cheryl, were exposed to many varied experiences. In addition to traveling on the inland waterways, the family visited the cathedrals in Norwich and Ely, sometimes staying for the open markets and holiday festivals.

At an early age, Robert developed a keen sense of loyalty and kinship toward his close friends. On one occasion, he and Jim Cadle were returning home after making a delivery of materials to a neighbor's home. Riding in an open, horse-drawn wagon, Robert sat on the hard wagon bench with the reins in his hands. Although he was only fourteen, his body was growing strong from the hard physical work he performed at home and on his job. At his side sat his long-time friend who had grown up with him and had worked with him on several construction projects. Even though they were steady workers, they sometimes acted like the boys they still were. The empty wagon taunted them a little on such a bright autumn day as they rode through the fields east of Lynn. The conversation went something like this:

"I bet this old horse is just wishing he could run a little ways. You think, Jim?" asked Robert.

"Well, it's mostly open country out here. We did get rid of the cargo. And I'm pretty sure this isn't a race horse we're guiding, but he probably would like to stretch his legs a bit," Jim replied.

"OK. Let's see," said Robert. With a snap of the reins, the wagon lurched forward. Unaccustomed to running with the wagon, the sturdy horse became spooked with the bouncing and bounding noise behind him.

"Whoa, whoa," yelled Robert, pulling hard on the reins.

Jim could see a gully at the end of the field. He cried, "Slow him down now—before we reach the gully."

"I can't pull any harder," replied Robert.

Just as Jim reached over to help, the reins began to burn through Robert's hands, and as they reached the gully, the horse broke loose turning northward across the field. The wagon overturned and careened into the gully, pinning Robert underneath the wagon while Jim was thrown against the bank of the gully.

Robert blinked in the dark, unable to see more than the shadows. His leg screamed with pain. He barely whispered, "Jim, Jim?"

The weak reply came from a stream of light. "Over here, I'm OK. How about you?"

"No, my leg—it's stuck under the wagon, I can't move it, and the wagon is so heavy. You will have to get help."

Jim crawled away toward the sunlight, and when he was within closer range of Robert, he said, "Robert, you are going to be all right.

Hang on tight, I'll get you out of there. I'll go for help. Do you think you can wait?"

"What else can I do?" came Robert's dire reply. "Go as fast as you can."

As Jim dashed off, Robert fell in and out of consciousness. He didn't know which was worse, the pain in his leg or the mental anguish going through his mind about the aftermath of the accident. The evening sun light had completely disappeared when, finally, he heard a voice.

"Robert, it's Jim here and I have brought help. We will move the wagon and get you out of here."

"Thanks, Jim, I'm ready to go," came Robert's weak but grateful reply.

As Robert was loaded into the back of another wagon, he saw that Jim was limping and that he had suffered an injury to his right shoulder. When Robert asked about the extent of his injury, Jim was quiet, but one of the helpers responded.

"Yes, we tried to get Jim to get stay in town to nurse his wounds, but he insisted on coming back to find you. Probably a good thing, 'cause we never would have found you down in that gully."

Robert didn't say anything else. He could hardly hear his friends' voices as the wagon carried him back to town. But he thought about Jim's admonition of "hang on tight, I'll get you out of there." He knew that Jim had saved his life.

Robert determined, then and there, that loyalty and friendship were the most important traits of character in his life. He vowed to extend his loyalty to his good friends and his kinship. Thereafter, for Jim and the rest of Robert's close friends, loyalty and friendship were the hallmark of their relationship with Robert.

The period from 1550 to 1565 was a prosperous and productive time for farmers and merchants in Norwich County. The demand of products, including cattle, sheep, fish, mustard, wheat, oats, and timber was strong. Trade was brisk on the River Nar. Lynn itself became known as the "Warehouse of The Wash." To support the sale and transportation of these native commodities, the shipbuilding business was growing steadily. That growth and prosperity would continue into Robert's adulthood as the number of small merchant ships increased from seventeen to sixty in the Lynn seaport from 1562 to 1587.

At the same time, the Crown had additional reasons for increasing shipbuilding. The Spanish continued to escalate as a serious threat to English shipping, forcing Queen Elizabeth and government officials to be concerned about potential enemy attacks at sea. The Queen issued a formal request calling for an increase in building capacity. In addition, there was a plea from her court for merchant ships to be prepared to support war ships in case of emergencies.

Besides the growth of commercial shipping, new construction was widespread in Norwich County. New facilities were built at the Greenland Fisheries. The new Tuesday Market Place was under construction and a new building was under construction at Thoresby College. These projects provided good employment for young and capable workers.

Fortunately, Robert healed quickly after his wagon accident. Because of his youth and stamina, he soon returned to work where he developed a strong and durable appearance.

In 1563, when Robert was sixteen, he traveled with his father to London. Robert, who had heard stories from his father about the glamour of London for years, was thrilled to see it for himself. The trip took seven days, leaving Lynn at the Ouse River dock, traveling to Hunstanton, Great Yarmouth, Aldeburgh, then to the open sea, south to the River Thames, and then westward to London. Robert jumped at the chance to assume a seaman's duties on the ship, where he spent extra time watching and learning navigation from Reginald Wright, who accompanied them on the trip. As the ship sailed into London, he was awed by the panoramic views and historic sites along the waterfront.

After docking, Robert helped unload the ship, while his father John left to meet with shipping officials and government representatives. As John passed along the docks, he heard news that would affect trade back home. Rumors persisted that Spain had sent its warships to the Netherlands and many people believed that they were preparing to invade Britain. John was given a comprehensive report by the Queen's Guard that expressed grave concerns for further confrontations with the Spanish fleet.

Prior to returning to Lynn, Robert's father gave him a brief tour of London, including the grounds at Westminster, St. Paul's Cathedral, and the Royal Exchange. Robert was most impressed by the excitement and trade carried on by the merchants in the central market and the Royal Exchange. Robert vowed to come back to London someday as a successful shipbuilder and merchant.

Upon his return to Lynn, Robert expanded his studies of shipbuilding, working with master builder Reginald Wright. Expanding his navigational interests, he began making a record of the ships entering and leaving the Lynn docks. He learned to identify ships that could be converted in times of war and possibly used in support of the British fleet. With advice from his father, he began to communicate with shipping companies and the Lord of the Admiralty.

Often in the fall, Robert accompanied his father and other friends for hunting trips north in Lincoln County. Over time, his parents became friends with Ben and Doris Adams, a family living near the village of Stamford. Ben Adams was an active sportsman and his wife, Doris, was an accomplished artist. The Adams had two daughters, Sally and Abagail, who were often relegated to entertain Robert and his sister Cheryl while their parents socialized. Robert grew to admire Sally and when he reached full maturity, he began to visit the Adams family with his courting eye on Sally. In time, Robert prepared to ask for Sally's hand in marriage, but obtaining her father's permission was a traumatic time for a person as shy as Robert.

One day Robert sat astride his mount riding next to Ben Adams, after the pair had been off on a riding excursion supposedly to hunt for deer. Actually, the men had discussed the future of Ben's daughter, Sally. Both men grinned as this trip had been successful in more ways than one, with Ben's approval and blessing for their marriage.

"There she is waiting on the porch for you. If you'd like, I'll get one of the older lads to care for your horse so that you can talk with her alone before the rest of the crew steals her away from you," said Ben Adams.

Robert replied, "I'd be most grateful, though I'm not too clean at this point. Perhaps she won't have me in this condition."

"Go on with you—as if she hadn't seen you after a hunt or a long ride before." Robert dismounted, striding a few feet toward Sally before he realized the reins were still in his hand, and his tired and dusty horse was following along. He turned and hitched the reins onto a post before setting out toward Sally one more time.

"Well, what did father say?" asked the petite and charming Sally.

"He said he knows I'm young, but he also knows I've been working for five years already. He says he can see my workmanship in the ships we're building, and he believes I have a keen eye to expand the kind of ships we build."

"And did you just talk business the whole time?'

"Well no. He also said that since I have been coming around so much, I might as well become part of your family—but your mother is the one that keeps the family in proper line."

"Mum? Why she could hardly keep to her painting while you were gone. She kept talking about traveling to Lynn and how different it will be for us to live in Lynn."

"Nothing seems to pass by your mum's eye. Lucky for me, your father gave me permission for us to get married."

"Well, Robert Kynne," replied Sally, "you may have my parents' blessing, but I don't think you have asked me yet."

Robert obediently dropped to one knee and, looking at Sally, asked, "May I have your hand in marriage, my lady?"

Sally paused a moment with delight, gave a wide smile, and stretched out her hand prior to a romantic embrace with Robert.

Robert and Sally were married at St. Andrew's Church near Stamford. They moved to a small house on Southgate Street in Lynn, close to the Saturday Market Place and within commuting distance to the shipbuilding yard on the River Nar.

As Robert's father, John, became more active in politics, Robert became more engaged in merchant trading and the shipbuilding business. He continued to study the strategic relationship between the naval warships and merchant vessels. With new and larger ships, their vessels could serve as supply ships and carriers of important communications to the galleons of Queen Elizabeth's Navy.

Robert visited and toured the *Mary Rose*, one of the mightiest warships at the time. With some new ideas, he made changes to improve the speed and maneuverability of their ships. He experimented with two and three masts with different shapes for the sails. The experimentation paid off with new sales and increased interest from some of the leading merchants.

In 1568, Robert and Sally lost their first child in childbirth. In 1571, Sally became pregnant again, giving birth to a son named Thomas. Thomas was an energetic and healthy baby who one day would grow to inherit the family estate. In 1574, they had another baby named Nichole. Nichole had a strong family resemblance to her mother and she grew to be a cheerful and spirited child. She loved the outdoors and, in time, she coveted adventure, wildlife, and spirited horses.

John died in 1573. Following a period of consolation, Robert and Sally moved ahead to assert the family's prominent role in the community. About this time, Robert decided to standardize the spelling of the family name to "Keney."

Robert concentrated on the family business by expanding new trade routes to Kirkcaldyin and Dieppe in Scotland. But he found it necessary to discontinue the lucrative trade business in Amsterdam and keep his ships closer to home. The small cargo ships had become popular with private merchants, which had the added benefit of increasing the Queen's inventory of supply ships that could be converted for maritime use in case of a war.

As Robert built his business and raised the children with Sally, the threat of an attack by Spain continued to grow. There were increased reports of British ships being attacked, especially along the trade routes to the Netherlands. Robert continued to correspond with the High Court of the Admiralty (HTA).

In 1584, when Queen Elizabeth visited Scrooby, Robert listened intently to the Queen's address as she pleaded for readiness and volunteers in case of an invasion by Spain. Robert quickly volunteered and began to organize some local troops in Norwich County. He offered a gift to the Queen's Royal Navy of one supply vessel, the one which led to his receiving his knighthood honor.

Following the ceremony, Sir Robert and the troops prepared themselves for the seemingly inevitable invasion of the Spanish troops. Using all available resources, including his supply ships and trading partners, Robert obtained guns and supplies for the troops. He supervised their training and created a transportation system to replenish important supplies. In July 1588, word came that the Spanish troops were expected to sail into the British Channel and land somewhere on the northern shore of Britain.

Robert, with about 250 members of the Lynn militia, traveled to Camp Tilbury to await further orders. Robert's group joined other British troops, estimated to include over 5,000 men in total. While training in camp, they received an announcement that Queen Elizabeth would visit them. On August 18, 1588, Queen Elizabeth arrived in Tilbury with the Earl of Leicester Robert Devereaux, the Earl of Essex Robert Dudley, John Norreys, and her traveling court.

Robert and the troops were assembled for full review, awaiting the arrival of Queen Elizabeth, when a gigantic roar rang out among the troops. Upon a gray gelding rode the Queen arrayed in a stunning white velvet outfit. Robert watched as Sir John Norreys, the Captain General, escorted the Queen and her inspection party. Proceeding slowly, the Queen looked out upon the troops. She seemed to like what she saw. As she moved about, her confidence grew and the troops responded with dignified approval.

Then she began to speak. The cheers died down until silence once more reigned. Amazing, thought Robert. She speaks with such sincere affection for her troops. He looked on her with increased respect when he heard her pledge that she, too, was prepared to lay down her all for her people, her honor, and her blood.

Elizabeth boldly stated, "I know I have the body of a weak and feeble woman, but I have the heart and stomach of a king and a king of England, too, and think foul scorn that Parma or Spain, or any prince of Europe, should dare to invade the borders of my realm . . ."

At the end of the day, after the Queen retired to her temporary quarters, Robert and the other field captains were invited to pay their respects to her. Lord Essex received the officers who had been so inspired by their leader. The men willingly renewed allegiance to the Queen, vowing their own willingness to pay the ultimate sacrifice to defend the borders of her realm.

Robert and the others walked in silence back to where each found his troops preparing for nightfall and anticipating a deadly battle with the Spanish invaders. Searching his belongings, Robert grabbed a small journal, then jotted down a few details from this momentous day. Robert would cherish forever his brief moments with the Queen and the everlasting memories with the troops. He wanted to share this story with Sally and his children exactly as it had happened. God willing, he and the men would soon be home, free of the scourge of the Armada and the Spanish threats on the seas.

Days passed, during which the troops heard numerous rumors about the Spanish Armada. Finally, reliable reports arrived that stated Admiral Drake had defeated the Spanish in a massive battle on the

North Sea and that Spanish ships were torn apart and forced to flee in random directions. Robert and the troops celebrated the victory for England. They shared a great relief for evading the bloody battle that would have been fought if Spanish troops had invaded the mainland. Within several days, the troops were released from Camp Tilbury and sent home. Their deployment, which lasted many weeks was over.

Robert and the militia returned to Lynn as triumphant warriors without firing a shot at the enemy. They had established many friendships and shared a kinship with troops throughout East Anglia that would last for many years. To Robert, kinship involved a common bond with the other soldiers who trained to fight together and share their mutual success and/or failure. Regardless of the consequences, they were a band of brothers.

Their loyalty to the Queen would not be forgotten. Preparing for the campaign had been physically demanding and difficult for Robert. He was worn out, but gratified to be part of the apparent success of the mission. England would be safer for merchants and his children's future appeared to be free from the threat of military invasion.

Robert spent his final days in Lynn with his family and friends. He returned to work at the shipyard, although a severe case of arthritis and gout cut short his working career. He suffered from a debilitating leg injury, which was believed to have originally been caused by the crushing blow to his right thigh in the wagon accident. His thigh bones never healed properly and he walked with a painful limp. When he returned from Tilbury, the arthritis extended throughout his body, making standing for long periods very difficult.

Robert became an advisor and confidant for his son Thomas as he became the leader of the family's business. Although Thomas was willing and made a gallant effort to be a successful merchant, his passion was directed to the reformed Church.

Nichole pursued her enthusiasm for show horses which would continue when she and her husband built a horse farm in Lincoln County.

Robert's health continued to deteriorate, leading to his death in 1590. Upon his death, the family library, which consisted primarily of biblical literature and family records passed on to Thomas and Nichole. In Sally's later days, she often welcomed comrades from Camp Tilbury and their children and family friends for visits in her home.

Sally survived until 1598. She was buried next to Robert in the church yard at St. Margaret's in King's Lynn.

Although Robert and Sally introduced Thomas to the religious difficulties of the times, his own commitment to finding the right place for Christian worship would lead the family to a conflict with church authorities and an eventual flight to the New World.

Bishop's Lynn (King's Lynn) Mayor, Benjamin Kine

St. Margaret's Church, King's Lynn

Chapter 8

Sir Thomas Keney
1571 – 1618
Puritan Baronet

STEADFAST IN FAITH
AS DANGERS MOUNT

Following a solemn and lengthy prayer, Thomas Keney unfolded his hands, lifted his head, and stood upright. God seemed to know his path and had been preparing him for this moment. His father, Sir Robert Keney, was dead, and Thomas, his only son, just nineteen years old, was now the head of the family.

His father seemed to know that he wouldn't have much time to train him in the important ways of the family business. When Thomas was barely fifteen, he had sent him to an apprenticeship at St. Thomas School in London, even though it meant that Thomas might inherit his family responsibilities early. His father had fulfilled his commitment to do whatever he could to keep the Spaniards from invading English soil.

By the time his father had gone off to Tilbury, Thomas was already back home preparing to care for the family's business. Fortunately, his father had not seen action, but the months in the field had taken their toll. Arthritis and gout had spread throughout his body, leaving him to limp with a swollen right leg. Thomas welcomed a much older father home. Still, Sir Robert was considered a local hero for his military leadership and devotion to the Queen. As much as he could, in the two years since his return, he had been teaching Thomas everything about the business with an increased sense of urgency.

Now it was up to Thomas to watch out for his aging mother Sally and younger sister, Nichole. Thankfully, his father's business-now his–was in sound financial condition. The business customers and other merchants, as well as the citizens of Lynn, considered Sir Robert to be a national hero. He had many loyal friends, now spread throughout Norfolk County. Thanks to people such as Robert, the community could again prosper without the threat of aggression against their merchant ships.

Growing up, Thomas was devoted to his mother and had learned to abide by her strict instructions. She was a dominating teacher, educator, and caregiver who carefully guarded his growth and development. Consequently, Thomas acquired punctual work habits and became an avid reader and diligent student.

Thomas' father, Sir Robert, also had a striking influence on his son, centered around his business, his affiliations in the community, and his status in the Church. Thomas remembered one homecoming reception for his father when his parents didn't know he was listening. The conversation was likely this:

"It's so good to have you home, Robert. How was your trip?" his mother Sally said as she hugged his father and led him into the anteroom. "I'll call the children-they have missed you and they will want to hear about your journey."

"Oh Sally, it's good to be home," replied Robert as he settled in his favorite chair by the fireplace. "Ely and Cambridge are beautiful in the spring. We had a wonderful gathering of Puritans at the Downing House in Cambridge. I believe our beloved Queen Elizabeth has brought new optimism and there is hope for our Puritan reforms within the Church."

Robert continued, "The flowers along the Ouse River are coming into bloom and the sales at the Saturday Market were brisk with eager buyers. The bakery in Ely ordered another full load of wheat–they like the full and hearty grain that we have been selling them from Cavender's farm. If sales continue to increase, we will need to order another supply boat to fulfill the new orders and . . ."

Robert stopped short when Nichole and Thomas bounded into the room.

"Hello, Father, did you bring us a surprise?" was the immediate inquiry from Nichole.

"Sure have," was his reply, as he reached into his travel bag and pulled out three wrapped packages.

Thomas and his sister quickly opened their presents and Nichole beamed with a new toy doll. Thomas frowned when he opened his present and gazed at some kind of new measuring device.

"What is it, Father?" he inquired.

"It's what they call a compass and if you hold it with the right angle to the sun, you can tell all the other directions. Wherever you go, on land or sea, you will never get lost. I'll show you how it works tomorrow when we go down to the docks."

Sally tried to change the subject and began opening her present. "Why it's a beautiful new necklace. It must have been very expensive. Thank you, Robert. Business must be very good."

"Business is good and I am grateful to you, Sally, for caring for the children and taking care of our home when I am away." Sally smiled, with respect, knowing that all too soon, her husband would be leaving again to sell some wheat or barley, as he spread the gospel, all for Puritan reform.

Thomas' parents lived in a comfortable home, which was spacious for the times. His parents hosted many social events, including tea parties and study groups for the prominent ladies in the community. Thomas' father hosted many of his business associates, including the farmers he represented as their merchant. Lively discussions about current affairs abounded at many parties held at their home. At the time when the upper and middle class were acquiring wealth and improved stature from increased trade and commerce, the lower class and many farmers seemed to be suffering and growing poorer. In addition to the ongoing changes in the church, reformers wanted to improve conditions for the poor and improve moral standards throughout the country, which drew Robert and Sally to some new ways of thinking.

Ever since she had lost their first child in childbirth, Sally turned to the Church for consolation and guidance. Over a period of time, she became a conscientious student of the Bible. With Robert and her children by her side, she had searched for a "faith community" that was compatible with her spirit for moral righteousness.

Sally traveled to Thetford, a village southeast of Lynn at the conjunction of the River Thet and the Little Ouse. She attended meetings in the home of William Dennis, who was a follower of the teachings of John Greenwood and Henry Barrowe. John Greenwood, a graduate of Cambridge in 1580, was the first to preach a religious doctrine known as Puritanism or Congregationalism. Initially, he advocated simple reforms of religious doctrine within the Church. Later, he adopted many of the reform policies of the Separatists movement. In accordance with the Act of Supremacy, he wanted to abolish the bishops and eliminate candle burning, the shrines, and chants within the services. He favored a simplified church facility with a bare room and a pulpit for the minister to read straight from the Bible without music or other distracting ceremonies. This new approach appealed to Sally.

When Sally returned from one of the meetings in Thetford, she was full of excitement and eager to discuss her findings with Thomas' father. She said, "Robert, I must tell you about this fellow John Greenwood who spoke to our Bible study group last week."

Robert replied, "My dear, it's good to see you so inspired. I've heard that Greenwood has been speaking throughout Norfolk County for several years. He has influenced many lives, but he seems to be very idealistic. What did he say?"

Sally replied, "He wants to elevate the morals of all people and bring equality for religious worship to everyone. He seeks ways for the poor, the farmers, and others associated with agrarian life styles to improve their quality of life. He talks of reforms leading to economic and religious freedom for all people."

Robert replied, "I can understand how his talks appeal to so many people. People want change—they want to live according to God's will. But I'm uncertain whether reform will come within our existing church or independently. This man Greenwood must be careful not to offend the Crown nor the Bishop of the Church of England."

Sally continued, "I believe these reforms will come, and hopefully our children and future generations will live in harmony with the chosen word of God as stated in the New Testament of the Bible."

Nonetheless, Thomas' family continued to live within the rules of the Church of England, attending services at St. Margaret's Church. Sally hosted study groups, led by the Reverend James Nyland in their home. When she was invited, she continued to participate in biblical studies at the homes of her friends.

In this environment, Thomas and his sister Nichole grew up with the consistent influence of the Puritan and Separatist ideology all about them. They had a growing library of religious books. Reading from the Tyndale Bible became a daily ritual, and Thomas grew to become an avid reader and a devoted reformer.

By birth, Thomas inherited the rights of "friendship to trade." In preparation to become a merchant, Thomas was sent to London to serve an apprenticeship. At the time when the country's merchant fleet was bracing for war with Spain, Thomas was introduced to the London docks, the riverfront, and the untamed life in London. For a young, naive lad, the experience was more enlightening for his expanding character than for his business acumen. While he fulfilled his working commitments and learned to work with the merchant accounts, his lasting personal impressions rested with the squalor and unfair labor practices spread throughout the city. He spent much of his leisure time in religious studies, rather than on inquiries into the ships, merchant practices, and navigational discoveries of the time.

When Thomas returned home, his father was in the midst of preparing the militia to defend the country from the invasion of Spain. Those services would likely require his father's absence from home for an extended period of time. Consequently, Thomas was expected to assume the operations of the family business. Thomas, who had a deep and abiding trust in his parents, wanted to please them. He accepted his family's responsibilities for the time being and became heavily engaged in the business.

Thomas joined the Trading and Merchants Guild. In cooperation with friends and business contacts, he solidified the merchant accounts with active farmers, including some of his relatives in Norfolk County. He sold their wheat, hay, mustard, cattle, and sheep to buyers in Cambridge, Boston, Portsmouth, and London. Eventually, his trading business prospered while the shipbuilding operations declined.

Thomas was well prepared to handle the family's business by the time his father died in 1590. As the years passed, he began to combine his business trips with meetings of church leaders, including the Puritans throughout East Anglia.

The period following his father's passing was an exciting time for exploration, adventure, and discovery. Since Admiral Drake and the British Navy defeated the Spanish Armada, new exploration began across the seas in earnest. Sir Walter Raleigh was exploring new trade routes in the Americas. The Dutch, French, and Portuguese sent new expeditions to the New World.

In England, William Shakespeare's career as a London playwright began and his production of *Midsummer Night's Dream* was completed in 1595. In Italy, the opera was born when Italian Jacopo Peri wrote *La Dafne* in 1597. The Globe Theater was built in 1599.

In Lynn, Thomas married Martha Eaton, a vivacious young lady who was eighteen years old at the time. Friends said Thomas must have loved his mother greatly, because he found a bride with many of the same characteristics. Martha attended Bible study classes with her mother in a manner similar to the classes Thomas attended with his mother. They even had similar Puritan upbringings with strong commitments to the faith. Martha and her family were active communicants at St. John's Church, where the wedding was held. Their wedding was a much attended event for everyone in the St. John's congregation and for many friends of both families.

Shortly before the turn of the century, John Greenwood and Henry Barrowe were executed by hanging. Prior to their executions, they were imprisoned for their refusal to return to the Church of England. While in prison, they wrote several books, which were later printed in Holland. Barrowe willed his estate to the Puritan Church, which used the money to pay for the printing and the distribution of his works. His writing left an indelible impact on young Puritans, including Thomas and his wife Martha.

After the executions of Barrowe and Greenwood, the English Parliament passed a law referred to as "Due Obedience," requiring all of the Queen's subjects over the age of sixteen to abide with strict atten-dance rules at only the Church of England. Any violations would be met with severe punishment, which could include prison, banishment from the country, or even hanging.

Another important event occurred in 1603 when Queen Eliza-beth passed away. She left a legacy that spanned almost half a century. During her reign, England defeated the Spanish Armada and become a great nation, recognized as a world leader. She skillfully maneuvered to establish Protestantism as the national church. With her passing, James Stuart, a Scotsman, ascended to the throne, marking a new era for England.

During the changes, Thomas and Martha moved ahead with the family's trading business and the expansion of their family. Their family prospered with four children. Their first son named John was born in

1600. The family grew to include a second son, William, born in 1601. A daughter, Elizabeth, was born in 1609 and another son, Thomas, was born in 1611.

Martha was a self-appointed community leader and a strong and dominating mother. She took it upon herself to educate her children and guide them into proper avenues of development. When Martha was not tending to her children, she taught school and worked at the Town Hall. When the family income declined in later years, she worked in several positions, including some clerical and maintenance positions. She was frugal and she primarily used her savings for her children's necessities and education.

At the Town Hall, Martha kept abreast of the local gossip, including reports and stories about the exploration and travels throughout England and the New World. When news describing the landing at Jamestown in the Americas reached Lynn in 1608, Martha was quick to comprehend its significance. With new discoveries, she anticipated that her family must be alert and prepare for future opportunities.

Meanwhile, Thomas continued to work as a merchant representing the farmers and fulfilling his calling with the Puritans. His religious duties gradually consumed more of his time. His heart and passion was with the Puritan movement. He supported the Puritan Church with his money, his time, and his teachings. Hoping that the Church could be reformed from within, he advocated that the true and righteous path was through Christian worship, the sacraments, and the teachings of Jesus Christ.

Thomas began to follow the Reverend Robert Browne, who began his ministry in neighboring Norwich, the dominant city in Norfolk County. Reverend Browne initially espoused the Puritan cause, but with time he became disillusioned. His following among the Separatists dramatically increased, even though there were threats and sanctions mounting against all non-conformists. Thomas and many others remained hopeful and optimistic that the Crown would be tolerant of the Reformation movement, especially the Puritans in East Anglia. Unfortunately the pressure for conformity to the Church of England mounted and Puritan leaders and Separatist clergy who did not conform with the Church were restricted and gradually expelled from the Church of England.

Thomas and other Puritan leaders had been hopeful that King James would favor the Puritan movement and spiritually return to what they called the "pure" church. Instead, in 1604, King James called for a conference at Hampton Court where he issued his famous proclamation, "I will make them conform themselves, or else I will harry them out of the land, or else do worse. Resolve to conform to the Church, or leave the Country."

To appease the Puritans, he called for the study and translation of the Bible into English. Eventually, his resolution led to the creation of the King James Edition of the Bible. But the persecution of the Separatists, Puritans, and other non-conforming groups intensified.

Thomas was thirty-four years old when Guy Fawkes and a group of conspirators attempted to blow up the Houses of Parliament and assassinate King James. Although the explosion and fireworks caused considerable damage, the King escaped. Fawkes was captured and his conspirators were seized later to be imprisoned or executed. Their torture was so gruesome that all Englishmen thought twice about crossing the King in any manner. To mark the historical event, England still celebrates with fireworks and bonfires on November fifth every year.

Thomas was disappointed with both the proclamation and the position of King James. But, with small children at home, he resigned himself to concentrate on the growth and development of his family and business. His trading business for sheep, cattle, and grains was steady and provided a stable income for his family. But in 1607, there was a devastating flood that caused heavy damage in the lowlands, and resulted in changing the water routes for small ships. Thomas worked hard to minimize the losses sustained by the farmers and by many of his friends. He shared the losses and attempted to salvage the produce that could be saved. He provided credit to many families. His loyalty paid off and when the farmers recovered in the good years that followed, they continued to trade with Thomas and repay the loans.

Over the years, Thomas maintained contact with many of his father's friends. In the course of his trading, he also cultivated some helpful contacts on his own. Mindful of his family's legacy, in 1612, Thomas submitted the family coat of arms for approval. He traveled to London to seek support, but he found that many of the family's friends were gone. London had changed. The Court of King James seemed to be indifferent to his request.

When Thomas returned to Lynn, his homecoming was one of mixed emotions and went like this:

Martha saw him from a window upstairs. She knew immediately that he wore more than the weariness of travel. Sighing, she strode toward the stairs and hurried down to greet him. Before he could reach the doorknob, she threw open the door.

"Welcome home," she called.

"Ah, Martha, it's nice to see a friendly face."

"So, how did it go?" she asked.

"Let's step inside first, OK?" Thomas looked out on the street wondering if he really knew who among his neighbors was friend or foe.

Martha shut the door with a bang and then looked into his face. "London was none too friendly, is that what I am to gather?"

"Well, King James' court seems to have forgotten the legacy of the Keneys. The coat of arms is not a go."

"Any reason why?"

"Aw, Martha, London's a much colder place these days. I don't think these days are so good for a man willing to declare that he sees God differently than the Church of England does. I start to wonder if pure faith can exist in this country."

"What would you do about it then?" she asked. "Are you starting to see why I suggest that maybe England itself hasn't been elected to reform God's work?"

Thomas replied, "I see why many have escaped to Leyden. Yet so far, my customers and friends have been loyal and still trade with me."

He continued, "These are uncertain times. From what I hear, there are those who may not be so interested in trading with a Puritan, no matter what his record or family traditions. Martha, I know that the teachings of Jesus Christ have been ignored for a long time, I cannot support the wrongs and injustice I see. Yet, if it affects you and the children..."

Martha interrupted, "Thomas, you know what is right. You can count on me to help our family, even if it means that I must turn to a menial position. My salvation comes from Christ, not from wealth or approval from the Crown."

Thomas replied, "And if things change so that we must worry for our very lives? Then what? Are you prepared to leave?"

Martha boldly replied, "Indeed, even to the Americas."

Thomas grasped her hand, grateful for her faith and strength. "God willing, that won't be necessary. We will do what we can here in Lynn. It's important to show our commitment for other followers who may be wavering."

Martha smiled. "Coat of arms or no, you can still tell your children the tales of their grandfather, great-grandfather, and all the rest. Should I call them so they can give their father a hearty welcome? They have missed you so. They can't wait to hear about your journey and, of course, to see if you found them anything in London."

"Yes, yes." Thomas answered as he checked his pockets and baggage for the treasures he had brought home for the children.

Thomas settled in his comfortable chair and spoke to his children, "I have tried hard for the past few years to obtain the approval of our family's coat of arms. But it now appears that I have been unsuccessful."

His son John intervened, "I'm sorry, Father, but why is that so important?"

"Well," said Thomas, "it would have been nice for the deeds of your grandfather to be recognized by the authorities, but I have come to believe that it is more important for you to know that your grandparents were good Christian people and that you should be very proud of them."

"I don't understand," said son William. "How can I learn from Grandfather when he has been dead for so many years?"

"That's true," answered Thomas. "We really cannot do much about the past, but you can do a great deal about your future. Your mother and I simply want you to have confidence, with knowledge of your ancestors, so that you can improve your lives and live as free and as abundantly as possible."

William said, "So that's why you and mother tell us stories about Grandfather Robert defending Queen Elizabeth at Camp Tilbury?"

"Yes, son," said Thomas. "I'm glad you understand."

In time, the oldest son, John, was trained in the family business. He had an outgoing, pleasant personality, conducive to working with other people. With a natural ability for building things, he worked at various construction jobs about town. He developed sound leadership skills, taking an active role in school and extended activities with his classmates. John was a sensitive child, highly influenced by the Puritan movement, who developed a deep-seated passion to live in accordance with Biblical scriptures.

William was the second child. Under his mother's careful eye, William was taught to be independent, yet very diligent and precise. He was a good student, with exceptional capabilities in math and the physical science. With a carefree spirit, William liked to spend time in the outdoors, often fishing and sailing. When he grew up, he spent an apprenticeship at the Nar River Shipbuilding Company and eventually would become a master carpenter.

When their only daughter Elizabeth was 7 years old, she caught a terrible fever and died in the winter of 1616. It was a dreadful time for the family, especially with the unrest and turmoil accompanying the religious upheaval. Thomas and Martha suffered the pain and sorrow of losing their daughter in the midst of a multitude of other problems.

Thomas was the youngest child, who was highly dependent upon his caring mother and older brothers. As he grew older, he witnessed the pain and suffering resulting from the family's allegiance to Puritanism. He would rebel and pursue a more conventional lifestyle as a merchant, selling and trading agricultural products.

In 1616, King James issued another edict calling for church reform. This edict again stated that everyone must attend and support the Church of England or suffer penalties and pay stiff fines. Violators were publicly humiliated. As pressure from the Church of England mounted, Thomas' business and family reputation slowly deteriorated. The family wealth declined, even though many farmers remained loyal to Thomas. It became more difficult for Puritans to practice their religion. Thomas remained steadfast in his devotion to the Puritan movement, becoming known and respected by his associates as Sir Thomas, the Puritan Baronet of Norfolk.

The pressure and public humiliation for his family was taking a toll on Thomas. His health declined rapidly as much of his energy was drained with increasing threats of censure and punishment from government authorities. He often met in secret sessions with other Puritan leaders. He even arranged the departure of some of his friends, who joined an escape party with some of the Separatists from Lincoln County. Determined to remain faithful, he was gratified with news from Holland that the faithful were successful in reaching a sanctuary in Leyden. Thomas hoped to find religious freedom for his own family and he began to consider an escape route.

But his health deteriorated and he died from what was believed to be a stroke in 1618. To prevent further harassment and humiliation for the family, his remains were laid to rest in the city's Saddlebow Road Cemetery, just south of Lynn. Many of the family's records, including the membership rolls for the Puritan Church, were destroyed to prevent further persecution of Martha and her children.

Martha retreated with her children from public exposure. She was determined to protect and raise her still-young children into adult men. Following the pretense of abiding by all government edets, she followed a daily routine that would not call for questions nor investigations from authorities. The boys grew strong and energetic, with many similarities to their father. Martha proved to be the guiding force for the family, doing whatever was necessary for their care and survival. Her dreams were fulfilled as she watched all three of her boys reach maturity and begin their own families.

John, the oldest son, would follow in his father's footsteps with a deep and abiding commitment to follow his parents religious teaching. With fervent convictions, he would pursue a course eventually leading his family to the New World.

With recognition for Sir Thomas' steadfast devotion to follow the word of God, a fitting epitath for the Puritan Baronet was taken from Deut 33:27 as follows:

"The Eternal God is thy Refuge."

Martha died in 1629 and was buried next to her husband in the Saddlebow Road Cemetery.

Road near Queen Street, King's Lynn

Tower of London

Chapter 9

John Keney
1600 – 1627
Man of God, Builder

PAYING THE ULTIMATE PRICE FOR RELIGIOUS FREEDOM

John returned home from a trip to London and walked into his home where he lived with his younger brothers, William and Thomas, and his mother. He found his mother sitting next to a window where the afternoon sun still shone brightly on this day, October 4, 1618. In his hands, he carried what looked to be an official notice.

"Mother, I've got news. You'll never guess."

Martha Keney looked up, much aged since her husband's death in March. "Well, tell me. Just because you are the man of the house now, doesn't mean you have to keep your mother waiting for news–you know how I love to hear what you did in London and what is happening in this world."

"This isn't just about the world, it's about us. Father, God keep his soul, should be here this day to celebrate. He so cherished our heritage and he worked so hard to protect our family's reputation, even while maintaining his faith."

John continued, "Mother, I have received official notice from London that the Keney Family Coat of Arms has been approved."

Martha jumped up from her chair and grabbed John's hands. "Oh, yes, your father would be so happy. He worked so hard and wanted to fulfill the family's request for official recognition." She sighed and then continued, "It's just that we don't know who is and who isn't our friend these days. Loyalty in the face of persecution can be a difficult thing."

"Yes," replied John. "I worry when I see families who used to do business with us, but now they are afraid to be tainted by our faith."

John handed his mother the official paper and reached for another paper in his pocket. "Mother, I have more news. I hear that even in Leyden, the authorities search for William Brewster. The Separatists are free to practice their faith there, but only if the Crown thinks they cannot reach the rest of us. But look what I have here."

Martha shook her head as John pulled a pamphlet from his pocket. "Not from Brewster's press, is it?"

John replied, "Yes, as a matter of fact it is, and it offers new hope for religious freedom. I am beginning to believe that Father was right when he said the English Church is beyond repair, and that, maybe, Brewster and Robinson make more sense than those who would have us change the Church here from within. I have become more enamored with what John Robinson has to say. We all know that we cannot worship and publicly live the Puritan way. Things are getting worse here. I'm thinking about leaving for Leyden and starting over."

"Now, John," cautioned his mother. "I hear that even the Separatists have become frustrated with Holland. Their children become more Dutch by the day and they find it so hard to find decent work to support their families. When you and Sarah marry, you'll have a good wife, and, God willing, young children for your caring. Besides, aren't the faithful ones in Leyden really looking for a way to get to the new colonies in America?"

"So I hear," replied John. "Perhaps new opportunities will soon allow them to find a new home in America if the first settlers are successful."

John wanted to assure his aging mother so he continued, "Mother, I will work hard to provide for you and the family, and I will be loyal to our Puritan values as you and father have entrusted to us. But you need to know that my conscience tells me to watch closely the behavior of our government authorities so that we will not be treated unfairly for our faithfulness to our principles nor our family's historic loyalty to the Crown. Although uncertainties are everywhere, I will care for our future." John spoke with authority and determination which seemed to satisfy his mother.

John was born in 1600, the first son of Martha and Thomas Keney. As the oldest, John did his best to be a good role model for the younger family members. John's early years were happy living with his parents, brothers, William and Thomas, and his sister, Elizabeth. He participated in outdoor sports with his brothers, but lacked the size and instincts to compete against bigger boys. Instead he developed a special talent for music and sang in a choir with six schoolmates. The boys gathered on Saturdays to practice and learn new songs. Their singing was much in demand and they sang at parties, dances, and weddings.

John was compassionate and grew even more so with the premature death of his sister, Elizabeth, in 1616. He provided comfort to his mother whom he adored. As best he could, he accepted this loss knowing that God's hand was involved in everything. Without complaining, he moved ahead.

Norfolk was a prosperous county in the early 1600s. The farmers in the rich agricultural country were providing cattle and sheep, as well as hay, barley, and oats for sale throughout the Kingdom. The fishing industry was flourishing and the north end of Lynn was growing with additional docks, warehouses, and homes for the fishermen. Markets in Lynn, Norwich, Cambridge, and Portsmouth were thriving, not only for the sale of goods, but also as attractions for traveling minstrels and occasional theater productions. James Burbridge brought traveling shows to Lynn, including some works by Ben Jonson and William Shakespeare. Shakespeare was known to be working on his masterpieces, *King Lear*, *Macbeth*, and *The Tempest*.

John's parents exemplified the hopes of the Puritans when King James was crowned. But after the gunpowder plot of Guy Fawkes, King James extinguished their hopes when he became more intolerant and defensive.

Things became worse for John when he became a teenager. In 1616, government officials began to enforce the King's decree calling for strict adherence to the rules for the Church of England which meant that other religious sects, including the Puritans, would not be tolerated. John was torn between his family's strong Puritan background, his classmates and friends, and his patriotic loyalty to the Crown. On some occasions, he began to be excluded from school and social activities.

The family, following strict directions from John's father, disobeyed the government edict and continued to attend Puritan services. Traveling as necessary in secret, Thomas became more aligned with the Separatist believers. In Lincolnshire and Scrooby, he met with followers of Reverend John Robinson. In time he became involved with some of their secret plans, including the ongoing correspondence with the Separatists in Leyden.

But in the midst of all their difficulties, John and his brother, William, still found time for fun. They traveled to the annual fair in Lincoln. Since their father stayed home, one can assume that the two boys felt carefree and rambunctious and able to do move about and eye the young maids without their father's watchful eye.

William nudged John, who then looked in the direction of his gaze. There John saw several attractive young ladies congregating near a booth selling hot cross buns.

"Didn't you say you wanted a hot cross bun?" asked William.

"Maybe later."

"Later? Why it's been hours since we last ate. I think you are afraid of the surroundings, especially those pretty girls."

"No, I'm just not hungry."

"Well, I am." William turned and strode toward the booth. John shook his head. His brother was so bold. John was just fine watching from afar, but he knew William would only embarrass him more if he waited.

John joined William as he was bowing toward the girls in the group. A lively brunette paused with her conversation in mid-sentence to listen.

William spoke, "Good morning, ladies. I am William Keney and this is my brother, John. How are you doing today?

"Very well, thank you," replied the apparent leader while a few others suppressed giggles. "Are you perchance the sons of Thomas Keney from Lynn?"

"We are. And who are you?"

"Sarah Cheever. My father knows your father, it seems. I have heard him praise you father's courage regarding our faith." The girl's demeanor suddenly turned serious. "It's good to have strong examples in our community."

This time John spoke up. "Our father cannot do otherwise. His commitment extends to everyone in our family. I admire your loyalty and courage to speak your piece. I'm sure our father would like to send his best regards to your father."

Sarah turned to look at John. An awkward silence followed before Sarah smiled again, only this time her smile was directed toward John. His face turned red as he focused on her penetrating eyes. He almost forgot to return her radiant smile, and without saying anything more, they seemed to communicate very well for a carefree young lady meeting a handsome young man for the first time on a warm summer day.

William understood that his quieter brother had somehow bested him. With a shrug, he looked around and asked, "Now, who wants a hot cross bun? My brother would like to buy one for each of you. Since I am the younger, he is the one with the purse and the money. John?"

John's eyes narrowed, darting toward his brother, before fixing on the girls in front of him, especially Sarah Cheever. Then he reached for his purse, knowing everyone in the group was going to enjoy a hot cross bun at his expense. But maybe it was the best investment he ever made, knowing it gave him a good reason to call again on the attractive Sarah Cheever.

During this period, John was working on various construction jobs, including one at the Wymonham Market, which was being rebuilt after the Fire of 1615, and another, at the Customs House that was completed in 1620. John had an unusual talent for heavy construction and reclamation work, including dredging and earthmoving to facilitate waterways for shipping. When John was younger, his father had converted some of the family's small merchant boats to dredges and working boats that would float in shallow waters. There was a need to repair the docks and dredge the River Nar to accommodate the larger ships.

John was a conscientious worker. He wanted to expand his working experience away from the family's trading business. Construction work, especially along the distant waterways, allowed him to use his talents well and keep a low profile away from religious controversies.

Although the government continued to intimidate the Puritans and Separatists, John and Sarah were married in 1620. The private wedding ceremony took place at St. Paul's Church in Lincoln. Shortly after their wedding, the Bishop in Norwich issued a warning that all marriages and baptisms must be registered with the Church of England. Further, the Bishop reiterated that all parishioners must make their pledges of loyalty to the Church and attend only their services. This was taken as another threat to the Puritans and all minority religious groups.

In 1621, John remained busy with his construction work. He and Sarah were expecting their first child in the spring of 1622.

John learned that the ship, the *Mayflower*, had sailed to the New World, and that a copy of the Mayflower Compact was circulating in England. John followed the news closely. Additional reports continued to arrive from Leyden where Separatists were restless. Rather than sailing on the *Mayflower*, John Robinson stayed in Leyden and continued to accommodate new refugees. There were additional reports that a close friend of John's, Richard Blake, and a group of parishioners from Scrooby had arrived safely in Leyden.

Leyden had become a haven for Walloon and English refugees

seeking religious freedom. Now, many who had left for Holland since 1608 were feeling the need to find a new home. As conditions in Holland worsened, they considered Leyden only a temporary shelter, with hopes of going to New England or Ireland as soon as travel arrangements could be made.

News arrived in spring 1622 that John's cousin, John Jenney, who previously lived in Norwich, was accepted for passage and was planning to go to America on either the *Anne* or the *Little James* ships. Meanwhile, public exposure of the non-Anglicans continued to mount. When a group of Separatists and Puritans attempted to escape, they were caught just prior to embarkation and returned to Lynn where they were put on public display and treated as outlaws. John's efforts to console the travelers were met with public ridicule. Authorities targeted John and warned him against further religious pacification. Those caught found the public humiliation to be unbearable and thereafter, they were forced into secret hiding places. Religious services and all plans had to be conducted in privacy with strict secrecy.

John heard from his friend, Richard Blake. He wrote to John describing Leyden as a fair and beautiful town with numerous windmills and peaceful streams and waterways. A university was located in Leyden and it was hopeful that some religious studies would be available to the immigrants. John Robinson personally welcomed the Blake family and others to services at St. Pieter's Church. However, housing provisions were very limited forcing Richard and his family to live in temporary quarters, sharing facilities with other refugees. It was difficult to converse in Dutch with the local people and there seemed to be a limited number of jobs available. Richard had planned to continue his work as a tailor, but the major clothing business was in Amsterdam, not Leyden. For now, Richard worked in a cloth factory as a weaver and wool comber. Richard was happy and relieved to escape the wrath of the Church of England. But he was still determined to find a better life for his family.

In Lynn, the winter was long and cold, which made it difficult for

John to work on construction projects. The government continued to expose and threaten the dissenters, making common religious services and friendships with parishioners almost impossible.

In the spring 1624, John and Sarah were expecting a second child who would join their daughter, Alexandria. During that time, at a small gathering of Puritans, a friend, William Higman, told John of another plan to escape to Leyden. There would be room for John and Sarah if they chose to go. After long deliberations, they decided that soon after the birth of their next child, they would join the next traveling party to Leyden.

Their son, Henry, was born in Lynn on July 6, 1624 amid preparations for their journey to Leyden and the start of a new life.

On August 24, 1624, William Higman led a group of Separatists and some Puritans to the docks on the River Ouse to board the ship bound for Amsterdam. John and Sarah, with their toddler daughter, Alexandria, and their not-yet two month old baby boy, Henry, boarded the ship under the cover of darkness. They only carried a few earthly possessions, including a small wooden box of family records and some other family treasures. John's brother, William, accompanied them to the ship and bid them farewell.

Once out to sea, the waters were cold and rough. Sarah and the children took space in amidships, with as much protection as possible from the cold winds. John was expected to take his turn with the ship's crew, serving as a lookout and assisting with the navigation. John took every opportunity to protect Sarah and the children and to keep them warm and comfortable. But the cold winds were menacing for John and soon he caught a bad cold with a high fever.

The trip took four days. They arrived in Amsterdam in late afternoon on August 28th. The port at Amsterdam was much larger than that at Lynn, and Sarah and John were awestruck with the splendid sailing ships in the harbor and the bay. Upon arrival, they were taken to St. Nicholas Church where they were given a warm meal, beds, and accommodations. John sent Richard Blake a letter informing him of their arrival in Amsterdam and their plans to journey to Leyden as soon as possible.

During the period from 1620 to 1635, Amsterdam was a vibrant and active seaport, considered a major trading center of the world. Dutch ships traveled throughout the known world and their trading business was thriving. Dutch explorers were searching for new trade routes and there were reports of colonizing New Amsterdam in America. In 1624, the Dutch were bartering for rights for what would be called Manhattan Island.

John and Sarah stayed in Amsterdam for about twelve days before departing for Leyden. Amsterdam was ablaze with summer flowers scattered in the parks and pathways. After resting at the church where John received care for his fever, they took the children on a walking tour of Amsterdam. They saw the marketplace and watched the small boats travel the inner waterways. They attended services at St. Nicholas Church where they met local Christians who shared their meals and welcomed them to their homes.

On the 10th of September, they left Amsterdam on a small boat, traveling on the coastal and inner passage to Leyden. Leyden was located about thirty kilometers south of Amsterdam. John and Sarah were filled with hope and great expectations as they traveled to see their friend, Richard Blake. The trip was pleasant, as they stopped several times to rest, replenish their provisions, and see the countryside which was still colorful with many fall flowers.

Richard Blake had received John's letter and was at the docks when they arrived. After an emotional reunion, they traveled into the Leyden neighborhood where other refugees lived and where they would share quarters with Richard's family. The first Sunday in Leyden was another emotional reunion for John when he and his family attended church at St. Pieter's, meeting many friends from Lynn, Norwich, and Lincolnshire.

John and Sarah met some new friends including Mary Putnum who offered to help Sarah get settled. John was especially pleased when the

Reverend John Robinson gave the sermon at church and welcomed their family to the congregation. It was a tremendous relief to be safe in Leyden, even though they knew that soon they would face new challenges.

Leyden was a prosperous and active community, yet much smaller than Amsterdam. Its natural beauty attracted many artists. The local university provided an environment for intellectual curiosity. Basic foods were available since the neighboring farms were growing wheat, rice, barley, and flour. The flour mills were busy and commercial trade was brisk throughout the area.

Since it was fall, John felt confident that he could find suitable employment before winter. Some of the immigrants were working in the clothing and woolen mills. John had hoped that with his experience in several areas of construction, he could find a good job. However, his health was still not good for working outdoors, and he found it difficult to converse with potential employers when he didn't know the Dutch language. Until he found a satisfactory job, John helped at the Walloon's Church and worked part time at the printing shop at the university.

The first winter in Leyden was cold, long, and difficult for John and Sarah. They took comfort in their family and friends from Lynn, and for their freedom from the threats and reprisals from the government. But their quarters were very small, their savings were dwindling, and the cold and bitter weather repressive, especially for John and the children. His health did not revive.

When spring finally arrived, the warm weather and flowers were a welcome relief. During the winter, John and Richard had constructed a dual baby carriage for Sarah, and she delighted in taking Henry and Alexandria for long walks. There were many artists in Leyden and some of them were studying at the university. Sarah came to know many of them as she made her rounds about town. The artists had their favorite sites for painting. Frans Hals lived in Haarlem, but occasionally painted west of town by the beautiful waterways. Jan Lievens and Rembrandt Van Rijn, who was born in Leyden in 1606, often settled by the flour windmills near the Central Park. Gerrit Dou was often found painting by the open markets and the parks.

Some of the artists were friendly toward Sarah and they asked that she stay awhile and pose for their paintings. She would often let Henry and Alexandria play in the parks where they developed a natural love for the outdoors. They loved to run and jump as the artists painted and visited with Sarah. Henry soon learned to walk during these outings.

During the first two years, Richard Blake provided the main income for the family. John continued to work part-time at the printing shop, but his health prohibited him from full-time employment. Richard would occasionally go to Amsterdam, where he would find the latest news about trading and sailing ships to America. He grew more interested in the opportunities in America and he began to plan just how he could arrange to make the journey.

Sarah made friends easily. She was naturally cheerful and friendly, even under the most difficult of circumstances. She became active in the family care center at the Walloon Center and St. Pieter's Church, where she provided care and comfort to other families who were in transit to and from Leyden. She was hopeful and optimistic that the right opportunity would come along for her family. In the meantime, she was devoted to her children, Henry and Alexandria. She was their inspiration and their teacher and she fed and nourished them with loving care. The children grew strong and developed godly discipline and healthy habits that would last a lifetime.

Life in Leyden was difficult for the faithful. They learned to help and support each other. Sarah and John made friends with the parents of Henry Curtis, Robert Taylor, and Victor Hubbard. Vincent Potter, a young merchant working in the cloth trade, took a special liking for Sarah and John. Richard Blake continued to be a valued friend. He shared his home, clothing, and food with the Keneys.

The Reverend John Robinson died in 1625 before he could lead others to the New World. The Separatist community helped each other, but with the death of Robinson, they lacked leadership and direction for their future. The people lived day to day, some returning to England, others becoming more Dutch with each passing day. Still others, like John and Sarah, continued to dream about their opportunity to go to the Americas.

In fall 1627, when John was working on the docks in Leyden, he contracted pneumonia. His health had never fully returned and the harsh northern winds and cold temperatures had become overwhelming to him. He gradually lost his strength and, after a lengthy struggle, he died in November 1627. John's unrelenting battle to protect his family and their rights for religious freedom came to a sad end when he was just twenty-seven years old. The Puritan and Separatist families joined together with other friends from the Walloon Church to support Sarah. Unfortunately, death was common in most families.

Richard Blake returned from a trip to Amsterdam in the spring of 1629 with news that he could obtain passage on a ship to America in the summer. He planned to take his wife and children and offered to take Alexandria. Once they were settled in America, Sarah and Henry would join them. After long talks and deliberations with Sarah, the plan became acceptable to all parties. Parting would be very difficult for Sarah, but she was convinced that it would not be long before she and Henry would join the Blakes. Richard had been so helpful to them. He had assumed the leadership of the family after John's death, and now it seemed important for him to take advantage of the opportunity to go to America.

Sarah told Richard about John's distant cousin, Robert Keayne, who was believed to be in London and planning to go to America soon. Robert was known to be an ambitious gentleman who had a solid background and was likely to become a successful merchant. She hoped that Richard would find Robert and that he would be helpful with their settling in New England.

Sarah resigned herself to make the best of the situation in Leyden until the time came for herself and Henry, now five years old, to go to

America. She found work where she could, including a part-time job at St. Pieter's Church. She cared for the children of Adam Winthrop, Henry Curtis, and Taylor Carr. She found time to teach English classes to students including Vincent Potter, Ted Hubbard, and Steven Winthrop. After cleaning at the university, she performed maintenance work for several artists including Jan Lievens. But most of all, she was devoted to her son, Henry, who was growing up rapidly in a difficult and challenging world.

Henry would learn to make the most of the meager income his mother could supply. She taught him to persevere, to be strong under adverse conditions, and to respect and trust his close friends, primarily those who shared their devotion to the righteous principles of the Church.

Occasionally, news came from England, confirming reports of the ongoing religious turmoil within the country. There were more warning signs of an imminent civil war. In 1629, King Charles dissolved the English Parliament. Unfortunately, shipping was limited, causing merchants to avoid dangerous ports for fear of major losses. Consequently, it was difficult to send and receive letters to friends and relatives.

There were neither letters nor news from Sarah's friend, Richard Blake, her family in England, nor from her distant relative, Robert Keayne. One year became two and then three. Sarah gradually became discouraged about the prospects for traveling to America, causing her to feel gravely ill from the loss of Alexandria. She was exhausted from her various jobs. But she continued to care for the children of Dutch and other families in the area. Henry spent much of his time with some likeable playmates including Teddy Hubbard and Caleb Carr. Sarah channeled most of her energy toward Henry as he began to read and write in English and Dutch. He was growing strong and showed signs of being a healthy and precocious young man.

Sarah contracted dysentery around Christmas of 1632. She tried to bolster Henry's spirits, thinking that she would soon be better and that they might yet prosper in the New Year. Instead, her weakened condition invited other illnesses. She spent time caring for children who had what would later be called scarlet fever. Consequently, Sarah soon felt ill again. She ached so much that she could not move from her bed.

Sensing the seriousness of her illness, Vincent Potter moved Sarah and Henry into the Potter home where he and his friends could care for them. Sarah's body continued to alternate between fiery heat and a frigid chill to match the February gloom. She tried her friends' remedies, but they were helpless against her fever's rage. Few moments passed when she responded to anyone, though often she seemed agitated without the ability to fight back.

She called for Vincent Potter in her final days and spoke as clearly as possible under the dreadful circumstances. She must have convinced Vincent to talk with Henry, which he probable did when Henry returned home from his work of cleaning up around the woolen mill. When Henry entered the home, Vincent began:

"Young Henry, we need to talk."

"What is it? How's my mum?'

"She was able to speak with me today."

"Is she better?"

Vincent winced at the hope in his voice, then replied, "Henry, I think her time on this earth is soon to pass—I've seen this condition with both my mum and father before God called them home."

Henry looked him straight in the eye, with a look far too old for his nine years. "All right, then. Can I see her?"

"Yes, she would like that, but I wanted to talk with you first about my conversation with your mum. She spoke as clearly as I used to hear Pastor Robinson preach. She wants to make sure you won't be abandoned to the streets. Ah, good, gentle Sarah Keney. I will miss her wise counsel. I believe she has prepared me well to watch for you."

Vincent and Henry sat down in the chairs that faced each other.

"She gave me her blessing when I asked if I could take you under my wing. Of course, here in Leyden I am not a man of means, but I have been saving my earnings from the cloth trade, and when the time is right, I will buy our passage to America. You will be able to work off your debt as an apprentice in the New World. We'll practice our faith in secret if we must, but some day we will live in a community where we will be free to live and worship God as we please."

"And Mum is OK with this?" asked Henry.

Vincent reached down and tousled the boy's hair. "Henry, she believes you are one of God's chosen and that you must soon be part of building his great city. She wants the best for you and that involves God's plan. I want that plan to come true for you."

Henry replied, "With Mum's blessing, I believe in God's plan. I believe that someday, I will go to America."

Their conversation was interrupted by the attending nurse who said, "Sarah would like to see Master Henry. I'm afraid there is not much time for her."

Henry could barely see as he entered the darkened room. The air smelled of sickness and his mother lay motionless on the small bed. Though her eyes were barely open, she managed a brief smile for him and she began speaking, slowly yet firmly.

"Be a good boy and you will grow to be strong. Don't forget who you are, your kinship, and where you came from. You are a Christian soldier, with all of God's power. Within you lies all things great and small. And for your wonderful gifts, including a strong mind, body, and soul, you are solely responsible to God, our ultimate creator. Live according to God's law and you will be rewarded throughout your life and ultimately in the Kingdom of Heaven."

Sarah's voice drew faint and she closed her eyes. By nightfall, Sarah was gone. She was buried in the poor section of St. Pieter's Church, close to the burial location where her husband John rested.

Her friends bid a sad farewell to Sarah as they formed a support family for Henry.

Inland River near Leyden, Holland

Chapter 10

Henry Keney
1624 – 1709
Frontiersman, Progenitor, Soldier

BRANCHING OUT IN AMERICA

Henry was ten years old when Vincent Potter heard of another opportunity to travel to the Massachusetts Bay Colony. The ship, *Elizabeth and Ann*, with Master Roger Cooper would leave from London in the spring. Prior to boarding, all passengers must sign a certificate of confirmation pledging their allegiance to the Church of England. Vincent Potter and many of the Puritans and Separatists planned to sign the certificates if it meant safe passage and getting out from under the Church of England. He told Captain Cooper of the plight of young Henry Keney. They agreed that Henry would be considered a minor under his guardianship. Henry would not be registered in the ship's log and would travel as the sole responsibility of Vincent Potter.

All passengers were given a list of supplies, including food and clothing for the voyage and their initial necessities in America. Henry's preparations were minimal, consisting of his basic clothes, pants, shirts, a wool coat and hat, boots, and two pairs of shoes. He also carried three blankets, his family bible which included a family log, his mother's treasure box, three books, several drawings and paintings of his parents and sister, three small games, a hatchet, pocket knife, eating utensils, cleaning articles, candles, and a first aid kit. Vincent Potter supplied his share of the food and medicine for the passage.

Henry boarded the *Elizabeth and Ann* on May 6, 1635. Several of his companions, including Philip Washburn and Richard and Nathaniel Whitney, were already on board. Henry was taken to the lower mid-section, between decks where he met three other boys, John Johnson, Stephen Barrett, and William Browne. Like Henry, these boys were bound to become apprentices in America. They were told to be quiet and remain there for several days–until the ship was clearly out to sea.

Survival by staying healthy became the primary objective when living on the ship. Henry learned to take it one day at a time, stay focused, and remain incognito. He felt grateful to Vincent Potter and was determined to stay out of trouble for fear of punishment or even being returned to England. He stayed within a very limited space and relied on his friends to protect him.

Living on a meager subsistence, Henry obeyed the authorities and performed his duties and obligations without strife nor contempt. These lessons served him well throughout his life, as he was constantly reminded that if he were to live, he must abide by the unwritten laws of survival. Controlling his emotions and hiding his anger became common traits for Henry. While he was pragmatic with his habits for daily living, he developed a deep-seated resentment for what he considered immoral or indecent behavior, especially when it was directed at him.

He saw people beaten, punished, and even killed for insubordination and violation of conduct. Nevertheless, his philosophy was based, to a large extent, upon the Puritan doxology, that everything happens for a good reason. In accordance with the daily prayers aboard ship and the consistent message of the Puritan vicars, he followed the strict word of God, as stated in the Bible and interpreted by himself and those adults he grew to respect. He accepted others for whatever their beliefs and causes, but he disregarded and avoided the demands of others to conform to their thinking. He resolved to live according to his beliefs and let others live according to their beliefs.

The sailing took sixty-eight days. Once out to sea, Henry could move more freely within the area assigned to the passengers. Every morning and evening, prayers were said and, sometimes, there was communion and singing. The sailors were given daily instructions. Henry watched the sailors closely and began to anticipate and imitate their daily routine. They taught him to tie knots and to repair broken lines. He made friends with the night watch and pretended that he was a lookout searching the horizon. Scanning the ocean, he watched for whales and jumping fish. Studying the skies, he learned the basics of navigation using the moon, sun, and stars. All the time, he tried to be helpful and assist others, especially Vincent Potter.

Henry spent a great deal of time, especially during the storms at sea, reading his family bible and thinking about the future. When the sailors told stories about their hardships and escapades, he listened closely. There were scary tales about the native Indians and Henry grew hopeful to learn their languages. He was uncertain about what he would actually find in America, but he resolved to work hard and to make a new life for himself. Remembering his mother's final words, he was determined to survive and to be successful.

Henry thought a lot about his childhood and what had brought him to this day. Although he was told, he didn't remember King's Lynn, the town of his birth. Friends told him how his father John and mother Sarah had escaped with him and his sister Alexandria shortly after he was born. Try as he might, he could barely remember the early days in Leyden when the four of them lived together with other refugees.

Henry did remember the outings with his mother in the Leyden parks where he learned to enjoy the outdoors. There, one of the artists drew a picture of Henry exaggerating his broad smile and prominent western teeth, with a wide space between the top two incisors. As he grew, he developed strong legs and eventually became a fast runner and an avid skater. He was an inquisitive child and sometimes wandered away from his mother to chase the birds or ducks, or to find other playmates. Tops, Nine Pins, and Spin the Ovals were his favorite childhood games. Most of his toys were homemade by his father. Henry learned to make the most out of whatever was available, under very humble circumstances.

The family's activities, including their religious and social activities, were centered around the Separatist activities at the Walloon Center or St. Pieter's Church. The church provided the communications link for news from England and throughout the world. Henry's father, John, periodically sent letters to his younger brother William in King's Lynn and to his cousin, Robert, who was living in London. Sometimes it was difficult to find carriers willing to take letters. Consequently, it often took two to three months to get a reply or to have any assurance that letters were delivered. Neither William nor the other members of his family in King's Lynn replied. But his cousin Robert did reply, stating his intentions to go to New England.

Although many of Henry's childhood memories, including much about his father, were lost from the time he was small, he was told many things by Vincent Potter, a young boy from Essex, England who arrived in Leyden about 1621. When the Keneys arrived in the fall of 1624, Vincent took a liking to Sarah and John and was a helpful and kind neighbor. Like the Keneys, Vincent received the majority of his worldly news from other refugees and the leaders at church. He listened as the adults talked about the relatives they left behind in England and their future plans for traveling to America. Over time, Vincent relayed some of those stories to Henry so he could grow to understand his ancestry.

When he was growing up in Leyden, Henry had several playmates, including Toby Brown, John Fitch, Richard Whitney, and Henry Curtis. His mother Sarah was worried about his sister Alexandria because she seemed to be left without many close friends. Alexandria and Sally Blake, daughter of Richard Blake, seemed to be inseparable. They shared a room, attended church classes, and played together constantly. That was one of the reasons Sarah agreed to let Alexandria go with the Blake family to America in 1629.

At that time, Henry did not understand why he was losing his sister. For awhile Henry was deeply hurt and acted aloof and disgruntled toward his mother. Vincent tried to convince him that he should forgive his mother.

The majority of adults in the community supported Sarah's decision because they believed some good reports about successful villages in the New World at Plymouth Colony and Jamestown. They felt that Sarah would have some relief from caring for two children and the family would soon be reunited in America. At first, it seemed to be just a matter of a short time before Sarah and Henry would join them. Over time, Henry learned not to complain about missing Alexandria because it always brought tears to his mother's eyes.

When Henry celebrated his eighth birthday, his mother Sarah planned a special birthday party for him, including twelve friends. His friends sang songs and his mother led the celebration. Sarah gave him a new kick-ball and swimming gear, perfect for hot summer days in Leyden. His birthday was a happy and memorable time in the midst of a difficult period. Henry was growing up quickly, learning to take care of himself and care as best he could for his often ailing mother.

The physical and emotional strain of the past few years had taken its toll on Sarah. Shortly after Henry's eighth birthday party, she became deathly sick. She struggled for several months and fought hard, but died in February 1633.

At that moment, Henry had lost his mother and father by tragic deaths. He had lost contact with his sister and all other living relatives, including his distant cousin in London and his family in King's Lynn.

After his mother's death, Henry was fortunate to live with Vincent Potter. Within a few months, they moved back to Essex County in England where the Potters had other relatives. Vincent went to work there for a short time in the cloth industry. It was a difficult time for

Henry, but he showed tremendous courage and tenacity as he moved ahead day by day. He prayed daily for the chance to travel to New England.

Miraculously, the opportunity to travel to America finally came. And now, his life would begin in the Massachusetts Bay Colony. Master Roger Cooper, Captain of the *Elizabeth and Ann* ship had previously sailed several times to New England. The ship was a supply vessel that carried building supplies, tools, provisions for the settlers including guns and ammunition, and some special merchandise for trading with the Indians, including kettles, woolen garments, and fish hooks. Captain Cooper's experience was invaluable as he maneuvered the ship to avoid difficulties, especially as they approached Cape Cod and the mainland.

Henry celebrated his eleventh birthday on the ship at sea on July 6, 1635. Vincent Potter gave Henry a new pocket knife and Captain Cooper assured Henry and everyone aboard that they would soon land in New England.

Not long after his birthday, Henry heard "Land Ho." Cautioned by Vincent, Henry stayed below despite wanting to stand on the deck with anticipation as his new home came into view. After a brief stop in the Massachusetts harbor, the ship sailed north and anchored in the harbor at Salem. Once in anchor, there was much to do. The sailors lowered the small boats called shallops into the water. Captain Cooper, with several crew members, went ashore first. The greeting from the people of Salem, including John Endecott, was warm and exciting with lots of hugging and embracing. Prayers of thanksgiving were said on the ship and later, on land, as soon as people went ashore. Captain Cooper gave Mr. Endecott the official correspondence from the British Crown and the owners of the ship's company. Many people came to the shore and later to the community building, where letters from England were passed out to the people in Salem. They were eager to exchange news and find out what cargo had arrived. Gradually, the other passengers were permitted to go ashore.

With Vincent Potter, his guardian, by his side, Henry Keney came ashore in a shallop at the native town of Naumkeag, called Salem, Massachusetts on July 14, 1635. The Indian name Naumkeag translates to "fishing village."

The founders of this European settlement arrived in 1626, nine years before Henry and some six years after the first plantation at Plymouth. They called it Salem, which translates to "safe and peaceful," as they hoped their new home would be just that.

By 1635, there were already 825 residents, with some of the native Naumkeag Indians living nearby. The village was situated on high ground overlooking the harbor. On first impression, the village seemed very small compared to Leyden. Henry saw several community buildings, some houses, and scattered temporary huts. Numerous buildings were under construction. As Henry walked about the village, he could see the initial layout for streets and houses. Farm land stretched beyond the village borders and trails lead into the wilderness. In the distance, he could see rolling mountains and some magnificent forests, including beautiful ash, elm, and oak trees. There was a river, the Naumkeag, running by the village toward the bay.

No doubt the area appeared to have an abundance of natural resources. The river and bay must surely provide many kinds of fish. Henry could imagine the fowl and wild game in the forests. Oh, his mother would have appreciated the rich ground for planting her vegetables and flowers.

As Henry reached the edge of the village, he saw for the first time a group of American Indians from the Pawtucket tribe. A gentleman building a home nearby told him about the Nipmucks who lived to the west, the Massachusetts to the south, and the Pokanokets to the northwest. Since an agreement treaty was made with Massasoit, Chief or Sachem of the Pokanokets, the natives had been peaceful. Still Henry was told that the settlers must be careful in dealing with the Indians. Henry was warned to be on guard constantly when he was confronted by members of the native tribes.

Vincent Potter made arrangements for himself, Henry, and the three boys to stay in one of the temporary huts. The huts, which were made of mud, hay, and timbers, were small and confining. After months of living in the restricted confines of the ship, Henry planned to spend much of his time outdoors. Vincent reminded him that fall would bring colder weather and everyone would need protection from the elements.

There was a great deal of work to do, with unloading the ship and its preparation for sailing back to England. Henry spent the next week working with the ship's crew. The crew brought the farm animals, including the chickens, hogs, and cows to the shore. Then Henry and his companions, John Johnson, Stephen Barrett, and William Browne led them into the village and to their new homes. In return, they carried beaver skins and animal hides to the shore where the ship's crew loaded them into the shallops and onto the ship. Captain Cooper accompanied the merchants when they met with the Indians to offer supplies and merchandise to pay for the animal hides. Henry watched closely as the Indians examined their new kettles, ropes, and fishing hooks.

After about three weeks, the ship was cleaned, reloaded, and ready to sail back to England. As the ship was set to depart, settlers and towns-people gathered to bid the crew farewell. With mixed emotions, Henry watched as Captain Cooper left Salem Harbor bound for England.

After surveying the area and discussing his plans with Governor Winthrop, Vincent Potter selected a tract of land, about twenty acres, near Salem for a temporary house and a planting area. After making an agreement to trade work with other settlers, Vincent, Henry, and the boys began to clear the land and construct a house. In the course of working with other settlers, they began to meet other townspeople and explore the surrounding area.

Though the winter of 1636 was cold and the wind off the Atlantic Ocean bitter and damp, Vincent, Henry, and the three boys settled into their new house. In the spring, the boys returned to work in the fields.

They were growing rapidly and the hard, physical work was healthy for them. Henry had an insatiable appetite—it seemed he couldn't eat enough. He grew strong and durable, yet he maintained a slender appearance. Vincent's supervision helped him develop good work habits and Henry became agreeable in working the land and accepting new assignments.

Henry continued his friendship with his shipmates, Phil Washburn, Stephen Barrett, and William Browne. The boys would ask an Indian named Red Feather, who had a large red feather carefully entwined through his braided hair, to accompany them on fishing and exploring trips into the wilderness. Red Feather told the boys many things about the native people including stories about their Sachem Massasoit and his son Philip. Since Massasoit was responsible for the treaty with the settlers, other tribes were jealous and threatened war and retaliation with the settlers. Henry marveled as he listened to Red Feather's explanations about conflicts between the tribes, including their violent battles.

The Pokanokets had been devastated by epidemics of chicken pox and measles. Some of them blamed the settlers for their illness and threatened retaliation. Consequently, Red Feather warned the boys to be careful when exploring in the wilderness. Henry grew to respect Red Feather's advice and he developed a cautious sense of curiosity as he continued to explore the undeveloped lands.

In 1637, shortly after John Johnson, William Browne, and Stephen Barrett were placed in apprenticeship positions, Henry asked Vincent to discuss his future plans. Vincent was noncommittal and said that he wanted to postpone making any decisions. He was thinking about the cloth business and his family back in England. In the meantime, Henry was learning a great deal about farming. He was happy living with Vincent and considered him to be his family.

In the fall of 1638, Henry and Vincent set out on a trip by land to Boston. They traveled along the coast, visiting the villages of Lynn, Winnisimmet, and Cambridge. They crossed the Mystic River and traveled eastward toward Boston, or Shawmut, as the Indians called it.

They traveled slowly, meeting new friends, surveying the land, and casually inspecting the improvements in each of the villages along the way.

In Boston, they met with Robert Keayne, the distant cousin of Henry's father. Keayne, who was establishing a merchandise shop on Washington Street, was delighted to see young Henry and Vincent. Although he had been in Boston only a short time, he was wildly enthusiastic about Boston and the surrounding area. When Vincent asked if he knew anything about Henry's sister Alexandria, the Blakes, or the rest of his family, Robert unfortunately said he did not. He had neither knowledge nor news about them. However, they did share some current information confirming his belief of the likelihood of an imminent civil war in England.

Robert pledged to help Vincent as he established his trade connections. Among other things, he suggested that he contact his friend William Parke, who was a tanner and planning to expand his trading store in Roxbury.

Henry and Vincent traveled south to meet William Parke. Parke showed them around Roxbury, which was located about eight miles south of Boston. It was an ideal site for a trading store since all major traffic to and from Boston from the west and south, went through Roxbury by a narrow isthmus known as the Roxbury Neck. On the outskirts of town there were open farm lands, abundant forests, and some stone quarries with Roxbury puddingstone. There were good water resources and fertile land, hopefully ideal for growing fruits and vegetables. The townspeople had built a new meeting house in 1632, a good sign showing a progressive attitude for the community.

Parke told them of ongoing concerns that the Indian tribes might unite in open warfare against the settlers near Roxbury. In 1636 when Indians killed a trader named John Oldham south of Narragansett Bay, Governor Endecott led a group to Block Island to retaliate. Tensions remained high and, in 1637, the militia troops participated in what would become known as the Mystic Massacre. The settlers decimated all the Pequots in the area, killing the women and children as well as the warriors. The massacre sent a chilling message to the other tribes and to all settlers in New England.

Attempting to inform Henry and Vincent about the area, Parke told them another story about the area. The Reverend John Davenport stopped by his general store before he embarked on a exploratory trip to the area southwest of Boston. Aware of the demise of the Pequots, he explored some of the lands west of Saybrook. He was so impressed with the territory that in time, he organized a congregational church and settled in what would become New Haven, Connecticut. His church created a unique structure whereby members were voted upon for membership. It was considered to be an honor to be a member of the church. The success of John Davenport and his congregational church would be an important part of the eventual separation of church and state.

Vincent and Henry left Roxbury with a greater understanding of the growing communities in New England. As Vincent and Henry traveled back to Salem, Vincent spent time thinking about his future. He had kept in touch with relatives and he knew of the uprising in England. He thought about Robert Keayne's confirmation of an imminent civil war. After several months and extensive deliberations, he decided to have a meeting with Henry.

"Henry, I need to tell you something."

Henry straightened up, then looked hard at the only man he had known all his life, sensing that Vincent was troubled with something.

"Word comes from my brother that people tire of King Charles. John says we will soon have the opportunity to make our homeland into a country based upon Puritan values. But workers are needed to bring about God's kingdom. I want to be part of that, Henry."

"But how will you do that from here?"

"I can't. That's the problem—I have to go back. While I can, I plan to continue to trade with the citizens here—at least before the battles start."

"Vincent, its one thing to take on the Pequots, but against the trained soldiers of the Crown? You will be risking your life, even if you do not lose it in battle."

"I am prepared to do so in God's name. Too many have died for their beliefs. And how many live but are lost because they cannot hear the true word?"

"Is this the right time to return to England?"

Vincent paused, "I believe so. I hate to leave you and my new friends. But I worry about my family members who have remained in Essex. I know it is the right thing to do. I would rather make the passage now before God blesses me with other responsibilities."

"Then it is a done deal?" replied Henry as he walked off to stare at the Salem Harbor. "What will happen to me?"

"Henry, don't worry. Providence is good. Your cousin Robert Keayne has been true to his word. He recommended you to William Parke, and I have received word that Parke has agreed to take you into his services. You will be serving an apprenticeship with a great man whose influence grows every year."

Henry's shoulders relaxed a bit. Parke's reputation was solid and he liked him when they visited on their recent trip. He turned to ask, "In Roxbury, then? When do I go?"

"Your apprenticeship will begin shortly after you get to Roxbury, as arranged with Mr. Thomas Lechford, a Practitioner at Law. I will deliver you to Mr. Parke about two weeks before I board the ship for passage to England."

Henry embraced Vincent and then, with tears in his eyes, he walked toward a greater vantage point of the sea. He thought about it-another beginning for him. Some day he would be in charge of his own choices-God willing. But for now, he would gather his belongings and prepare for the trip to Roxbury.

Henry never did see Vincent again. Although Vincent and his comrades were initially successful in overturning the Crown's reign, eventually he would be convicted, along with others, in the execution of

Charles I. Potter reportedly would die in the Tower of London before his sentence could be carried out.

On his arrival in Roxbury, Henry met another apprentice named Bob Manion. Bob was a tall and robust fellow, considerably larger than Henry. He had a contagious smile and a warm, pleasant personality. Although he was about six months older than Henry, Henry felt immediately comfortable with Bob. They agreed to work together and share their responsibilities. They had an genuine appreciation for each other, knowing that they shared similar positions in life. Not only did they learn to do their jobs together, but they also spent most of their leisure time together, often hunting, fishing, and exploring the western frontier of Massachusetts. Within a few weeks of meeting each other, they were constant companions.

For the next eight years, Henry and Bob learned the tanning business and they helped run Parke's general store. William Parke traded with the natives and supplied them with many provisions including knives, axes, salt, woven textiles, fishing hooks, and cooking equipment. Parke had strict rules neither to trade guns nor liquor.

Henry and Bob developed a healthy appreciation and respect for the Native Americans. Over a period of time, they learned who to trust and who might resort to deception and warfare. As they traded, they dealt with many Indians who grew wealthy by selling beaver and other animal furs. But they also heard stories of hostile warriors who were preparing to attack some of the settlements.

Though Henry and Bob settled into developing their new lives, times were not easy. Although they worked long hours, they learned the tanning business and how to treat people with respect and fairness. William Parke proved to be a fair and compassionate businessman. His business prospered. He acquired much of his merchandise from Robert Keayne and other leading merchants in the area. The store supplied goods to many explorers including the Reverend John Eliot, the minister for fourteen praying towns and native villages.

Henry grew to full maturity during his apprenticeship. Although his total commitment was for eight years, William Parke provided substantial freedom and independent time for Henry and Bob after six years. He encouraged their support of the local militia. Henry was physically fit, ambitious, and energetic. He had saved some money and was anxious for adventure. His reading and writing skills were limited, but he could shoot with stunning accuracy and was a good horseman. He and Bob could be described as classic frontiersmen. With their friends Ed Rawson and Ben Briscoe, they joined the militia whenever there was an Indian uprising. Over time, they traveled the frontier, visiting trading posts from Kennebec to New Haven and Philadelphia.

In 1646, Henry and Bob went to Boston to visit Robert Keayne. It had been seven years since Robert Keayne had recommended him to William Parke and many changes had occurred within Boston. Robert Keayne had become a leading merchant in New England and was extremely popular with the citizens. He was serving in the state legislature and was known as the first captain of the artillery company. A distinguished gentleman, Clement Cole, was serving Robert as an aide and servant.

Robert, who was forty-six at the time of the visit, offered his friendly philosophy and some fatherly advice to Henry who was twenty-two at the time. In addition to his success in the business world, Robert was a professor of religion. He had experienced some conflicts with neighboring church officials and wanted to warn Henry of the evils of religious hypocrisy. He likely said, "One of the reasons for coming to America had been to shed the persecution of the Church, yet it was here again. We seem to have short memories."

Henry respected Robert's seniority and listened intently as Robert continued, "Be mindful of the dangers of men of the cloth when they grow infatuated with their own importance and disregard the sacred word of the Lord. They can limit the freedom of others." The sincerity of Robert's advice, coming from a well-respected member of his kin, gave

Henry valuable confidence that he would carry into his adult life.

On another subject, Robert advised, "There are wonderful opportunities emerging in New England. You have the chance of a lifetime to pursue your grandest dreams. To be successful, sometimes you must take a chance and work hard to make your dreams come true."

Robert Keayne's business success allowed him to become Boston's greatest philanthropist during his time. He generously gave money to the Boston Public Schools, the public market, and the water system as well as giving land for Boston's original town hall. His generosity and eccentric style upset the conservative ministry so much that John Winthrop and the Reverend John Cotton threatened an investigative court case. The case was heard and the Church, after a lengthy debate, decided to censure Captain Keayne. Later he was charged with stealing a cow and maintaining a slave. The negative attacks from the Church would have a depressing effect on Robert and, in an unusual way, he wrote an extensive treatise in conjunction with his will to justify his actions. He stated his vision for the right of free men to earn and spend their profits without interference from either the Church nor the State. Of course, the will would not be read until he died in 1655, but his statements would leave a mark, just as his civic contributions did.

Henry completed his successful apprenticeship with William Parke in 1647, and shortly thereafter, he was designated as a free man. Vowing to continue their close friendship with the Parke family, Henry and Bob Manion set out to explore the western frontier. They traveled throughout western Massachusetts, Pennsylvania, and New York, often visiting with members and friends of the militia. After about a year, Bob decided to return to Roxbury and settle near William Parke's store.

Henry returned to Salem where he had a joyful reunion with some old friends. Salem had grown substantially and some of his friends were living on nearby farms. They encouraged Henry to settle with them and he decided to spend time with two friends, Robert Prince and John Bond, whom he had met in the militia. For a time, Henry reportedly ran a tavern and associated with some rowdy and boisterous friends.

At that time there were constant concerns about Indian uprisings, so the men often joined forces with other neighbors to protect and care for each other.   One Sunday in 1648, Henry helped Prince and Bond move a cannon into a new location. It took about an hour to move the heavy artillery and adjust the firing mechanism into its new position. Mr. Endecott and other church officials brought formal charges against the men, accusing them of working on the Sabbath. The charges were eventually dismissed, but not before Henry and his friends spent some time behind bars. Henry had a court record and, adding insult to injury, the men had to pay a so-called hospitality fine. Henry dismissed the charges as ludicrous, but he was beginning to understand the sage advice of Robert Keayne. Yes, he could see that the omnipotent attitude of some church officials could sometimes be more harmful than good.

With a guarded attitude, Henry began to settle down. He attended church in Salem Village with regularity. Although his views toward the Puritan ministry had changed, he maintained a steadfast devotion to the Christian code of conduct and worship, as expressed in the New Testament. As a free man, he was determined to express his freedom and to live in accordance with the word of God.

One Sunday in 1649 after church services, Henry likely asked a wholesome young lady named Ann Howard Putnam to go for a walk away from the other church attendees. It was a romantic, secluded spot, likely under a tree that was ablaze with fragrant apple blossoms. Their conversation was something like this:

"Ann, you look lovely today, even better than this tree in all its glory."

Ann blushed. "You know, 'tis folly to think that we people can be compared to God's handiwork."

Henry replied, "Did he not make you? Indeed he did. And you know what I think about that? I think he meant for you to meet me all along. Imagine, just three years ago you and your parents were in England-in

Aylesworth back in Kent."

"Did he then?" She replied. "So all along he was creating me just to come to Salem Village and encounter you?"

Henry laughed. "By faith, it is so. Yet, I don't think his plan stops there, do you? I believe he was creating you to be my wife." The words hung in the air for a moment, Henry's earnest gaze fixed upon Ann. "What say you?"

Ann paused–a minute too long for Henry's taste–before she answered. "Well, if God wills it, then surely I cannot deny it." The mirth in her eyes betrayed the stern set of her chin.

Henry shook off the tension that had made it hard to concentrate throughout the whole morning. "That's a yes, then? Right?"

"Yes," gleamed Ann.

Henry wanted to sweep her into his arms, but there were too many watchful eyes nearby on this glorious Sunday.

"Ann, I thank God for you. I have been a long time on my own. You know about my parents and my sister. But you don't know the story of the kinship of my ancestors. My parents left behind a prosperous way of life and all their relations to seek a new way of life following God's plan. Vincent told me the tales, but the stories seemed like make-believe compared to the hard times we faced in Leyden. Knights, merchants, landowners- and then my mother cleaning and caring for others' children? They gave their all for the freedom to worship as God called them, but I am all that is left of this line. And I am tired of being alone. I want to be like Abraham."

"Abraham? Living in a tent? The winters in Salem are deadly," replied Ann.

"No," said Henry. "With descendants as numerous as the stars. I pray that God will bless us with many children of our own, so that I can know what my ancestors have known. A kinship within my family, with a good wife, several strong children, and an honest way to earn a living."

Henry continued, "Remember John 15:5 when Jesus said, 'I am the vine, ye are the branches: he that abideth in me, and I in him, the same bringeth forth much fruit: for without me ye can do nothing'."

Ann smiled. "You said it yourself–God has a plan. Now, let's go tell my parents. Or rather, you better go on your own and ask first. Father might have his own plan if you don't give him the respect he expects."

"Yes, I had given up on having a father, but perhaps there is still time to have one after all. But first you've got to help me–I have no idea what fathers expect from men who want to marry their daughters."

"In time you will. For one thing, Father might wonder how it is you know that God has this planned when God forgot to tell him. Don't give him a chance to say that. Tell him how you plan to support me and all those children and how you will be faithful to the family and the Church. Now go."

Henry proceeded until Ann's father, Edward Putnam, gave him his blessing. Henry married Ann Putnam on November 12, 1649. They settled into a home in Salem where in time, he became an accomplished farmer, commonly called a yeoman. In 1658, Henry purchased a home and three acres of land on Essex Street from John Putnam, next to Richard Addams on the south and William Flint on the north. In December 1662, Henry acquired thirty additional acres of ground.

Together, Henry and Ann worked hard to build a successful farm. They planted hay, corn, and barley. With modest provisions to begin their operations, they raised chickens, milking cows, and several pigs. Ann kept a small garden, where she planted some vegetables and seasonal flowers.

Beginning in 1651, they were to be blessed with eight children, six that survived. Two children, Hannah and Sarah died in infancy. Henry would get his wish for a large family. John, the oldest, was named after Henry's father. Their second son, Thomas, was born in 1655, and Hannah, the first girl, was born in 1657. Mary was born on May 3, 1659. Mary married William Pillsbury. Another daughter, Sarah, was born in 1661 and Elizabeth, was born in 1662. Elizabeth married Elder William Wentworth of Boston, who was a cousin of Ann Hutchinson.

Lidia was born in 1666 and Henry II was born May 1, 1669.

As time passed, Henry worked on his farm and cared for his growing family. He continued to serve with the local militia and was ready whenever emergencies arose in the area. In 1654, he was called to serve in the successful expedition with Major Sedgwick to take the French Fort at St. John. He also served under Captain George Corwin with the Essex Troopers during the War with the Narragansett Indians. For his military service, Henry received land grant number three entitling him to acquire thirty acres of land.

After years of serving in the military militia, he became known as the Corporal. In 1667, he petitioned the General Court for relief from serving on the military watch in Salem. He appealed, saying that distance and the dangers associated with leaving his family unprotected were so severe that he should be exempted from the watch. His appeal was denied. Consequently, he continued to serve on call whenever the threat of warfare was imminent.

As Henry grew older, he garnered additional respectability among his neighbors and townspeople. The records of Salem Village indicate that Henry, as well as his sons Thomas and John, were paid for their building services within the village. They worked on several projects, including a new meeting house, a new road, and a bridge at Beaver Dam, located fairly close to his property.

The records also indicate that Henry, on another occasion, went to Boston to secure the preaching services of Mr. Lawson. While gaining respect at church, he sometimes got into trouble by verbally attacking those with whom he disagreed including the Reverend James Bailey and his neighbor and friend John Putnam. Nevertheless, he was chosen as one of the constables for the community, a designation he cherished.

In 1687, several years after Henry's wife Ann passed away, his second son Thomas died from an infection. At that time, Thomas had four small children ages one, six, eight, and nine. Sensing an emergency for his son's young family, Henry was determined to care for his grandchildren. He offered to move Thomas' widow Elizabeth and the children to his farm. But Elizabeth declined and stayed at her farm. Henry and his sons and daughters who lived nearby spent considerable time trying to help Elizabeth.

Elizabeth was distraught, not only over her husband's death, but with raising the boys alone and the unusual witchcraft events that were occurring in Salem. Charges of witchcraft were prevalent, including some accusations against some of Elizabeth's friends. When Martha Cory and Rebecca Nurse were accused, Elizabeth attempted to come to their aid. But Elizabeth, Martha, and Rebecca were all distracted and thwarted with unwarranted attacks from the clergy and the prosecutors.

Even Henry's son, Henry II, joined Ed Putnam in a complaint against Martha Cory for "suspicion of having committed sundry acts of witchcraft." After her trial, Martha Cory was hanged September 22, 1692.

Henry continued to be protective of his own family, attempting to keep them away from the trials and the publicity. He appealed to church officials. But without success, he became involved in additional verbal attacks with Reverend James Bailey.

Meanwhile Elizabeth continued to suffer under the strain of her friends' prosecution. Within three years of the witchcraft trials, Elizabeth died, leaving the children to be raised primarily by the Putnams, the Cheevers, and other members of the Keney family.

Although he was approaching his seventieth birthday, Henry was determined to help support and provide a suitable home for his family. In 1698, he married a family friend, Mrs. Magdaleane Wiggins of Essex, Massachusetts, who agreed to help care for the family. Magdaleane and Henry enjoyed over ten years of marriage, including their help to the extent of their capabilities, for raising the four young boys of Elizabeth and Thomas.

Henry spent his final days at his farm in Salem with his family and friends. He had persevered and brought the Keney family back from the brink of extinction. As an orphan, he arrived in America in 1635. He survived and prospered as a frontiersman, a yeoman, and a soldier to raise six children and twenty-two grandchildren.

Henry lived a long life, dying in 1709 in Salem Village, near Danvers where he is buried on his farm.

At a family reunion of descendants of Henry Keney in 1884, many of his relatives told stories and presented memorials in honor of Henry. By then, some five generations later, there were estimated to be over 2,200 descendants living in America. George Kinney, a descendant from Chicago, was one of the ancestors who participated in the reunion.

An adaptation of an original quotation by Leo Buscalgia, a twentieth century professor, seems to be an appropriate memorial for Henry. This memorial, as altered to fit Henry, is paraphrased from the original quotation:

> *"Nothing is forever. In reality we never lose the people like Henry that we love and admire. Our kinship with him will live and become immortal through us and our children. Henry will continue to live in our hearts and minds, and he will participate in our every act, idea, and decision. He made our existence possible. No one will ever replace him and, in spite of the pain and sacrifice he suffered over time, we are richer for the years and memories he gave us. We are grateful for his determination, valor, and steadfast persistence to survive and flourish. Because of him, we have more to bring, not only to our personal lives, but to all our family's present and future relationships."*

While the majority of the American Kinneys would not exist without Henry's life and the births of his own children, the early death of Henry's own son, Thomas, is a grim reminder that settling the frontier was a risky proposition that not all survived.

Windmill in New England near the Kenney Farm

Henry Keney & Ann Putnam Keney Descendants

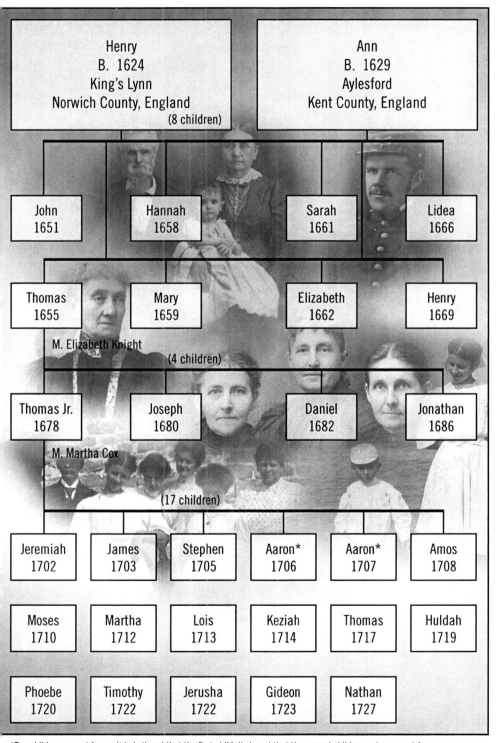

Henry
B. 1624
King's Lynn
Norwich County, England
(8 children)

Ann
B. 1629
Aylesford
Kent County, England

| John 1651 | Hannah 1658 | Sarah 1661 | Lidea 1666 |
| Thomas 1655 | Mary 1659 | Elizabeth 1662 | Henry 1669 |

M. Elizabeth Knight
(4 children)

| Thomas Jr. 1678 | Joseph 1680 | Daniel 1682 | Jonathan 1686 |

M. Martha Cox
(17 children)

Jeremiah 1702	James 1703	Stephen 1705	Aaron* 1706	Aaron* 1707	Amos 1708
Moses 1710	Martha 1712	Lois 1713	Keziah 1714	Thomas 1717	Huldah 1719
Phoebe 1720	Timothy 1722	Jerusha 1722	Gideon 1723	Nathan 1727	

*Two children named Aaron. It is believed that the first child died, and that the second child was also named Aaron.

Lucy Park Kinne

Chapter 11
Thomas Keney
1655 – 1687
Frontiersman, Farmer, Militiaman

PROTECTING
THE COLONIAL FRONTIER

Thomas Keney knew this might be the last sunny day before the weather turned and frigid winter set in. An active eight-year-old boy, he hated when the nor'easters came and his mother wouldn't let him leave the house except to take care of the livestock. Too bad his brother John, four years older, was off working in the fields with some of their neighbors. Thomas liked to pretend he was Little Beaver, the son of Red Feather, one of the Praying Indians in Salem Village. It was a lot more fun when Thomas and John could play warriors together. At least he was outside, not inside with his mother and little sisters. The baby Elizabeth had already been sleeping when his mom put his sisters Mary and Sarah down for their naps. Thomas loved their naptime because his mom often shooed him out the door.

All of a sudden Thomas heard leaves rustling as someone moved through the woods just beyond the barn. He thought it might be John or a neighbor. Instead three Nipmunk Indian scouts came in sight. His father often traded with the Pokanokets but he was gone on a trip to nearby Duxbury.

Thomas ran to the house, calling to his mother as he opened the door. "Mum, Nipmunks are outside and coming toward our house."

Ann Keney looked startled, a flash of alarm on her face. "Thomas, I've had such a time getting Sarah to sleep. You need to keep an eye on her for me."

The little girl Sarah, seeing her mother leave, let out a wail and toddled after her. Thomas wasn't prepared for how fast she could move now that she had been walking since last year. As he followed after her, he could hear the Indians haggling for some food, salt, and supplies with his mother. His mother did not like the offer because she was shaking her head and pointing for them to go away. Little Sarah grabbed onto her mother's skirts and soon was hidden in the folds.

"No, not today. Now, go on." Ann Keney said as she stood as tall as she could, staring into the natives' eyes until they began to back away.

Thomas was afraid they were going to strike his mother, but the natives continued to back away slowly, yelling something neither he nor his mother could understand. All of a sudden, the tallest one reached for a musket he was carrying and fired a shot into the air as he ran into the woods.

"The musket, Thomas! Get me the musket."

Thomas sprinted inside where he stretched to snatch the musket down from above the fireplace. Thank goodness he had grown a little. As carefully as he could, he jogged back to his mom carrying the long, heavy weapon. Ann grabbed the musket and aimed where the leaves were still crunching. The sound echoed through the woods even as his mother worked to stand firm against the gun's kick. She held it ready, but all the two of them could hear was the footsteps growing dim in the distance. After a few minutes of silence, Ann relaxed her shoulders, and then slowly eased the heavy weapon down by her side.

At once her eyes opened wide, "Sarah! Where is Sarah?"

Thomas looked around before answering. "Last time I saw her she was hiding behind your skirt, but now I don't see her. The noise must have scared her off."

"Oh, no, Thomas, run as fast as you can to the fields. Get your brother and the neighbors. I will look about here and stay here with your other sisters—but we are going to need help."

Thomas turned and took off running, wishing his legs were as long as his brother John's so that he could run faster.

They organized a search party as evening and a violent storm approached. Despite frigid temperatures, they searched all night. They found Sarah at dawn where she was hiding in a shallow cave. During the melee, she had become so frightened that she ran into the forest to hide. Sarah caught a dreadful cold which eventually turned to pneumonia. Her mother tried valiantly to comfort her, but she died in November 1663. Thomas would carry the scars from the provocation from the Indians and the unfortunate death of his sister for the rest of his life.

Thomas' youth was filled with constant threats from the uncertainties of the frontier, cold weather, unknown diseases, and persistent threats of Indian attacks. He was born March 11, 1655, and he was baptized at the church in Topsfield on April 12, 1656. Thomas was born at the family's farmhouse that his father had homesteaded and built in 1649.

The children grew up on the edge of the wilderness where they were constantly adapting and learning new skills simply to survive. The Henry Keney family had the barest of essentials, but with a strong Christian faith and dogged determination, they learned to use their resources well, wasting nothing and utilizing all possible means for nourishment and subsistence. Like so many others on the frontier, the men cleared the land, used the stones for fences, and cultivated those areas that were suitable for farming. Most farms had small vegetable gardens and carefully planted fruit trees. By providing care and protection for the farm animals, the settlers became largely self sufficient with their pigs, chickens, sheep, and cows. Using natural fibers, animal skins, and homespun cloth, they made many of their own clothes. If the clothes were durable, they would be shared and passed on to younger family members and to their neighbors.

Thomas learned the fundamental lessons of farming at an early age. He tended to the animals, worked in the garden, and assisted his mother and father whenever called upon. Working together, the family built a very strong bond, a kinship for caring and sharing within the family. Much of Thomas' knowledge came by observation and from following the instructions of his parents and older companions. Although Thomas' parents had a limited ability to read and write, educational opportunities were growing as life on the frontier became more settled. Consequently, he received his early literary education at the primary school in Salem and Sunday School at church.

Thomas' practical education also came from his older brother John whom he considered to be his best friend. John paved the way for Thomas by teaching him many things, including the basics for hunting, fishing, and abiding by their parents' discipline. Thomas and John shared a valuable kinship. Since it was customary for the oldest son to inherit the family farm, John, Thomas, and the much younger Henry, were raised with that expectation.

Thomas and John often worked in the fields together. They seemed to be inseparable when working or playing. They developed a strong bond of loyalty and confidentiality to each other. On one occasion, John climbed a large apple tree to pick some apples. Thomas tried to keep up by following him, but he could not extend himself to the distant branches. When he fell out of the tree some thirty feet, he fell on his right arm and they feared it was broken. For fear of punishment from their parents, the boys wrapped Thomas' arm in a temporary sling and promised each other not to tell their parents. Fortunately, his arm was only bruised and soon the incident was forgotten, except that such incidents became personal secrets and common bonds to the boys.

As Thomas grew, he remained slender, yet strong and physically capable of rigorous activities. He liked to explore the wilderness and could survive several days camping out and eating roots, berries, and whatever fish he could catch. He learned how to track animals and to navigate the streams and rivers. His father taught him to communicate with the Narragansett Indians and he often explored new areas with Little Beaver, the son of his father's friend, Red Feather.

Thomas had a natural aptitude for mapmaking, drafting, and making calculations. He was good at math and could calculate the distances between farms and villages with remarkable accuracy. He was also gifted with a good understanding of the workings of firearms. He could take apart a flintlock musket, clean it, and reassemble it within fifteen to twenty minutes. His father taught Thomas and John to shoot and to be respectful of the dangers as well as the potential power of the guns.

Thomas' parents were devoted church members. They observed the Sabbath and raised their children with obedience to the standards of the neighboring Puritans and the Congregational Church in Salem. Their social activities were bound by church activities, often spending Sunday afternoons with their neighbors and friends. Whenever newcomers arrived or when visiting clergy came to Salem, they were often invited to the family's home. Many of the neighbors would assemble to hear news from England and the other settlements in America.

Thomas' father was an active member of the Salem militia. He was ready on a moment's notice to come to the aid of his neighbors for any emergencies, including the threat of Indian attacks. Despite his militia service, Thomas' father was good friends with many natives of the Pokanoket tribe. The Pokanokets lived close by and had traded with him when he served his apprenticeship with William Parke in Roxbury. One native Indian named Red Feather traveled with Thomas' father and Bob Manion when they were apprentices. Since then, Red Feather had converted to the Christian church. He became known as Redford, one of the Praying Indians in Salem.

Redford taught Thomas and John many ways of the Indians. On joint hunting trips, they often sat by the fire discussing the ways of the natives. Redford spoke of the great Indian spirits and how his people lived in harmony with nature including all the animals living on the earth. He spoke of a new kinship for all men with descriptive words like loyalty, allegiance, pride, and respect. Honor and trust were binding qualities between all men. There were traditional ceremonies to acknowledge this kinship by dancing, chanting, bloodletting, and pipe smoking.

Redford offered these traditional symbols of trust and agreement to his friends, including Thomas and John. But Redford admitted that sometimes he became confused when the settlers and the natives of different tribes broke their solemn agreements. Some natural ways of the spirits, including the use of hunting grounds, were not subject to agreements between men. He warned Thomas of retaliation if the settlers violated the spirits or broke the solemn agreements with the Indians.

As times began to change when more settlers arrived in the area, the friendly relations with the natives deteriorated. On one occasion, Thomas' father was called to ride with the militia to Taunton for a possible outbreak of a war with the Pokanoket Indians. Rumors were widespread throughout the region that the Indians were preparing to attack the settlers. John and Thomas watched with envy, pleading with their parents to allow them to join their father. Their mother was adamantly opposed and their father agreed saying that they were too young and that the time would come soon enough when they would join him. In this instance, the threat subsided as a temporary peace was agreed upon. Thomas' father returned home after about two weeks.

In 1670, after the fall harvest, Thomas traveled with his brother John and his father to Boston, Roxbury, and Cambridge. His father had recently celebrated his forty-sixth birthday. He wanted his boys to visit with his friends, Bob Manion and William Parke. For Thomas, it was a wonderful time to see Shawmut, commonly called Boston by the settlers. Boston was emerging as the capitol of New England and becoming known as an aggressive trade and commerce center. Thomas hoped to become familiar with the villages and trading posts along the way. The boys enjoyed the opportunity to see first-hand the expansion and emerging opportunities along the seacoast.

After a long church service in Boston, Thomas and John were feeling restless. Upon leaving the church, they met the famous minister, William Hubbard, a comrade of Thomas' father who was writing a historical paper about the formation of the New England colonies.

John was eager to get on with their excursions of the city, with hopes of seeing some new sights, the latest firearms, and possibly some young people. Their initial meeting likely happened like this:

"I heard that there are lots of pretty girls in Boston," said John.

"Girls?" replied Thomas. "You might care about that, but I'd rather talk with some boys about what they do here in Boston. It seems so different than Salem."

Just then their father came by with a friend. "Boys, I would like you to meet Mr. Joseph Knight who lives in Watertown and trades here in Boston. Years ago we met in Roxbury. He and his family are visiting today, too."

John and Thomas surveyed the Knight family. John's hopeful expression dropped when he saw that Mr. Knight's daughter Elizabeth was about his sister Mary's age. After the introductions, the adults began to talk. John and Thomas were left standing with Elizabeth. No one said anything until John threw an elbow into Thomas.

"Err, so do you like visiting Boston?" Thomas asked Elizabeth.

She responded, "Oh, it's nice for a day or two, but I prefer my home in the village. How about you?"

"Sure, it's OK. I like to hunt and fish more than I like to hang around in shops and be around all the noise. Besides, I'm pretty much ready to go out with the militia next time any of the Nipmunks cause trouble." John poked Thomas again. "Well, Father says I'm too young, but soon I'll be ready to go."

"Oh, how old are you?" John asked.

"I'm twelve," replied Elizabeth.

Thomas wrinkled his nose. "I'm sixteen." John winced and snorted aloud. Thomas tried again. "Well, I'm almost sixteen and I am just about ready for the militia."

"It must be scary living on the frontier. You should write to me and tell me what goes on where you live. You write, don't you?"

"Oh, sure. I went to school for six years, but I'm done now. I help my parents with the farm–and especially the hunting. Say, do you like maps? I can draw you a map where I live and maybe even a map of all the places in between here and there. Father says I am really accurate at calculating the distances between farms and villages. I've been taking notes this whole trip."

"Yes," replied Elizabeth. "Send me some maps, OK?"

"Mother says it would be good for me to practice my writing skills."

Just then Henry Keney turned to the boys. "We need to get moving, boys. Say goodbye and we will be on our way."

As they walked away, John said to Thomas, "I thought you didn't want to meet any girls."

Thomas replied, "She is just a little girl. I only talked to her because maybe Mary will want to write to her. She'd like to have a friend from faraway."

John chuckled, "Right, let's tell Mary when we get home."

In Roxbury, their father had a grand reunion with William Parke. The boys heard many stories about the times when Thomas' father was an apprentice, working with Bob Manion. Parke was happy to report that it had been a good year–the harvest was plentiful and hunting parties were returning with record numbers of beaver pelts and hides. At the same time Parke also told them about potential trouble with the Indians. Times had changed since Thomas' father had lived in Roxbury. Several of the great leaders of the Colonies were gone. Myles Standish, the military leader, had died. His reputation throughout the Colonies was legendary since he brought an end to the uprising of the Wessagusset

Indians when he killed Chief Wituwamat. The diplomatic leader of the Pokanokets, Massasoit, had also died. His son Wamsutta or Alexander promised that he would abide by the peaceful coexistence established by his father. But he had been killed mysteriously back in 1662.

Wamsutta's brother named Metacomet or commonly called Philip was twenty-four years old when he succeeded him as the supreme sachem of the Pokanokets and Wampanoags Indians. Philip was known as ambitious and arrogant toward the English settlers. His haughty behavior caused the Puritans to refer to him as "King Philip." Like his brother, he abided with the peaceful relations for a short time, but soon he began to build warring alliances with other tribes. William Parke believed it was simply a matter of time before Philip would gain sufficient strength to avenge his brother's death and attack the English settlements.

Thomas returned to Salem with a better understanding of the fragile conditions supporting the peace with the Indians in New England. Working on the family farm, he gained maturity and a solid physical presence. He showed exceptional interest in military skills, especially marksmanship. When his father gave him a flintlock musket for his sixteenth birthday he learned to fire it with stunning accuracy. He would imitate the movements of the Salem militia and sometimes anticipate the imaginary moves of the Indians.

In 1674, Thomas' father was summoned to attend a meeting of the militia in Taunton. King Philip had assembled a group of warriors and it appeared that they were about to attack. In attempt to avert the confrontation, King Philip was required to attend the Court in Boston where he was given a strict sentence to relinquish his arms and pay an annual fee to the Court. Again the threat subsided and Thomas' father returned to his farm in Salem. The settlers were lured into a period of complacency. However, King Philip immediately began selling more of his land to acquire money for purchasing arms. He appealed to the Pocassets, the Nemaskets, and the Nipmunks to join him as he prepared for war against the English settlers.

Thomas' father was kept abreast of the movement among the Indians through messengers carrying news from William Parke and the militia members. In 1675, John Sassamon, a Praying Indian, warned Josiah Winslow, the Governor of Plymouth, that King Philip was on the warpath. Subsequently, John Sassamon was murdered while he was traveling between villages performing his missionary work. Three members of Philip's tribe, including an Indian named Tobias, were charged with the murder. They were convicted and sentenced to hang. When King Philip received word of Tobias' hanging, he instructed his warriors to attack some of the settlements in retaliation.

King Philip's warriors attacked Swansea, where they destroyed eighteen homes, including the home of the Minister John Myles. As the warriors continued their rampage, an urgent request for the militia was passed along by messengers sent throughout the colonies.

When the request reached Salem, Thomas and John were old enough to join their father to ride with the Salem militia. Their younger brother Henry would stay with his mother and sisters on the farm. The Keneys rode to Taunton, where the Salem militia joined forces under the command of Captain Appleton. The total forces for the United Colonies of Massachusetts, Connecticut, and Plymouth were approximately 1,000 men. King Philip had successfully organized the Narragansetts, the Pokanokets, and the Nipmuck tribes. However, the Mohegans and many of the Praying Indians deferred and remained loyal to the English settlers.

The rampage of the Indians continued with raids on Dartmouth and Rehoboth. They burned houses, destroyed crops, livestock, and murdered settlers. The Indians made violent ambush attacks and then fled to the marshes and forests. Other raids were reported at Deerfield where fifty-seven Englishmen were killed and at Bloody Creek where sixty-four settlers were killed.

The reaction of the colonists called for a united front, with cries of retaliation against all "cutthroats." Unfortunately, some of the Indian fighters called for retaliation against all Indians. One of the most notorious Indian fighters, Captain Samuel Moseley sounded the battle cry of "the only good Indian is a dead Indian."

Thomas, John, and their father were riding with the Massachusetts militia when they were called to Brookfield after the Beers Ambush at Northfield. By the time they arrived, the Indians had fled to the south toward Hadley. The speed and ability of the Indians to hide in the swamps and forests made it difficult for the settlers to follow. Wherever they went, they were warned to be prepared for an ambush. They continued to follow their trails and, by December 1675, they were situated and prepared for a major battle at Fort Narragansett in Rhode Island.

They joined other militia from Connecticut and Plymouth for the assault on Fort Narragansett. All the troops united under the direction of Josiah Winslow and Benjamin Church. The battle turned into a bloody exchange with hand to hand fighting when the troops entered the fort. The Keneys engaged in a massive charge that sent the Indians into the marshes and forest. Both sides took heavy losses, including over 200 militia men and over 600 Narragansett Indians.

Although the Narragansetts were nearly destroyed, those who escaped joined other warriors and reassembled in obscure areas in the forests. They continued to raid towns and villages, then hide in the dense swampland. The Massachusetts militia, along with Thomas, John, and their father, continued in pursuit of the Indians. The "great swamp fight" that followed was exhausting for both sides.

In the spring, the war entered a new phase. The militia had suffered heavy losses, causing some militia members to be relieved of their duties. John Keney returned home to Salem in time to prepare for the spring planting while Thomas and his father stayed with the militia. Scattered raids by the Indians continued while the militia had limited success due to the speed and versatility of the Indians. However, the coalition of the Indians was breaking down. Some surrendered and others withdrew from the fighting.

Benjamin Church appealed to the Mohegans and the Praying Indians to join the English militia. Church suggested a new approach in fighting their "hit and run" warfare. Church wanted to infiltrate King Philip's forces with friendly Indians, so that he could learn their strategies and plans for their movements.

In the spring, Thomas and his father were assigned to Medfield, Sudbury, and Groton, where they anticipated attacks. Instead, the Indians struck in Lancaster, where they kidnapped Mary Rowlandson, wife of the minister, John Rowlandson. She would not be released for several months. The militia raced to Lancaster, but the Indians had moved away, continuing to be evasive and hiding in desolate locations.

Benjamin Church continued to cooperate with the friendly Indians. He was able to convince two factions of the Pequots and the Niantics to join with the Mohegans to share information about the movement of the Narragansetts. The Sakonnet Sachem Awashonks also agreed to join forces with Benjamin Church. Together, their guidance and alliance proved to be very helpful with the pursuit of King Philip.

In June, Governor Winslow decided to send a select regiment of troops under the direction of Benjamin Church in the final pursuit of King Philip. In a midnight attack at Mt. Hope in Rhode Island, King Philip was shot and killed by Caleb Cook and a Pocasset Indian named Alderman. King Philip's head was secured on a stick and hung in Plymouth for years as a grim reminder of the consequences of the war.

Benjamin Church and a small group of soldiers continued in pursuit of King Philip's chief captain, Annawon. They captured him and told him of King Philip's death. Annawon then surrendered and instructed all the Indian warriors to lay down their arms. This submission by Annawon brought an end to the war.

The message that the war had ended spread quickly and, on August 17, 1676, the Pastor John Cotton led his congregation, as well as a relieved group of militia troops and many citizens in New England, in a

Day of Thanksgiving. Throughout New England, celebrations were held and the militia was praised and decorated.

Thomas and his father returned to their family farm in Salem as military heroes. The brutal war had taken its toll on both of them. They had been involved in some of the bloodiest battles of the war and they felt fortunate to have survived. Many friends and comrades had been killed. Others had been wounded badly. Thomas would never forget their sacrifice, remaining loyal to his comrades in the militia throughout New England. Over the next ten years, he kept in contact with many of his comrades, often hosting them when they visited him in Topsfield and Salem.

Thomas was twenty-one years old when he returned home after the war. After several trips, including visits with his comrades in Providence, Quincy, and Lexington, he was ready to settle down and build a farm of his own. Because his brother John would inherit the family farm in Salem, he looked elsewhere. His family and some friends helped him settle in a new area, north of Salem near Topsfield. For his service in the militia, he was eligible for ten acres of land. After careful exploration, Thomas chose a fertile area, where he envisioned a fruit orchard and a spacious meadowland. Beyond his chosen ground, there was a natural swamp.

Thomas attended a celebration in Boston where he renewed his courtship with Elizabeth Knight, the girl he had met around six years earlier. Thomas and Elizabeth had both grown up in difficult times, with vivid awareness of the hard times on a farm in a frontier settlement. Madly in love and eager to move on with their lives, they were married on May 23, 1677.

They wasted little time in preparing their homestead. With help from their families and friends, they cleared a substantial area of their land and built a family home with enough space for their family and visiting members of the militia.

Soon Thomas and Elizabeth had four children, Thomas Jr., in 1678,

Joseph, in 1680, Daniel, in 1682, and Jonathan, in 1686. Four boys within eight years and a new farm were challenging assignments for Elizabeth and Thomas.

In the peaceful time following King Philip's War, they settled into an annual routine involving farm operations: planting in the spring, clearing the land and growing the crops in the summer, harvesting in the fall, and hunting and fishing throughout the year. The winters was spent with a variety of indoor crafts and ongoing preparations for spring planting.

During this time, many colonizers continued to come to America, expanding the immigration for religious freedom. An English Quaker named William Penn began a settlement in an area that would become known as Pennsylvania.

In Topsfield, the Congregational Church became the center of the religious and social activities for the majority of the settlers. Thomas became an avid student of religious history, often studying with church elders. Elizabeth was a gifted reader and taught Sunday School classes. The boys loved her stories and they memorized many of the exciting tales she told. She taught all her children to read at an early age. Thomas Jr. soon became a devoted student of the Bible, while Joseph and Daniel favored adventure stories.

The boys were growing physically strong and capable. The outdoor activities and the work on the farm were healthy and good for their physical development. They often spent Sunday afternoons with the families of Thomas' brothers, including fourteen cousins and numerous other neighbor children. The children learned to play together, organizing ball games, throwing and jumping contests, and various acrobatic talents. The Keney boys grew to excel in the competitive games and often challenged each other with their sporting skills.

In the early spring 1687, several members from the Massachusetts militia invited Thomas to join them on an exploration trip to the northeastern edge of the frontier. Since the end of the King Philip's War, there had not been any Indian uprisings within forty miles of Topsfield. Although Thomas was planning the spring planting soon, he agreed to ride with his friends into the frontier territory.

It was spring and the trees were starting to blossom with vibrant colors as they rode north toward the Cherry Valley and Lake Ostego. It was magnificent country and they speculated as to when the territory might be developed and occupied by the French, the English, or possibly by American settlers from the New Colonies.

At that time, King William III of Britain was bickering with France in what would eventually lead to the War of the Grand Alliance. Both sides attempted to align themselves with the Indians, the English settlers, or whomever would fight for their side. Both the Iroquois and the Potawatomi Indians were partial to the French. The members of the Potawatomi Tribe were eager to prove their savage warfare and gain a fighting reputation in trade for favors from the French.

Thomas and his friends did not anticipate any fighting because the disagreements involved the English and the French, not the colonists. As Thomas and his friends rode north, they encountered few white men, but occasionally saw some Indians and several French trappers. They had heard stories about Indian skirmishes, but they were lulled into a dangerous state of tranquility by the beauty and grandeur of the country.

They were taken by surprise when they were riding through a dense forest in the late afternoon. They met a band of Indians most likely from the Potawatomi Tribe. It was believed that the Indians thought that Thomas and his friends were British. They opened fire without any warning, wounding Thomas who was riding in the lead position.

Thomas and his friends, Alexander Osborne and Robert Page, shouted and sent signals attempting to indicate that they were not British soldiers. Within a short time, the shooting stopped, but not before another colonist, Kenneth Card, was wounded. The Indians quickly disappeared into the brush, while the colonists tended to Thomas and

Card, his wounded companion. The shots were not fatal and the men were able to dress their wounds and return to their mounts after a short period. In view of the attack, Thomas and his friends decided to return home without further exploration.

Thomas was taken back to Topsfield where he was placed under the care of a doctor. An infection had set into his wound during his ride home causing him to become sick with a high fever. When the doctor advised Thomas and Elizabeth about the seriousness of the wound and the likelihood of its spreading throughout his body, Thomas quickly reacted to care for Elizabeth and their children.

He wrote a will, providing all his worldly possessions to Elizabeth and his children. He met with his creditors including Henry West, Joseph Horn, Mr. Endecott, and Mr. Lindale to resolve his obligations. He also turned to his friends, John Putnam and Alexander Osburn, whom he named as overseers of his will, with instructions to assist Elizabeth in case of his passing.

In his will Thomas was very precise with the identification of his assets. Among other things, he identified "4 cows and 2 steers of 3 years old, 1 calf, 2 (of 8) sheep, 3 lamb 6 small pigs and 5 young pigs 30/1 plough cart yokes (chains) and all without doors and iron tools, axes and 1 house and 10 acres of land and orchard improved and unimproved land and all fences belonging to swamps . . ."

Thomas died in early June 1687. The militia, including some members from distant colonies, attended his funeral en masse. The family gathered in support of Elizabeth and their children. Thomas' brother John offered to care for the children and Thomas' father Henry offered to have the children live at his farm for awhile. But Elizabeth chose to have all the boys stay with her on her farm.

Elizabeth and her four boys turned to their close friends and her church for help and consolation. Elizabeth had not expected this tragedy that came when the family was so young and when other things seemed to be going well. Unfortunately, premature deaths and family tragedies were common on the frontier.

The people in Salem searched for answers to the strange and bewitching things that were beginning to happen in their community. The children would grow up quickly in an atmosphere demanding endurance and maturity just to confront some vicious and unexpected attacks on the frontier.

As Thomas II grew up and began raising his own family, he prepared to make some personal adjustments to confront the effects of the witchcraft trials, including moving his large family to a new and bountiful country.

Henry Keney's Farm, Danvers, Massachusetts

Witch Hill, Salem, Massachusetts

Chapter 12

Thomas (II) Keney
1678 – 1756
Deacon, Farmer

THRIVING WITH DISCIPLINE
AND HARD WORK IN NEW LANDS

Thomas paused outside his grandparents' home where he had lived off and on with his brothers since his mother had taken ill. Now that he was older, he often stayed on his own family's farm, doing much of the work with his younger brothers on their land. Recently he had been surprised to note how all those chores were turning his compact boy's body into that of a still short but now muscular, soon to-be-adult young man.

Thomas shook his head, remembering how just a few months ago his mom, Elizabeth, had called him by his name. When he addressed her now, she just stared at him as if she hardly knew him. She acted confused and said, "I thought for a moment that you were your father just come home from King Philip's War." It was sad and painful to see her physical condition deteriorate so quickly. She was barely talking these days and what she said didn't make much sense at times. Winter had been hard on her declining health.

When the door opened, his grandfather Henry stepped outside. Henry stopped when he saw Thomas. He dropped his eyes before squaring his shoulders and looking right at the boy, then said "Thomas, she's gone now. She's with the Lord."

"When?" asked the startled lad.

"Not so long from now. Your grandmother's with your brother Jonathan, and I will go fetch Joseph and Daniel. Thomas, your brothers are going to need you to be their strength now."

Thomas responded, "God knows that my mother has been my strength since my father died."

"Yes, Thomas," said Henry. "I know it is not easy with both parents gone. But I was on my own much younger than you are now. You have loving kinship-brothers, many cousins, uncles, aunts, and myself. You've got property. It's yours now. All I had was my faith and some godly people like Vincent Potter. We will help you and you will get by. With renewed faith, discipline, and hard work, you will do more than just get by–you will have the opportunity to flourish and prosper in this growing land."

Thomas responded, "Probably helped that once you married, your house was full."

Henry smiled a bit, "Sometimes it did, sometimes it didn't."

Thomas furrowed his brow. "Have we been a burden, then?"

Sensing the tender heart of the boy, Henry responded, "No, a joy and a blessing in my old age. I loved your mother and considered her to be one of my own. You boys and your noisy games keep me from the deadly silence. So many friends who came with me to this country are now gone. But as you said, my house is full for I feel blessed and am at peace with the Lord."

Thomas' confidence grew and he said, "May God see fit to provide me with a full house too-I pray that my wife and I can grow old together-so our sons and daughters can prosper and care for us!"

Henry's gnarled palm brushed across Thomas' calloused hand for a moment. "God willing, God willing, my boy. Now go on inside and pay your respects. I'll be back with your brothers soon. Be ready, OK?"

Thomas nodded, then turned and grabbed the doorknob.

Thomas was nine years old when his father Thomas Sr. died. His brothers were only seven, five, and one at the time. By the summer of 1688, persistent unrest and apprehension permeated Topsfield and the eastern Massachusetts Bay Colony. Living on the edge of the frontier meant living with unexplainable conditions. In addition to the constant threat of Indian attacks, there were violent storms, insufficient food supplies, unknown diseases, and persistent uncertainties in dealing with the local government and church officials.

After prayers and meditation in respect for his mother, Thomas moved outside again and paused by his favorite evergreen tree to reminisce. His mother Elizabeth was a strong and courageous woman who drew support from her parents and from neighboring friends and relatives as she learned to live without her husband. She directed her attention and support to her four children, and with bold determination, she made the farm a self-sufficient operation.

She kept a loaded musket by the door and taught Thomas and all her children to use firearms. In a strict but caring manner, she also taught them to hunt and fish, to read and write, to work on the farm, and to care for and protect each other. In that guarded environment, Thomas and his brothers grew up with respect and a very special admiration for their mother.

Elizabeth had a set and predetermined routine whenever strangers or danger arose at her house. Thomas Jr. would stand guard, with a loaded musket at the rear of the house while Joseph, with another musket, would cover the east side. Daniel would take the baby Jonathan to the west bedroom, then Elizabeth would confront the stranger at the front door, with her musket visibly ready to fire. When strangers realized that there were three loaded muskets aimed in their direction, intruders generally vacated the area quickly.

Thomas' grandfather, Henry, had grown up in the Puritan and Separatist Church. He raised his children to live in accordance with fundamental biblical teaching. When Thomas and Martha moved to Topsfield, they chose to attend the Congregational Church. After

Thomas Sr.'s death, Elizabeth maintained a strong and faithful allegiance to the church. She felt that it was especially important since the young boys had lost their father at such an early age that she establish religious discipline and substantiate their faith. Since their daily lives on the farm prevented them from daily contact with other people, the Keney boys looked forward with great anticipation to Thursday evening meetings and Sunday socializing with their friends and neighbors.

Thomas grew up in an environment dominated by strict frontier discipline, strenuous physical work on the farm, and unwavering family loyalty. Children were taught to live by the Golden Rule and not to question their elders, including the ministers at the church. Thomas learned from his grandfather and the church ministers, becoming a good reader and an avid student of the Bible. He was polite, yet his manner was rough within the country style. He was cautious and always careful not to drop his guard, especially with Indians or with strangers.

As the oldest child in the family, Thomas was keenly aware of his family responsibilities, especially for the care of his mother and younger brothers. He developed a protective nature and a strong tendency to avoid conflicts with other people. From an early age, he memorized passages of scripture and short prayers to remind himself of his duty to God and to his family. One of his favorite prayers, which he self-adapted follows:

>*Dear Lord, as I go to my daily work, help me understand my duties and your guiding hand.*
>
>*Give me strength, patience, and courage to do what is right, to perform my duties to the best of my abilities, and to perform them in a timely manner.*
>
>*Help me understand that with my discipline and your great love, all things are possible.*

As Thomas entered his teenage years, he developed a popular social presence with other people. He often joined friends for "husking" parties, which were a typical way for friends and neighbors to provide basic necessities for newlyweds in their new home.

Although Thomas Jr. had the outward appearance of a calm and gentle person, he never completely forgot nor forgave the savage Indians who wounded his father and killed several friends. He assisted the local militia and was always ready on a moment's notice to assist his neighbors and friends. During his early years, the majority of the fighting between England, France, and the Indian nations was located to the north and west of Topsfield. Nevertheless, settlers built their homes with the community defenses in mind. They shared important information about any Indian conflicts, and when threatened, they shared guard duty and moved quickly to notify others of imminent danger to their families and farms.

Thomas was a quick learner involving many practical things, especially operational needs around the farm. He never considered another occupation, but consistently pursued a life on the family farm As a student of agriculture, he learned to rotate the crops, irrigate marginal lands, and use neighboring fields for grazing sheep. Adapting to new ways, he became a weaver, making clothes and blankets for his family. Always willing to lend a hand, he became popular for helping neighbors with building projects.

As time passed and Thomas and his brothers grew older, more ground was cultivated and the farm became more productive. In addition to providing the basic necessities for the family, the farm provided eggs, chickens, and sheep for sale at the public markets. Thomas would occasionally go with his uncle Floyd or his grandfather to visit the markets in Lynn, Boston, or others nearby villages.

When Thomas was about thirteen years old, he went to visit his grandfather Henry in Salem. After church one Sunday morning, he met Mary Wolcott, Abigail Williams, and Mrs. Elizabeth Hubbard. Thomas noted that Abigail acted strangely when playing hide and seek with the other children. She hid in strange places and avoided the other children. When the game was over, they could not find Abigail, and soon a search party was formed. After a lengthy search, she was found hiding in the attic in the church. Mrs. Hubbard took the girls home and nothing was heard from them for about six months. After that, several visitors from Salem began telling reports of strange and bewitching behavior involving Mrs. Hubbard and the girls from Salem.

Times had been troublesome in Salem for several years, including a series of unfortunate encounters with the Indians. In 1689, two citizens of Salem Village were killed and, by 1691, the neighboring county of Essex was forced to keep twenty-four scouts scattered on it borders to repel Indian attacks. The hostilities continued and, later in 1695, Indians killed fifteen people from neighboring Billerica, burning houses and kidnapping one person, never to be seen again.

The threat of Indian attacks was not the only ongoing burden to the citizens of Salem. Since the original charter for Salem was lost in 1684, there was uncertainty and a constant worry about their constitutional rights. The citizens were confronted with excessive taxes and ongoing appeals to support government authorities. The Salem seaport was attracting more ships and shipbuilding was becoming a prosperous business, but commercial trading was difficult with an increasing number of pirates sailing and terrorizing the eastern seacoast.

In this state of high anxiety and distress, the witchcraft delusions began to infiltrate into Salem County. There were reports of "afflicted girls" attending meetings where they participated in strange activities, including wild and incoherent contractions. The girls acted as if they could not control themselves, but were driven by some devilish powers. After an examination by a physician, Dr. Griggs, some of the girls were said to be "bewitched." His pronouncement led to more public attention and soon people flocked to see the afflicted girls. When one of the girls, Abigail Williams, attended church, she made a public spectacle by confronting a visiting preacher named Mr. Deodat Lawson. She admonished him to "stand up and read his text."

At that time, Puritan teaching held that nothing was caused by chance, but that supernatural forces were ultimately responsible for all things, good and evil. Perhaps these girls were manipulated by evil or devilish forces. Although many of the church members were offended by the unusual actions of the girls, several of the ministers tried to help them by offering prayers and consolation. But the weird and strange behavior persisted and on February 29, 1692, warrants were issued to several of the girls.

Grandfather Henry admonished Thomas and his brothers to tend to their own business, avoid the gossip, and stay away from the trials. Thomas' mother, Elizabeth, concurred and she attempted to keep her boys busy on the farm and away from the public spectacles. But it was difficult because Elizabeth knew many of the participants, including Abigail Williams, Martha Cory, Elizabeth Hubbard, and Mary Walcott. The strain of the trials wore heavily on Elizabeth.

The fury of the trials escalated and most everyone in the county was caught up in the legal proceedings. In time, over 160 people were accused of witchcraft, and before it was over, nineteen people were executed by hanging and six other died from excessive punishment.

The trial of Rebecca Nurse was especially excruciating for the Keney family. The Nurse estate was located about three miles from the Keney farm and both families often attended church together. The accused, Rebecca, was seventy-one years old at the time. She had four sons and four daughters. A granddaughter also named Rebecca, will reappear in the Keney family history.

The records of the Court indicate that a warrant for the arrest of the accused Rebecca Nurse, wife of Francis Nurse, was made on March 23, 1692. Magistrate John Hawthorne presided at the initial examination, which became one of the most publicized trials of the period. Known to be a pious woman, Rebecca was charged with "certain detestable acts called witchcraft." A neighbor, Ed Putnam, brought charges against Rebecca and called for the witnesses, Mary Wolcott, Abigail Williams, and Elizabeth Hubbard to testify. Mary and Abigail appeared to conspire together, both presented condemning testimony against Rebecca.

In the course of the proceedings, young Henry Keney, son of Thomas' grandfather, complained of his "amazed condition" in Rebecca's presence. But Rebecca denied that she had ever hurt anyone in her life. In response to the Magistrate Hawthorne's charges, she uttered her famous reply, "I can say before my eternal father, I am innocent, and God will clear my innocency." Magistrate Hawthorne was unrelenting in his interrogation and after an extensive examination, Rebecca was sent to prison. She suffered a brutal confinement and was hanged to death in July 1692.

Governor William Phips arrived in Boston after the interrogations had begun. He directed a commission to hear the witch trial evidence. Before it was over, even his own wife would be accused. Finally, in October 1692, Governor William Phips ended the court trials in Salem. Pending cases were transferred to the Superior Court and eventually all the cases were cleared and prisoners released. Several years later, the Puritan Reverend Peter Clark would say, "We no longer believe in the supernatural power of witches, nor do we believe that supernatural powers control our daily lives. We assume that the individuals executed at Salem were innocent."

But in the meanwhile, the trials left a sobering and lingering impact on Salem and the surrounding counties. There was a decline of the supernatural mentality, and most of the citizens turned their attention to their daily lives and improving their living conditions. The Puritan Church retreated and many parishioners drifted toward other parishes.

The lingering strain of the trials had taken its toll on Elizabeth. Her health declined and she died in 1694.

Following their mother's death and for the next six years, Thomas and his brothers concentrated on the steady production and the expansion of their farm. With record corn and hay production, their harvests were sufficient to supply their needs as well as many of their neighbors. Their chickens, sheep, and cattle provided profitable sales from the markets in Topsfield, Lynn, and Haverhill.

As life on the farm stabilized and Thomas matured, he developed a growing attraction for a popular and attractive young lady named Martha Cox. Over the years, Thomas and Martha participated in many joint social activities including thatching parties in Topsfield and Salem Village.

Martha provided a wide variety of delicious foods, including cornmeal muffins for all of the workers at many of the thatching parties in the area. Thomas' young brothers would accompany him, primarily to participate in the festive meals when the work was finished. But Thomas kept a steady eye on Martha, with some long term plans which included his enjoyment of her wholesome cooking. Thomas and Martha had a happy courtship, which steadily grew into a common bond for the rest of their lives. To the delight of both families, they were married on November 10, 1701.

Thomas became an accomplished yeoman and known throughout the area as a devoted Christian. Their marriage thrived and from 1702 to 1714, Thomas and Martha had eight children, five boys and three girls. The couple was steadfast in their ongoing work on the farm and the growth of their family.

Beginning in 1704, Thomas' brothers began moving away from the farm. It was common practice at the time for the younger siblings to seek new opportunities, which often meant new branches of the family. Thomas' brother Joseph married Keziah Peabody and moved to a farm near Preston, Connecticut. His brother, Daniel, moved to a new farm and his youngest brother, Jonathan, reportedly moved to New York. He married young Rebecca Nurse in 1709 and they had two sons who served in the Colonial Navy.

In about 1710 when Thomas attempted to expand his farming operations in Topsfield, he was restricted by the lack of available land. Higher taxes and lack of sufficient water for his crops caused him grave concern for his future. Over a period of several years, he became discouraged by his inability to expand his farming operations. He began to search for new lands and, in 1714 he made a trip to Connecticut to visit his brother Joseph.

When he returned, he likely walked the road toward his home with mixed emotions. Even in the cooler late days of October, he loved the place where he lived and where his children had been born. Unfortunately, this land wouldn't support his growing family.

He paused, thinking about the fertile land his brother Joseph had shown him. Now there was a place with room to expand. It wouldn't be easy for awhile, but at least the ground would grow more than rocks on a regular basis. He couldn't wait to see Martha and the kids. Oh, how he'd missed them—even if he did appreciate the quiet he had enjoyed away from the bustle of his large brood. He prepared to share good news for all of them.

His thoughts were broken by loud voices he soon recognized as belonging to his sons Jeremiah and James. No doubt their mother had sent them out to gather kindling, but they appeared to be playing some version of settlers versus Nipmunks or Potawatomis or whatever group of Indians grabbed their fancy that day. Setting down his knapsacks, Thomas grabbed a stick for himself and approached the boys in the quiet, pastoral manner his own father had taught him. As he let out a whoop, both boys jumped. Jeremiah recovered quickly, working hard to show a total lack of fear, especially since he considered himself so grown up these days.

James had no such illusions and ran straight at Thomas. "Father, you're back! How was your trip? Tell us about Uncle Joseph's place."

"OK, boys. First why don't you finish collecting that kindling? Your mother doesn't need more trouble than she's already got with the lot of you."

The boys ran to collect the branches they had scattered all around the yard. Martha, having heard the commotion outside, was standing at the opened door with baby Lois in her arms and little Martha at her feet. As she smiled, Thomas noticed how she had changed since he'd left. But unlike so many women who grew frail when with child, his Martha seemed to blossom. She appeared radiant, possibly growing even stronger as the time of delivery approached.

"There's my girls," he shouted, dropping his stick and climbing the steps to the porch for a homecoming embrace with his loved ones.

The little ones squealed with delight as they watched their parents share their mutual affection and tender care for the children.

"Martha, you look better every day. I don't know how you do it, with the farm and the children. How can I thank you?"

"Oh, Thomas, your homecoming makes it all worthwhile. But, you must tell us about the Connecticut Valley and your brother Joseph and Uncle John."

Thomas settled in and prepared to give a full report. "Martha, there is plenty of open space ready for new farms. Joseph has saved 150 acres next to his farm, and there are running streams and forest land nearby. The ground is rich and fertile with space throughout the valley for future generations. You will like the neighbors–they have established a church devoted to the worship of God as you and I have always wanted."

Martha interrupted, "So we are really going to leave Topsfield?"

"Yes, Martha, my dear. I think it is the right thing to do. Joseph has offered to help and share with the move. Our boys can help too. It is important to settle before winter so that we can prepare the land in the spring. You will have a house by the stream and your sister-in-law will be living on the farm next door. You won't be alone. The children and I will be with you."

"Thomas, it sounds marvelous. It really does–it's just that I would prefer some of my women friends help with the household packing. You saw how our sons handle the kindling. Let them pack your farm equipment with you and I will be prepared to move whenever you are ready."

About then, young Jeremiah tugged at his father's pants. "Father, is there a place for us to play in Connecticut?"

Thomas broke out in a wide smile. "There is lots of room to play and there will be lots of things to do before we can leave. Your mother and I need to plan a few things and we will need everyone's help. We want to move before the cold weather settles in. But tonight we'll use some of that kindling and have a warm fire in celebration of our new home."

Jeremiah turned to his brothers and called out, "We're going to Connecticut! I'll pack my toys and be ready to go by morning."

It was difficult to leave many friends, including the Putnams, Hubbards, and Coxs who had been friends of the family for over sixty years. The sale of his property, including the historic John Martin house, to Jonathan Putnam was recorded on a deed dated February 15, 1715. Thomas signed his name Kinne, but throughout his life, he is known to have spelled his name as Kinnie, Kynne, Kenny, and Keney.

By November, Thomas, his wife Martha, and their children had moved to Preston, Connecticut to a farm on the banks of the Pachaug River near the town of Griswold. He acquired the 150 acres saved by Joseph which adjoined his farm.

About the time that Italian Bartolommeo Cristofori invented the first piano-forte and when Johan Sebastian Bach began writing his cantatas, Thomas and his brother Joseph were creating a comprehensive plan for the development of their farms. With his previous farming experience, Thomas knew how to maximize the productivity of the area. He cut trees and removed rocks to prepare the fields for cultivation, teaching his children as he worked. After studying the natural movement of the water from rains and snowstorms, he planned the irrigation system including several holding ponds for domestic and agricultural purposes. With Martha's advice, he identified the site for the farmhouse, the outbuildings, and the barns. It was a massive plan for the times that would take years to complete. But Thomas and Martha considered it to be a golden opportunity. They felt challenged, yet happy and optimistic to use their past experience as they built the farm of their dreams. The move served to stimulate and reenergize both of them.

As they began their new life in Connecticut, they identified their goals and concentrated they efforts toward three major areas: their farm, children, and Christian faith.

In addition to the seven children that accompanied Thomas and Martha to their new farm, Martha gave birth to nine more children, making a total of sixteen—ten sons and six daughters. Their twins, Timothy and Jerusha, died in infancy. The other children were known to be healthy and robust.

Birthdays and holidays were special events on the farm with at least one member of the family having a birthday in every month of the year and several members in March, May, and December. Martha prepared the favorite meal for the birthday celebrant along with a birthday cake and homemade ice cream for the whole family. Sometimes neighbors and special guests joined the family for a party in the evening. Many of the birthday and holiday gifts were made by Thomas and Martha. When the children were small, they received dolls, toy soldiers, tops, spinning games jump ropes, jacks, and balls.

Most of the clothes were made on the farm and often the clothes were passed from one child to the next according to their ages and physical sizes. As they grew older, the children, too, learned to make gifts for others, including their parents. The children received a small allowance from their chores on the farm and learned to spend it wisely at the general stores or markets in the villages.

Thomas and his brother Joseph often traveled to the nearby villages of Sterling, Plainfield, Glasgo, and Norwich to sell some of their farm products at the open markets. Often they traded chickens, eggs, and dairy products for some of the necessities they needed on their farms. Market trips were also good times to hear current news from other locations in the Colonies.

Over a period of time, they developed a friendship with Edward Logan, the owner of a general store in the port city of Norwich. Norwich was located about fourteen miles to the west on the Pequot River, later called the Thames. The population of the Norwich area was growing rapidly. In 1717, Thomas suggested that they increase their farm production and sell their products directly to Edward Logan, who in turn would sell their products on a daily basis to his customers. Thomas Logan would receive a commission, resulting in a mark-up of a small percentage of the price of the products and their products would be available to his customers. Fresh products would be delivered to the Logan General store generally two times per week.

This marketing system began in spring 1718, running successfully for over forty-three years. Other than occasional interruptions due to weather and transportation problems, the people in Norwich received fresh and reliable food service while Joseph and Thomas Jr. earned valuable income to supplement their direct farm income.

Thomas Jr. and Martha were very proud of their children and devoted much of their time to mold their family kinship. The children grew up in a healthy environment. Their oldest son, Jeremiah, assumed the ownership and management of the family's farm. With a solid morale and physical upbringing, Jeremiah was well prepared to address the inevitable confrontation with British rule. He would lead the family safely through the country's revolution. Two of the other boys, James and Amos, showed interest in agriculture, and eventually developed their own farms in the Connecticut farming region just west of Preston. Amos served as a Lieutenant in the Colonial Army. Their son Stephen moved to New York, where several cousins lived. Their son Moses moved to Providence, Rhode Island and served in the Colonial Navy. Their son Nathan moved to Boston where he studied religion and eventually became a Protestant minister. Their daughters Lois and Huldah married young men from the Preston area and both settled in western Connecticut. Their daughter Martha married Joseph Skinner and moved to Taylor's Eddy, near Damascus, Pennsylvania. The Skinners had thirteen children, thus expanding the Keney family throughout the colony. In 1759, several years after Martha's death, Joseph Skinner would be murdered by Indians when he was transporting goods on the

Delaware River. Their daughter Phoebe married and stayed near the family farm. The other children married into prominent families including the families of Herrick, Robbins, Palmer, Reed, Skinner, Paines, Brown, Gallup, and Cogswell.

In his later years, Thomas helped to found a new church, the Second Church of Christ, which was often referred to as the Pachaug Church in New London County. The parishioners affectionately called Thomas the "Deacon." He was instrumental in creating a mission statement for the church, which initially read as follows:

> *Our mission is to enable people to encounter the living God as revealed through Jesus Christ and to serve God and Humanity in an ever changing society.*

Thomas and Martha spent their elder years on the farm in Preston. Jeremiah assumed control of the farming operations and he gained full ownership after Thomas' death.

One of Thomas' favorite verses was from Revelation 14:13 which was paraphrased as follows:

> *Blessed are the dead who die in the Lord, so says the spirit for they rest from their labors, and their works follow them in everlasting remembrance. Their bones are buried in peace, but their names and deeds live forever.*

Martha died in 1747, but "Deacon" Thomas lived several years more, dying in 1756 on the family farm. He was buried beside Martha on the farm in an area called the Old Kinne Burying Ground on the banks of the Pachaug River. Their gravestones remain today. Indeed "their bones are buried in peace but their names and deeds live on forever."

It's thanks to the bravery of Jeremiah and other revolutionary soldiers that his parents' bones are able to rest peacefully over two and a half centuries later.

Home of Jeremiah Kinne, Voluntown, Connecticut
circa 1756

Chapter 13

Jeremiah Kinne
1702 – 1798
Farmer, Patriot

A CALL TO ARMS

The sun was beginning to rise on the eastern horizon as Jeremiah and his sons prepared to enter the side door of the Green Dragon Inn, a popular tavern in Boston. The conversation went something like this.

"Jeremiah, is that you?"

"Yes, Abagail, it's me. Don't be frightened."

"Well, I declare, I hardly recognized you, with your face all darkened and that weird costume on—you look almost like a savage—where have you been all night and what is going on?" Abagail was the innkeeper at the Green Dragon Inn Jeremiah liked to frequent when he was in Boston.

"Abagail, we finally told those Tories where to put their tea as long as they had a ridiculous tax on it. I just returned with my sons, David and Spencer, and the other Sons of Liberty from a party down on the docks. We raided the British cargo ships and threw their tea into the ocean. We caught them by complete surprise. What a party! That ought to send a message all the way to King George in London."

"It surely will," replied Abagail, "and it will send the British troops here to find you and your comrades. You had better hightail it, for they will be coming soon." Abagail grabbed two water pails and headed to get some fresh water–Jeremiah and his sons would need to clean-up quickly and scatter before the British soldiers arrive.

After cleaning up and a few hours rest, Jeremiah, his sons, and four other comrades from the Connecticut Militia left Boston to return to their homes in Voluntown, some eighty-five miles southwest in the Connecticut River Valley. They rode at a brisk pace, stopping in Providence to rest their horses and to spread the news throughout Rhode Island from where it would soon spread to the southern colonies. They traveled west, with several other stops for visits with friends and farmers along the way. They knew that this incident, which became known as the Boston Tea Party, was only one event in a long series of confrontations and skirmishes that might lead to a full scale war with England. However, this single event became symbolic of the patriotic spirit of the colonists. And this single event marked a dramatic change for Jeremiah and his family as they moved from their long-standing allegiance to British rule to a new loyalty and personal commitment to American independence.

Looking back, there seem to be a number of decisive events and important influences in Jeremiah's life that eventually led him and his family to alter their philosophic thinking and became patriots for the new colonies.

Certainly one of the initial influences centered on Jeremiah's structured childhood in a conservative Christian family. He was born in 1702 in a farming community near Topsfield, Massachusetts. Making a living on the farm at the turn of the eighteenth century was difficult at best. The New England winters were long and cold. Days were filled with strenuous physical work, while evenings and nights were often spent near the family's fireplace, simply to keep warm. Food and supplies for the farm were carefully guarded, and, sometimes, they were rationed to survive through difficult periods.

During this period a great awakening swept through the British colonies in the Americas. Traveling preachers caused a religious fervor stressing the individual's relation to God as being all-important. In time the ideology weakened the colonists respect for British authority and strengthened the movement toward independence.

Jeremiah was the oldest of sixteen children born to Thomas, Jr. and Martha Cox Kinne. His early years were characterized by his family activities, working on the farm, and observing strict devotion to the church's doctrine. Without questions nor hesitation, he was well-disciplined and, with guidance from his parents, he responded quickly to directions and instructions. He inherited a strong respect for authority, including training and teaching from his parents and church leaders.

By the time he was twelve, he would have five younger brothers and two sisters, soon after his parents moved to Voluntown, Connecticut. From an early age, Jeremiah developed a strong sense of kinship within his family. As the oldest child, he was expected to show leadership, which he did, serving as a good role model. He became a good teacher, instructing his brothers and sisters with some of the rudimentary chores around the farm.

Topsfield had a primary school where Jeremiah received his first formal training. His teachers were impressed with his progress and they recommended him for additional studies.

Jeremiah was small in stature, yet physically adept, agile, and a fast runner for his age. He had a natural liking for the outdoors. There were many trails in the area, including some undercover paths, which became shortcuts to get to his great-grandfather's home in Salem Village, some six miles away. If an emergency arose, Jeremiah could take the shortest route, and get to his great-grandfather's home in a little over one hour.

As Jeremiah grew older, he would travel with his father to the markets in Salem and Lynn. Occasionally, the family would travel to Boston to visit relatives. Shortly after Jeremiah's tenth birthday, he and his father went to visit Mary Kinne, a relative who had married William Pillsbury.

The Pillsbury's oldest children were grown and had moved away from their home while two children still lived at home. In the course of their visit, Mary took a liking for Jeremiah. She recognized Jeremiah's prodigious aptitude and she decided that under the right conditions, he could be an excellent student. Mary Pillsbury likely asked Jeremiah, "What do you want to be when you grow up?"

Jeremiah paused thoughtfully, before answering, "I have always assumed that I will work on the farm, since that runs with my family and I enjoy working outdoors with the farm animals. But I also like to be with lots of people and play kickball and other competitive games. My mum says I am a natural leader, but I'm not sure what that means."

Mary suggested, "Maybe you want to be the captain of a ship?"

"No, I don't know how to swim and I've never been on a ship," was Jeremiah's reply.

"How about a merchant, a tailor, or a town council member?" she offered.

Jeremiah was a bit perplexed, "I don't know what they do, but I'd like to find out."

"Hum!" said Mary. "With your curiosity and talent, you need to be exposed to all kinds of things in Boston. I think we can do something about that."

She convinced her husband that they should invite Jeremiah to live with them, a practice that was common with large families in the area. Jeremiah could attend the primary school in Boston and return to the family's farm in the spring. With his parent's permission, Jeremiah accepted the invitation, moving to Boston after the fall harvest was completed.

Mary showered Jeremiah with affection and gave him steady encouragement as he made his way in the new school. He called her his grandmother, but she was actually his grandfather's sister. There were so many branches of the Kinne family living in the greater Salem area that no one seemed to care about exact relationships and, in time, she felt like his grandmother due to the maternal kinship she had adopted.

The classwork and new studies were a challenge for Jeremiah since school in Boston was so different from the small school in Topsfield. He excelled in math and science, but his understanding and grades in Greek and Latin were marginal. He was a conscientious student—he worked hard to satisfy his teachers, the Pillsburys, and his parents. He did not want to disappoint them, knowing that the schooling was a great opportunity for a farm boy.

Jeremiah made friends easily. His athletic prowess made him a popular among the boys, especially for the sporting teams. After school, the boys tended to play together as they wandered about Boston. He became more confident and outgoing as he developed friendships with his classmates and, eventually, with local innkeepers and merchants. Using his adventuresome instincts, Jeremiah developed a good sense of the city's geography. He identified key landmarks and found shortcuts among the footpaths, hills, and trails within Boston.

Mary's husband, William Pillsbury, was a kind and gracious gentleman. He tended to let Jeremiah keep to his own affairs, but he served as a major influence to Jeremiah. He read stories with him in the evenings and introduced him to the newspapers, including the *London Gazette*. As Jeremiah's interest increased, Pillsbury explained some of the major stories, including the ongoing war between the French, British, and Indians, commonly called Queen Ann's War. Discussing the news stories helped Jeremiah to develop an inquisitive nature. He learned to gather information, distinguish the facts, and form his own opinion. This informative routine became a personal habit that Jeremiah carried for the rest of his life.

Another major influence of William Pillsbury's came from his trips with Jeremiah to the waterfront and to the offices of the shipping merchants. As a youngster, Jeremiah watched with amazement as Pillsbury visited with sailors and traders to discuss sailing dates, merchandise, cargo, weather conditions, and current exchange conditions in England, the West Indies, and throughout the Colonies. It was Jeremiah's first exposure to foreign commerce and the political and military exchanges between England and the Colonies.

The two school years in Boston made a bold impression on Jeremiah. They opened his eyes to many new and exciting things that he would confront in the future. His friendship with the Pillsburys transformed his personal experiences into meaningful relationships with them and with other friends in the Boston area. In the spring of 1714 Jeremiah bid farewell to the Pillsburys and his friends and returned to the farm in time to begin the planting season.

Summer passed and in the early fall, Jeremiah's father, Thomas Jr., announced that he was planning to move the family to a new home in eastern Connecticut. Thomas purchased a farm adjoining his brother's property near the Pachaug River, where each family would have a farmhouse and share some of the outbuildings. The plan called for the family to move to Connecticut in the late fall and be settled before the winter. It would take extra care to prepare the children for the trip.

There were four wagons in the traveling party, which included a neighbor, Thomas Cuddington, and a nephew, Jacob Kinne. A nurse-maid, Peggy Jones, helped Jeremiah's mother with the children. The men assisted with the wagons and directed the oxen and cattle. Jeremiah was assigned to help care for the small farm animals, including the chickens, goats, and pigs.

As they traveled, they visited with occasional riders along the way who provided helpful information about the trail conditions, crossing the rivers, and likely places to camp each night. The trip took about three weeks to get to Voluntown, where Joseph and his family met the caravan. There was a grand reunion with many of the Kinne families living in the Connecticut Valley.

In the following days, the men spent much of their time completing the farmhouse that Uncle Joseph and some neighbors had begun during the summer. Until the house was completed, Jeremiah and his brothers stayed with neighbors in temporary facilities. Anticipating the delivery of their new baby, his mother, father, and the small children stayed with

Joseph and his wife in their home.

The first important task for Jeremiah was to get the small farm animals into new pens. The chickens needed a henhouse and the pigs needed secure pens, capable of keeping the foxes away. It was a busy time with lots of help from their new neighbors and friends.

The frontier community in the Connecticut Valley brought a new spirit, as well as a new opportunity for Jeremiah's family to build a strong and lasting future. There was a simplicity of life, based upon a daily routine of working on the farm, caring for young children, and constantly expanding and improving the land. Simply clearing the land to make it productive for crops or for grazing was a ongoing endeavor.

In the course of their work, Jeremiah learned to use all of the available natural resources. They used their own timber to build a barn and additional outbuildings. With the remaining timber, they made chairs, cabinets, and tables. Using numerous stones from the fields, Jeremiah learned to build stone fences, something that came to represent the unique craftsmanship of the stone masons in the area. Many of those stone fences remain in place and can be seen today near Voluntown.

Jeremiah's grandfather's brother, John Kinne, was one of the early settlers in the Connecticut Valley. He was one of the first volunteers from King Philip's War to receive a land grant (number forty-four) from the lottery for the war veterans. Like Jeremiah's own family and many others at the time, John had a large family including seventeen children. Soon after his children began raising their own families, there were so many Kinne relatives that people referred to the area as the Kinne Valley. Two of the trails that eventually became roads were named Kinne Road and Kinne Street and a small stream is called Kinne Brook.

John Kinne was one of the early member of the church in Glasgo, which was known as the Pachaug Church in New London. This church called for increased authority to its members, yet held many fundamental practices and teaching of the Puritans. Jeremiah's parents also joined the church, where his family became thoroughly engaged in its worship, social, and community activities.

As Jeremiah grew to full maturity, he gained a wider understanding for managing the operations of the farm. His father and Uncle Joe proved to be good teachers. They experimented with fruit trees and found that apple and cherry trees grew abundantly in the area. They increased wheat and corn productivity with extended irrigation during dry periods, offset with decreased watering during wet periods in the spring. They built extra water ponds to conserve water for other purposes, including domestic and agricultural use.

Many of the family's farm products were sold at the open markets in the neighboring villages of Norwich, Preston, and New London. Jeremiah became a good salesman, as he had a natural liking for talking with people. He learned to barter and trade farm products for supplies and household merchandise that his mother could use. His father gave him a small commission for his sales, primarily for the his chickens and eggs. Consequently, he quickly developed a personal incentive to sell his farm products for a profit.

When Jeremiah's father and Uncle Joe established a sales agreement with Edward Logan in Norwich, Jeremiah and his cousin Willy often made the trip to Norwich in a wagon to deliver the dairy products and fresh produce. The trips were not only a good way to sell their products, but also a source for obtaining information about happenings throughout the Colonies. Since Norwich was located on the Pequot River, later called the Thames, many merchant ships arrived on a regular basis. They brought supplies and information from seaports all along the east coast. Jeremiah and Willy enjoyed their time on the docks visiting with seamen, as well as gathering newspapers, mail, and other supplies to deliver to farmers along the way on their return trip to Voluntown.

Thursdays were special days for Jeremiah because the family would gather for lecture meetings at church. Since Sundays were restricted and devoted to the Sabbath, Thursday's gatherings were more informal, giving the congregation more time to socialize and meet newcomers.

Jeremiah met Mary Starkweather one Thursday evening after a lecture. When members of the congregation gathered in the common room, Mary assisted by serving punch and cookies. I suspect Jeremiah had a special craving for Mary's sweet cookies, because over time, he was known for his perfect attendance on Thursday evenings. They visited weekly and discovered many common interests, including a passion for adventure and a love of the outdoors. In time, their Thursday meetings were extended to include weekend picnics and occasional visits to the Starkweather's home.

The Starkweathers were a large and well-respected family in the valley. Their frontier family was originally from Ipswich, Massachusetts and, later, they lived on a farm north of Griswold near the village of Danielson. Mary's great-grandfather came to America from the Isle of Mann in 1640.

Each year after the harvest, Jeremiah and some of his cousins or other family members liked to take an exploratory trip. Jeremiah's favorite city to visit was Boston, where he could visit with the Pillsburys and see some of his former schoolmates. Jeremiah also visited New London in 1720 and Philadelphia and New York in the following years.

In 1723, Jeremiah and Willy made a special trip to Boston to pay their respects to Mrs. Pillsbury following the death of her husband the preceding year. After spending time with Mrs. Pillsbury, Jeremiah and Willy called on their cousin, David Keney, who was working at a trading office on the Boston waterfront.

David was enthusiastic about business opportunities and trading with British merchants. One of David's assignments was to check the inventories of merchandise coming into port and those leaving Boston. He told Jeremiah about some ships leaving Boston without full loads and what needed to be done to establish sales of farm products to the sailing merchants. Jeremiah took the information that David provided and returned to Voluntown to share this news with his father and Uncle Joe.

After due consideration, the men's reaction was not to pursue selling their merchandise to the Boston merchants. Their established market in Norwich was doing well and it would be easier to expand their markets into New London. Nevertheless, Jeremiah's newfound familiarity with the Boston waterfront would prove to be valuable in his future.

Shortly after Jeremiah's twenty-fourth birthday, he proposed to Mary Starkweather. After their marriage in the fall 1726, they moved into a small home near the Kinne Farm. Since Jeremiah was the oldest child, fully capable and well trained, he was expected to assume the management and eventual ownership of the family farm. He had a good sense of his family responsibilities, not only for his immediate family, but also for his younger brothers and sisters and aging parents.

Jeremiah and Mary were well suited for each other. They had similar backgrounds, strong moral characters, and diligent work habits. They shared a faithful and abiding love, which became an inspiration for all their family.

The family farm prospered for the next fifteen years. The acreage for cultivation gradually increased as more forest land was cleared and the land plowed for new crops. The rolling hills and fertile valleys proved to be good breeding grounds for dairy cattle. Their milk production steadily increased. Yet, the demand for the farm products grew more rapidly than the farm's capability to increase production. New settlers were coming into the Connecticut River Valley, arriving from the northeastern colonies and from the seaport at New London. In addition to providing farm sales through Logan's General Store, some fresh products were being sold to a shipping merchant in Norwich who was transporting the products to New London. New London was becoming a strategic port for distribution to southern colonies and the eastern seaboard. By 1735, settlements were well established in Georgia and North and South Carolina.

Jeremiah and Mary's marriage was blessed with caring relatives, helpful neighbors, and many new babies. The family's Bible recorded the births of their children as follows: Mary, a beautiful, precious baby, January 28, 1728; John, a robust brother for Mary, on August 10, 1729; Spencer, healthy and strong, February 3, 1731; Eunice, a fine sister for Mary, June 1734; David, small, with strong vocal chords, November 11, 1736; Miriam, petite and gentle, August 5, 1738; Manuel, muscular and rambunctious, August 13, 1740; Jerome, distinctive features with a touch of red hair, August 21,1743; Ruth, smiling and happy, April 30, 1745; Daniel, playful and happy, May 10, 1747; Elizabeth, beautiful eyes and strong features, March 23,1749; Suzanna, slender and playful September 9, 1751; and Samuel, husky, dark hair, and calm demeanor, April 13, 1753.

Mary had a natural maternal instinct whereby she showered each child with tender love and care. With a strong sense of personal independence, she encouraged each child to develop as quickly as possible to his/her full potential. And when danger arose, she was like a mother grizzly bear, poised and ready to repel any danger. She had a gift for nursing and caring for children when they were sick. Using natural remedies, she was often called upon to give medical advice to their neighbor's children as well as their own.

Jeremiah's allegiance to an independent government within Connecticut grew as the people of Connecticut established their own self-rule. The early settlers in Connecticut were very progressive in attempting to form a government focused on strong individual rights. In its formative years, the Connecticut territory operated under a charter known as the Saybrook Colony. The Dutch and English both claimed the territory. When the French and Indian Wars were raging in the north and in Canada, and with England, France, and Spain fighting in Europe, it was a confusing time to attempt to clarify or update its legal status. Nevertheless, many early settlers consistently attempted to update their colonial status. As time passed, the General Court of Connecticut voted allegiance to the British Crown and asked for a new charter. Also, the Court attempted to change the name of the Mohegan River to the

Thames and the name of the city of Nameaug to New London.

Those were difficult times in Britain. Since King Charles I had been rejected by the British Parliament and then executed in 1649, the English government was substantially under the control of their parliament while Oliver Cromwell was the Protector of the Commonwealth. Charles II ascended to the crown in 1660.

As England regained its stability, the people in Connecticut decided to present formally a new proposal. In March 1661, they submitted a draft of a new charter and selected Governor John Winthrop to sail to England to obtain the King's approval. The new charter was accepted and signed by King Charles II on April 23, 1662. The charter was described as "extraordinary" because it clearly gave the people of Connecticut the unqualified power to elect all their own officers, enact laws, and administer justice without any appeal to England.

The charter established a new era for the people of Connecticut, which eventually spread to all the Colonies. The literal interpretation and promise of the charter led Jeremiah and his family to become very protective of their rights. Thanks to this charter's existence, Jeremiah and the people in Connecticut resisted any new threats to their personal freedom.

Jeremiah was elected as a deputy to the Connecticut General Assembly in 1754. The assembly met in New Haven where he expanded his family of colonial friends and allies. During this time, Jeremiah gained a valuable understanding of the relationship between a state and federal government and the importance of unified support for all the colonies.

The Connecticut Assembly attempted to clarify its geographic boundaries which was a difficult task in view of the westward movement of people from New York and Pennsylvania. To the south, there were reports of the Virginia Company exploring areas and possibly moving settlers to the west. News of the English Army's defeat at Fort Duquesne reached the Connecticut General Assembly in 1755. In addition, it was learned that General Braddock had been killed and that young George

Washington had assumed command of the troops. The farmers in Connecticut watched with great concern, becoming even more protective of their own boundaries. They united in opposition to intruders including Governor Andros and others who attempted to take their land and alter their property rights.

After a bountiful harvest in 1763, Jeremiah was expecting record profits from his crops. In addition to the sales in neighboring villages, about half of his sales of hay, alfalfa, and corn were made to farm agents who in turn sold the products for shipments to cities along the eastern coast. The agents quoted fair prices, but delayed payments, causing Jeremiah and other farmers to carry the accounts.

Over the years, Jeremiah had become apprehensive about extending credit to intermediary buyers. There had been a dreary succession of excuses for late or reduced payments. During the Queen Ann's and King George's Wars, the farm agents tried to issue paper money for the crops. Some farmers accepted the paper money, then lost half of its value within six months when the paper money was devalued.

After the close of the French and Indian Wars in 1763, there were substantial debts within the Colonies. The British government imposed taxes on the Colonies in attempt to assist in paying their own debts which exacerbated the economic conditions. Jeremiah and the farmers in the Connecticut Valley strenuously objected. Many of the farmers and men from Connecticut who had served with the British in the Seven-Year-Long War rejected further economic burdens. Trading or purchasing British goods became more difficult because of the cost, including the British taxes that had increased substantially.

On a trip to Boston after the harvest in 1769, Jeremiah was eager to see his friends and spend some time in his favorite city. He visited with friends at the Green Dragon Tavern and went to Faneuil Hall to hear the new organ in a music recital. As he wandered throughout the city, he was startled to see British troops armed and patrolling the streets. He heard even more discouraging reports about the stubborn

British economic policies. With friends, he discussed the possibilities that the British Crown would revoke some charters and likely impose its omnipotent rule throughout the Colonies. Connecticut, Rhode Island, and New York would likely be the targets for British troops. He was told about the Boston citizens' resistance and that some of the colonists were secretly preparing to confront the British soldiers.

David Keney, who continued to work in a warehouse on the Boston dock, took Jeremiah to a meeting of friends who were sharing information about the British military's presence in the city. The group joined with other patriots, including some representatives from the Sons of Liberty and the Committee of Correspondents. They appealed to Jeremiah, who by this time was considered to be an elder statesman. With his knowledge of Boston and his influence in the Connecticut Valley, Jeremiah's support would be influential and a valuable sign of leadership for younger colonists.

When Jeremiah returned to Voluntown, he carried a renewed spirit of patriotism for the Boston citizens-and possibly for a new, independent country. He had an unblemished record as a successful farmer, family man, and Christian gentleman with a long record of loyalty and dedication to the Crown.

Without disrespect to the Crown, Jeremiah believed in the human rights and freedom as codified in the Connecticut Charter and substantiated by the British philosopher John Locke. He argued that if the government abused an individual's right to life, liberty, and property, the people had a right to rebel. All men should cherish their independence and, if necessary, Jeremiah was prepared to fight for it. Since he had physically worked hard to provide for his family, now he was determined to extend this new opportunity to his children and future generations.

In the succeeding months, he helped organize farmers and merchants in the Connecticut Valley. He traveled to Lebanon, Tolland, and New London to organize militia troops. A network of communications developed and he followed the news with periodic reports from

Boston and Norwich. The *Connecticut Gazette* of New Haven, the *New London Summary*, and the *Connecticut Courant*, gave ongoing reports of the skirmishes on the Boston streets. The British rule became confrontational, with sporadic fighting in the streets. The colonists began to spread a war cry of "no taxation without representation." In March 1770, several colonists were shot by British soldiers. Reports of the incident spread rapidly and grew out of proportion, becoming known as the Boston Massacre.

As tensions mounted, Jeremiah increased communications with the Sons of Liberty. In late November 1773, Jeremiah was asked to join a troop of volunteers going to Boston to support the local colonists in retaliation for a tax that was levied on merchandise coming into Boston. Some of the Boston merchants, including John Hancock, were reportedly smuggling some merchandise to colonists without paying the British taxes.

When Jeremiah and his comrades arrived in Boston on December 12th, they were told about several ships in the Boston harbor waiting to be unloaded. Under a plan reportedly put together by Samuel Adams, the Sons of Liberty planned to board the ships and throw the tea into the sea, preventing the British from collecting the appropriate taxes. The execution of the plan worked smoothly on the night of December 16, 1773. In the morning, the surrounding beaches smelled of the pungent fragrance of British tea.

The reaction of the Colonies was mixed. Boston patriots reacted with stunning approval. Celebrations were held in Philadelphia and New York. But some colonists were upset, including Benjamin Franklin who described the act as a "violent injustice" and said the raiders should be punished.

The British were so furious their parliament passed an act closing the Boston port. Consequently, Boston became the center of the dispute and the event moved the Colonies closer to outright war. Boston became a desperate town, cutoff from British trade with limited communication with other seaports. Other towns and communities, including the

Connecticut Valley had to provide supplies, food, and other support to the Boston commonwealth.

Jeremiah returned to Voluntown before the year's end. In the succeeding months, word spread quickly throughout western Massachusetts, Rhode Island, and Connecticut that the British would reinforce their troops in the area. Shortly after the first of the year, Jeremiah went to Lebanon to meet with farmers and other colonists. The farmers agreed to send supplies to Boston and to recruit troops for the Connecticut militia.

Jeremiah's sons John, Manuel, and Spencer volunteered to serve in the Connecticut Militia. His daughters, Mary and Elizabeth, volunteered for service at the hospital in Providence. Joseph's son, Jacob, served in the Sixth Regiment and his son Ezra was in the Eighth Regiment of the Continental Army. Joseph received a commission and served as a Captain. Amos Kenny, a nephew, served in the Colonial Navy on its only ship under the command of Seth Harding.

As the fighting began, Jeremiah stayed in Connecticut, primarily maintaining the farm and supplying food and supplies to the troops. In addition, he substituted as vicar at church and served as Justice of the Peace for Windham County. When the British invaded Connecticut at Stonington in 1775 and Stanton in 1777, Jeremiah volunteered to lead the local resistance. However, the British did not advance further into Connecticut after their initial attacks. When the British attacked and burned New London in 1781, Jeremiah went to Norwich in anticipation that the British would move northward. Fortunately, the British troops retreated to New York.

When the Treaty of Paris was signed and the War ended in 1783, Jeremiah was eighty-one years old. His wife Mary died in 1785. Several years later, Jeremiah was designated by the Daughters of the American Revolution as a "Patriot" for his service in Boston in 1773 and for his ongoing support of the Colonies during the Revolutionary War.

Jeremiah lived the rest of his life on the family farm near Voluntown. He spent much of his time with his son, John, who assumed the operation of the family farm and with his son, Manuel, who assumed the pastoral duties of their church.

Manuel developed a unique interest in keeping historical records of the family, members of the church, and citizens in the community. In addition, he had a strong passion for sharing the biblical lessons of the church with young married couples. Combining these interests with his pastoral talents, he became a well respected pastor and influential leader in Windham County.

Jeremiah died in 1798. He and Mary are buried in the family cemetery in Griswold, Connecticut near the family's farm. His tombstone reads:

> *In memory of Jeremiah Kinne Esq.*
> *who departed this life June 24th AD 1798*
> *in the 96th year of his age.*
> *A soul prepared needs no delays.*
> *The summons comes, a saint obeys.*
> *Swift was his flight, short the road.*
> *He closed his eyes and saw his God.*

Kynne Family Historian Roger Kinney in King's Lynn

Manuel Kinne Homestead, Plainfield, Connecticut

Chapter 14

Manuel Kinne
1740 – 1828
Farmer, Preacher, Patriot

BLESSING THE BONDS OF MARRIAGE, FAMILY, & COUNTRY

"I now pronounce you man and wife." Those were the felicitous words Manuel Kinne declared to over 200 couples as they exchanged wedding vows and began their married lives. Manuel blessed the bonds of so many marriages that he was known in the Eastern Connecticut Valley as the "marrying parson." Manuel would be called that, by the end of his life, for personal reasons as well as for his matrimonial services. In addition, he was the keeper of vital records, including marriages, baptisms, and death records, for Plainfield and Windham Counties.

It was customary at the time for a magistrate, a justice of the peace, or a "man of dignity" in the community to officiate at the wedding ceremony, called the contraction. A sermon covering the conditions for matrimony was presented to the bride and groom at the contraction. Manuel was known for electrifying sermons and strict instructions to newlyweds. Following the ceremony and a three to four day waiting period, the couple would have a "coming out" party at church, when the couple would be presented to the entire congregation. At that time, the minister of the church would say prayers and formally bless the marriage. Usually, the bride and groom chose the text for the sermon which the minister delivered at the Sunday services following the wedding.

Manuel took great pride in preparing young couples for their contraction and wedding ceremonies. According to Manuel, marriage vows were not to be taken lightly. If young couples didn't understand their roles in the marriage contract, Manuel would clarify the customs and provide detailed advice for the bride and groom.

However, the colonists were known to marry when they were very young and if there were a death or the marriage was annulled, which rarely happened, they married often. Bachelors were frowned upon. Widows and widowers were often quick to join other families after their spouses died. Match-making, negotiating, bargaining, and matrimonial-calculating commonly went along with a fashionable courtship. But sometimes the execution of the marriages didn't go as planned.

Walter Brown, Jr. was a fun-loving young man, eighteen-years-old, when he began courting Arin Kinne, Manuel's niece, in the spring of 1784. Known as a jokester and prankster among his friends, he had stolen his older sister Carole's birthday cake from her party and had a party of his own with his conniving pals. When the girls at church went on a retreat in the woods, Walt and his friends dressed like goblins and scared the girls until they ran for help. On another occasion, Walt absconded with the clothes of his friends, Freddy Leonard and Phil Warner, when they went swimming nude in the river outside of town. Consequently, there were lots of people around town who wanted to get even with Walt if they ever had a chance.

When Arin and Walt decided to be married, a notice was placed on the church door for the whole congregation to see. Their friends began plotting revenge. Immediately Arin and Walt met with Manuel Kinne and established schedule of events leading to the wedding. They studied biblical verses, choosing Eccles 4: 9-10a for the following reading: "Two are better than one, because they have a good reward for their labor. For if they fall, the one will lift up the other." They chose several prayers to be said and asked for Reverend Joel Benedict to bless the wedding at the

Sunday services that would follow the contraction.

When Walt's sister told Freddy and Phil about the wedding plans, the trio decided it was time to get even with Walt. At that time, the sport of stealing brides was common in the Connecticut Valley. The day after the contraction services, Freddie and Ray arranged to take Arin on a secret trip to an inn near the old stone quarry, about four miles away. Walt's sister, Carole, and several other friends detained Walt long enough to prevent him from chasing after Arin. When Walt realized she had been kidnapped, he searched frantically but did not find her until Saturday. By that time, all their friends, including Freddie, Carole, and Phil had enjoyed a boisterous party at the old stone quarry.

Walt and Arin returned home and went to the church just in time to confront Manuel who was preparing the church for Sunday services. The conversation likely began with a greeting from Manuel, "I'm so glad to see you, Arin and Walt. I've been hoping for several hours that you would come by the church."

Walt responded, "We have been busy preparing for Sunday services with some of Arin's friends. They seemed to have had some special advice for her."

"That's nice" replied Manuel. "And Walt, did they have any advice for you?"

Walt paused, while observing a wily smile on the older man's generally somber face. Then he replied, "No, not really, they seemed to leave me out in the dark. They think I can take care of myself. But I've learned that there are times when a fellow needs some real friends he can count on."

Manuel quickly noted, "That will be true throughout your marriage. Sometimes, we learn such lessons like this in the most unusual ways."

Walt searched the preacher's eyes but couldn't tell if the wise man was passing on advice as a married man-or if he knew more about Arin's disappearance than he was admitting.

Arin agreed, "Yes, it was unusual. I think Walt and I both learned a good lesson from our recent experiences with our friends."

Without dwelling on the details, Manuel suggested, "Then let's move on and prepare for the proper observance of the Sabbath and your coming out ceremony here tomorrow."

If Manuel Kinne and Reverend Joel Benedict knew anything more about the kidnapping, they kept it a secret to themselves.

Manuel came by his Christian education and religious training naturally. He was born on August 14, 1740 into a family with a devoted Christian history. He was the seventh child of Jeremiah and Mary Kinne, with three older brothers and three older sisters, all subject to strict discipline by their parents.

If children or any colonists got out of line, there were numerous forms of punishment to remind them of their righteous ways. As a youngster, Manuel was aware of the whipping post, the stocks, and the pillory in town. Closer to home, children were scolded, given extra chores, or taken behind the barn for a whipping if found necessary.

Manuel's early years centered on his physical growth and maturity on the family's farm. The Kinnes lived according to the seasons, with primary attention to the success of the annual harvest and to the production of calves and lambs from their dairy cattle and sheep.

Manuel's mother Mary was a kind and gracious lady who comforted and guided him and his siblings in their early years. She was a wonderful cook and she prepared special treats including bread pudding and fruit pies. Her voluminous meals generally consisted of hearty meat dishes, potatoes, and vegetables, basically grown or raised on their farm. There were fifteen people at each meal and when guests and relatives visited, Mary increased the portions accordingly. Her scrupulous care and old-fashioned, natural remedies for colds and children's ailments is credited with maintaining the children's good health and their strong physical constitution in a time when many children did not make it to adulthood.

When Manuel was five, he was sent to a primary school, called a "Dame" school, where he learned to read and write under the direction of a strict overseer. At an early age Manuel showed an interest in reading and could recite passages from the Bible and the *New England Primer* by the time he was seven. Following directions from his older brothers, he learned to build things with his hands. Using local woods, he built model toys, including spinning tops, hoops, and some kites. As he grew older, he built some small furniture, some bird houses, and shelters for the small animals.

All of the children in the family were given daily chores around the farm. During the planting and harvest seasons, they joined forces to accomplish the necessary work, sometimes within a restricted time period. Weather conditions played an important role, which often resulted in working from sunrise to sunset when it was necessary. As the children grew, they assumed more responsibilities. Manuel learned the fundamental lessons for operating a farm and he grew to be physically strong and muscular.

Part of ongoing work on the farm involved clearing the land for agricultural purposes. This included gathering the rocks and broken stones, which were used to build protective walls and fences around the property. Without using an adhesive, the stones had to be placed in strategic order to maintain the shape and withstand any storms. Manuel had a natural aptitude for building the stone fences, some of which were so sturdy and graceful that neighbors considered them a work of art. Sometimes stones had to be broken or chipped so that they would fit properly into place. One day when Manuel was chipping a stone, a part of a stone flew into his right eye causing terrible pain. The doctor could provide some physical comfort, but he would remain partially blinded for the rest of his life.

As a child, Manuel had some difficulty hearing and it was determined that there was a blockage in his inner ear. Although it likely caused some permanent loss, the blockage gradually dissipated. When he reached his elder years, it reappeared and he became about fifty percent deaf.

By the time Manuel was fourteen, he had three more sisters and three more brothers, making thirteen children in the family. Along with his brothers, he often delivered their farm products to the market in Norwich. On special occasions, he visited New London, Boston, and New Haven.

Manuel grew restless on the farm. His parents wanted him, as well as all of their children, to be well trained and to be exposed to new opportunities. His father discussed some possibilities. He suggested that Manuel consider another working experience, even an apprentice-ship. His father spoke with his brother Daniel who had friends living near New London. Daniel had three sons with similar ages. Manuel liked his cousins, Timothy, Jerusha, and Gideon, and when he turned sixteen, he went to live for a time with Uncle Daniel. Later, he lived with Daniel's friends near New London. Manuel hired out, taking a job at the Larson Building and Mercantile Company. He worked hard, learn-ing the building trade. In addition, he attended some classes, including some history and religious studies at the Congregational Church and the Coventry Divinity School.

During this time, New London was a growing seaport. Ships were sailing to and from Boston, New Haven, Philadelphia, New York, Charleston, and occasionally to and from foreign ports including London and New Amsterdam. Small ships carried food and supplies to Norwich and Hartford. With his cousins, Manuel wandered about the streets and docks in New London. But his work fell primarily within the warehouse district, assisting with the inventory, loading and unloading products and supplies. Outgoing shipments included some of the farm products from the Connecticut Valley and incoming shipments involved supplies and machinery for distribution within the interior cities in Connecticut.

During the warmer months, Manuel worked with the construction crews building additional warehouses and dock facilities His knowledge about construction increased substantially and he developed an under-standing of the construction trades necessary to make a building project successful. Working with architects and building planners, he studied the buildings along the docks and contemplated the future compatibil-ity and efficiency of the shipping business with the agricultural products from his family's farm. He offered suggestions to his supervisors. To prevent spoilage, it was very important to protect the farm products and to deliver them in a timely manner. He discussed the importance of adequate water supplies, including maintaining the water-storage facilities and the improvement of all sanitary conditions around the edible products. After a fire in one of the grain warehouses, he suggested a plan to separate food from other products.

Manuel and his cousin Timothy often worked together in the warehouses and on the docks. They grew to know the crews of some of the merchant ships. After proving their workmanship and dependability and, likely, after a couple of social drinking occasions, they convinced the captain of a merchant vessel to take them on board as part of their crew. This practice started on some of the shorter trips to New Haven, Boston, and New Amsterdam. But as time passed, they sailed to Philadelphia, Charlestown, and Baltimore. They heard firsthand reports from British sailors about the British War with the French and the Indians in Canada and the northern colonies. Some of the British ships were recruiting volunteers to join their troops in the north. Manuel watched as some volunteers from Connecticut joined their forces and departed on British ships from the dock in New London.

In 1762, Manuel's father sent him news that some farm land in a neighboring village of Plainfield would become available the following year. Manuel was ready to return to farming so he decided to move back to the Connecticut Valley. But before he left New London, he completed a warehouse construction project for the family of Silas Dean, a prominent businessman in Connecticut. After the building was ready for occupancy, Manuel and Timothy set out on horseback traveling first to Boston, then to Philadelphia and Washington before returning to Voluntown.

Manuel returned to his family's farm in the spring of 1763. With his father's guidance, he purchased some raw land near the Quinebaug River. The majority of the land had a dense forest so a substantial number of the trees had to be cleared. A meadow near the river was ideal for grazing cattle, so Manuel built a barn for the cattle after the farmhouse was completed.

Some of the ladies at the Congregational Church worried about Manuel-he seemed to work all the time and he didn't have a wife. There weren't many available young ladies in town, but Manuel took a liking to Martha Gallup. Martha was pretty as a picture, innocent, and only fifteen years old. The Gallup family lived on a farm near Sterling, where Manuel visited throughout the summer of 1764. Manuel was twenty-five when they married on November 22, 1764. By that time, Manuel had built a cozy farmhouse, a barn, and several shelters for the small animals. With his building experience in New London, Manuel could construct a durable, new building as fast as anyone in the valley. He quickly became a popular neighbor and often assisted others whenever new construction was planned.

After his marriage, Manuel had a renewed sense of direction. He devoted his energy to the establishment of his new farm. For the next five years, he worked hard to clear the land, establish irrigation channels, increase his dairy cattle and sheep production, and plant the crops that would support the large family he and Martha hoped to have.

When Manuel and Martha were getting settled in their new home, the conflict between the colonists and the British was escalating. As the French and Indian War in the north was coming to an end, the British began a series of taxes with infringement policies on the colonists. The taxes were designed to make the colonists pay a greater share of the debt, largely accumulated by the British to pay for the wars of the past fifty years.

Manuel's father was becoming more involved in the resistance movement against the British. At his father's suggestion, Manuel began reading various periodicals, including a series of letters from John Dickinson, a farmer from Pennsylvania whose works appeared in the *Pennsylvania Chronicle*. The theme of Dickinson's work dealt with the unconstitutional nature of the British legislation on economic matters and how such legislation was unfair and unlawful to the rights of Englishmen living in the Colonies. The enlightening letters, with their poignant message, hit a vital chord with Manuel and many of the farmers throughout the agricultural communities.

Twelve letters of John Dickinson were printed in pamphlet form and distributed in England as well as in the Colonies. The letters were used as a basis for farmers to unify their resistance and establish their position against the ongoing intrusion into the rights of American colonists. Manuel's father became an active leader of the farmer's resistance. He conferred with leaders of the militia and began traveling to Boston and Lebanon for strategy meetings.

Manuel and Martha had their first child, Levi, a boy they called Leroy, on April 13, 1766. He was followed by a girl, Mercy, in June 1767 and, a boy, Jeremiah, in May 1769. The pattern of having a new baby every two years continued. By October 1780, Martha and Manuel had seven children, four boys and three girls. Martha's last pregnancy was very difficult, and the doctor had to operate to protect Martha and save the baby. Thereafter, Martha could not have other children. The perpetual strain and hard work associated with seven children under the age of fourteen took its toll on Martha. She lost considerable weight and her health gradually deteriorated.

While the general economy wavered, Manuel continued to expand the farm's production and increase the sales of his farm products. With an abundant water supply and grazing land, the dairy cattle and sheep thrived on his farm. Manuel's stock became well known for high-quality wool and healthy lambs. He began selling some of his stock to buyers in Norwich and New London, with some other shipments to farmers in the southern states.

As hostilities with the British increased, Jeremiah became convinced that the conflicts would lead to a full scale war. An appeal was sent throughout the valley for volunteers to enlist and be ready for an invasion of British troops. Some of Manuel's brothers, cousins, and nephews were the first to enlist. Manuel conferred with his father and decided to volunteer for the local militia. His partial vision curtailed his marksmanship ability, but he was able to shoot from his left side. His militia status would keep him in a ready, reserve military position, and he could maintain the supervision of his farm. He would work with his father and other farmers to provide supplies and food to the troops. If the British invaded Connecticut, he would be called with other members of the militia to defend the state. Periodically, Manuel trained with other members of the Connecticut militia. They drilled on the village green in Lebanon and they conferred about military strategy when reports from the front lines reached home.

In 1775 when General George Washington traveled through Connecticut en route to Cambridge, he made stops in Norwalk and New Haven before traveling up the Connecticut River to Hartford. Manuel's militia unit met Washington's party in Hartford and later helped to escort him to Governor Trumbull's farm near Lebanon. The farm was converted to a supply depot which became a strategic location for Manuel. He delivered food and supplies to the depot and later, he made deliveries to the troops with supplies from the depot.

The Kinne family and most every household in the greater Connecticut Valley had fathers, sons, and daughters working for the war's causes. Manuel's older brothers, David and Spencer, joined their father in some of the first raids with the Sons of Liberty. Later, they served in the Connecticut militia. Uncle Joe received a commission and became a captain in the Continental Army. His sons, Jacob and Ezra, also enlisted in the army. His son Caziah served with the Virginia militia. Manuel's younger brother Daniel joined the army and fought with the Eighth Regiment. Manuel's sister Miriam married captain Robert Cole who served under General Nathanial Greene and General Israel "Old Put" Putnam. Throughout the war, colonists joined together and listened intently as news from the battlefields found its way back home. Connecticut was second only to Massachusetts with the number of citizens serving in the military.

In August 1776, a plea came from Alexander Hamilton for supplies to aid the troops who had retreated from Canada and were stationed in New York and New Jersey. Manuel and several members of the Connecticut militia organized a shipment of food and supplies from the supply depot near Lebanon to be sent to New York. Thereafter, on regular basis, Manuel acted as a supply chief. He managed the harvest on the farm, stored the food, butchered the cattle and sheep, and delivered the food and other supplies to the troops and, sometimes to families in need within the Connecticut Valley.

During the war years, Manuel and his father served as the ministers at the church in Plainfield. Manuel officiated at Sunday services and provided spiritual services at the homes of parishioners when requested. He conducted marriages, baptisms, and funerals. With family news coming and going to the troops, Manuel began keeping a record of vital information. His recordings grew in importance and eventually became part of the legal records for Windham County.

In July 1779 the British troops were moving south raiding Horseneck, Greenwich, and New Haven. When the militia was called, Manuel joined forces under the command of General Andrus Ward marching to New Haven. By the time they arrived, the British troops had sailed away and rerouted for attacks on Fairfield and Norwalk. The militia marched to Bedford and Ridgefield, but again Manuel missed an encounter with the British.

By the spring of 1780, the British had captured Charleston. Reports circulated that the French had responded to the American's appeal for help and were sending additional warships to the southern colonies. General Washington, with his chief aide Alexander Hamilton, made another trip through Connecticut with stops in Lebanon and Norwich on his way to Newport, Rhode Island for a conference with French officials. Manuel was a member of the militia's welcoming party for General Washington and Alexander Hamilton at Norwich.

Later, Manuel reported with 38,000 other Connecticut troops

who were called by Governor Griswold to defend Connecticut against further attacks. But the battlefields moved to the southern colonies and the Connecticut militia disbursed without further orders.

News of the Battle at King's Mountain where patriot sharpshooters defeated the British in October 1780 heightened confidence throughout the Colonies. Accounts of another stunning victory at the Battle of Cowpens in South Carolina reached Connecticut in late January 1781. The Americans had overrun a superior British force on January 17, 1781. As spring approached, the tide of the war seemed to turn in favor of the Colonies. After months of steady pressure from the colonists, a showdown came in September at Yorktown. With the support of the French warships that blocked British ships from entering Chesapeake Bay, the British troops were isolated in Yorktown without help from their navy. In 1781, at the dramatic siege of Yorktown, British General Cornwallis acknowledged defeat, leaving over 8,000 British soldiers and sailors isolated. General Washington demanded complete surrender and, in a historic ceremony, British General Charles O'Hara presented his sword indicating complete surrender to his second-in-command, General Benjamin Lincoln, who symbolically accepted the sword and then returned it to him.

Sporadic fighting continued for several more months. The British troops gradually left other southern cities and their headquarters in New York. General Washington informed Congress of the victory at Yorktown. But he waited until April 1783 to declare that the war was over.

There was a slow transition to peace time, as troops returned to their homes and gradually rebuilt their lives.

Manuel directed more time and effort to his farm and to his church. While his regular chores of milking the dairy cows and tending to the animals became part of his daily routine, his diary reflected some of his other activities, including the following entries:

Monday–repaired the fence on the north and west boundary.
Tuesday–cut lumber, made shelves and split rails.
   Used some rails to reinforce the walls of the vegetable cellar.

Wednesday–Went to the market with a load of potatoes and apples. Sold them for 65 cents per bushel.

Thursday–Sister Joyce died, wrote a sermon and visited with her family.

Friday– Made a coffin for Sister Joyce. Afternoon, made soap, boiled sugar and worked on the farm house.

Saturday–hunted for deer, dressed two pigs and a calf torn by the wolves.

Sunday– Observed Sabbath, gave sermon at Church and visited with neighbors. Read poetry.

As Manuel concentrated on the affairs of his family and his congregation, the nation wrestled with the formation of a new government. A Constitutional Convention was held in Philadelphia in 1787. A friend who served in the war with Joseph Kinne, Oliver Ellsworth, was selected as one of the delegates from Connecticut to the convention. After widespread debate, Connecticut delegates offered a solution to the stalemate of whether the membership in congress should be based upon equal representation from each state or be based upon the size of the population of each state. The Connecticut compromise created two houses of congress incorporating both concepts. Once written, the constitution required approval from the majority of the states. In 1788, Connecticut approved the new federal constitution by a vote of 128 to 40.

Manuel followed the convention and the ratification of the constitution by reading periodicals from Boston, Philadelphia, and New London. After Benjamin Franklin's careful distinction between a Republic and a Democracy, Manuel subscribed to and heavily endorsed a Republic as the country's form of government. Although many of the farmers supported a strong position for state's rights, Manuel became a strong advocate for a strong federal government, following the federalist doctrines espoused by Alexander Hamilton. His casual meetings with Hamilton during the war gave him a personal feeling of attachment to him and to his philosophy. He followed Hamilton's career anticipating that his leadership would influence the stability and makeup of the new government.

In the winter of 1789, Martha came down with chills and a severe cold. By February she grew very weak and her illness turned deadly. She died in 1790, at the age of forty-one.

Manuel and Martha's oldest son Levi was then twenty-four, and their youngest son, Thomas, was ten at that time. Levi, who married Hannah Gallup in 1787, moved to Sterling and was already living and working on the Gallup's family farm. Their second son Jeremiah had moved to Herkimer County, New York, while their third son, Isaac, stayed on the family's farm in Plainfield to work with his father.

In 1789, George Washington was elected President, John Adams Vice President, Alexander Hamilton was named Secretary of the Treasury, and Thomas Jefferson was Secretary of State. Manuel was convinced that the federal government was headed in the right direction. New states were added in 1789 with North Carolina, in 1790 with Rhode Island, and Vermont in 1791. The nation's capitol, originally in New York, was later moved to Philadelphia. Representatives from the southern states were plotting to move the federal government and build a new capitol across the Potomac River from Virginia, just east of Maryland and south of Pennsylvania.

For about the next six years, Manuel supervised the operations of the farm, preached with increasing regularity, and dutifully recorded the vital records of the community. He became more scholarly by studying the great men of the time. Benjamin Franklin was one of his favorites and he read his pamphlets, including the annual *Poor Richard's Almanac* almost as if it were his bible. On a trip to Philadelphia in 1795, he visited the famous library founded by Franklin and his Junto Club. He often incorporated some of Franklin's sage advice into his sermons and conferences with young people.

On October 7, 1797 Manuel married Lucy Starkweather Park, an attractive and high-spirited lady from Boston. Lucy was the daughter of a cousin of Manuel's mother. She was a widow, forty years old, and experienced with the wifely chores of running the farm. Her former husband, David Park, was accidently killed in a hunting accident several years previous in western Pennsylvania. Since Lucy's birthday was October 7, 1756, her marriage with Manuel was a happy occasion on the date of her forty-first birthday.

Lucy and Manuel fit right into the common pattern of life on a Connecticut farm. Both assumed their familiar roles, and within several years, they had two children, Robert in 1798 and Ezra in 1801. Lucy was a good mother and spent much of her time nursing and caring for the newborn, as well as her stepchildren. The children grew to be strong and healthy, but in 1807, Lucy suffered from severe coughing and a bronchial disorder. Doctors diagnosed the problem as a form of tuberculosis. Manuel sent Lucy, along with the small children, to Boston in spring 1808 to visit the Park family, with hopes of restoring her health. Lucy's former father in-law, Henry Park, took a special liking to the children while his wife tried valiantly to nurse Lucy back to good health.

About this time, the French Revolution was raging in Europe as Napoleon was subduing large parts of Italy, Spain, and Portugal. To help finance his war, Napoleon sold the Louisiana territory to the former colonies, thus nearly doubling the size of the United States.

This was also the great age of European classical music, with the works of Mozart, Haydn, and Beethoven readily available. Henry Park, his wife, and some friends introduced the Kinnes to some classical music, playing their violins and harpsichord to the receptive ears of Lucy, Robert, and Ezra. Ezra was so motivated that she studied the masters and eventually became an accomplished pianist. Robert didn't play a musical instrument, but he developed an appreciation for music and savored the special attention from his relatives.

Lucy, with the children, returned to Plainfield in the fall of 1808. But her condition worsened and she died in January 1809.

Her death brought considerable pain and suffering to her children who had witnessed the agony of her failing health. The young children felt alone and stranded without their mother. Robert blamed his father, while Ezra withdrew and began to associate more closely with her older half-sisters, Bridgit and Anna. Attempting to console Robert, Henry Park devoted much of his time to Robert resulting in a strong bond between the two, even though there was an age differential of some sixty-five years.

Manuel turned again to his church for consolation. Some of the ladies of the church were quick to console him and in a routine manner, they set out to find another mate for Manuel. They introduced him to Zipporrah Pattridge, a widow with a prominent social standing. She was thirty-eight years old, without any experience on a farm, and had a strong inclination for socializing with rich and prominent merchants. Without much fanfare, Manuel and Zipporrah were married in 1809.

After a long and cold winter, Zipporah was eager to leave the farm and engage in some spring social events. But spring on the farm meant that planting was top priority. Manuel and the older children were needed to assist with the planting and the caring for the new calves and lambs. So when everyone on the farm went to work, Zipporah disappeared. She reportedly went to Philadelphia, but she never returned to Manuel nor the farm. It is believed that Manuel worked it out with church officials to annul the marriage. Since he was the keeper of vital records, including marriage documents, the records reflect that a legal annulment was made.

As time passed, Manuel's son Isaac assumed a major role of managing the family farm. He built a farmhouse about one mile away for his family and his three young children. His sister, Anna, and his younger brother, Thomas, lived with Manuel in the family's original farmhouse.

When Manuel turned seventy, his family had a special birthday party for him at the church. It was a festive occasion and many of his friends and neighbors attended the party. When they surprised him with a gift, a new fishing pole, Manuel told them that he had a surprise for them. He announced that he was going to marry Edith Curtis, a young widow whose family had been friends of his family for many years. Edith was thirty-five, young enough to be Manuel's granddaughter. But she was ready and willing to marry Manuel.

Manuel's reputation as the "marrying parson" took on new meaning with his marriage to Edith Curtis. It was his fourth marriage, and people began to tease him about how many times he would marry. He responded saying that it was the obligation of every man not only to get married, but to have children and raise a family. He practiced what he preached. Within a year, Edith gave birth to a baby boy whom they named Charles. Two more children, Mary and Moses, were born in 1815 and 1817. Again Manuel settled into a daily routine on the farm and in the church dealing with the life of raising a family and serving God.

Manuel lived to be eighty-eight years old. In his elder years, he devoted much of his time to his church and to his expanded family in the Connecticut River Valley. With a passion for preaching and telling stories about the Revolutionary War, he extolled the distinguished war record of his extended family. His manuscripts and notebooks containing the vital records of Plainfield were given to Windham County and eventually some of the records were shared with the Danielson Museum. In addition to the county records, Manuel updated the family records and gave a copy to each of his children.

His son, Robert, who had grown up on the family farm, faithfully kept his copy of the family records as well as some of the family's relics from the Revolutionary period. Although he had rebelled against his father after his mother died, Robert found a way to seek adventure and fulfill his patriotic calling by fighting in the War of 1812 prior to moving west with his family.

Upon his passing in 1828, Manuel was buried at the Union Cemetery at Mousup, Connecticut.

His widow Edith Curtis Kinne lived to be ninety years old. She raised and educated their three children Charles, Mary, and Moses. She remained on the family farm which was managed by Isaac, and later by his son Jacob. Upon her passing in 1867, she was buried next to her husband at the Union Cemetery at Mousup, Connecticut.

Birthplace of Robert Kinne (Kinney), Plainfield, Connecticut
circa 1816

Chapter 15

Robert Kinne (Kinney)
1798 – 1870
Militia Fighter, Farmer, Pioneer

WESTWARD
AFTER THE WAR OF 1812

Robert and his companions stood and watched in quiet amazement as they scanned the fire red sky from their vantage point on Arlington Heights in northern Virginia. The capitol city, Washington, was ablaze. He and the other members of the Connecticut militia had retreated, first from the Battle at Bladensburg, then from the city of Washington under strict orders from Colonel Thomas Hood.

The excitement and awesome intimidation caused by the invasion of the British troops caused a scurry of activities with seemingly conflicting orders all the way from President Madison down through the ranks to Robert's militia unit. Orders first indicated that American troops would take a stand at Bladensburg on August 22, 1814. The militia, under Colonel Thomas Hood, was ordered to guard the southwestern flank of the defense forces. Robert stood in combat readiness, deathly frightened, but prepared to meet the enemy. His military unit was considered the third line of defense behind the regular army and the seasoned troops who were ahead of them to the east.

When the British troops, under the command of General Ross, overpowered the Americans on the first line of defense, American

General Winder gave orders for a full retreat from Bladensburg. With American troops retreating, the British had an open road to what became an undefended Washington. As the British troops prepared for the final assault, American men, women, and children scurried to save their valuables and evacuate the city. The president's wife, Dolly Madison, was one of the last to leave as she gathered valuable documents and many national treasures. Robert's militia unit moved to the hills in Virginia.

The British considered the capture and burning of Washington to be a fitting retaliation, for earlier in the War of 1812, the Americans had burned the British Capitol at York in northern Canada. When British General Ross issued orders to burn all the government buildings, the British soldiers sent a volley of fire bombs through the windows of the White House, the Capitol, both houses of Congress, and the Treasury. Several nearby homes were destroyed, including one originally owned by George Washington. The only government buildings left standing were the post office and the Patent Bureau. The blaze, which began about 8:20 P.M. on August 24, 1814 could be seen from the distant hills in Virginia and Maryland. One of Robert's friends in militia, Denny Wheeler, said, "I'll never forget the destructive majesty of the flames, and the overwhelming magnitude of the destruction. Flames reached skyward as if to scream for help and awaken the country."

A violent rainstorm followed the blaze and by morning, the fires were roughly contained within the city. Shortly thereafter, the wet and soggy British troops began to reassemble and return to Bladensburg and then back to Cape Henry. In the eyes of General Ross their mission of retaliation was successful. They had humiliated the American nation. But to Robert and his comrades and the citizens of Baltimore, there were more battles to come and the resolve of the American troops would be rebuilt with more energy than ever before. It had been thirty years since the Revolution and this was the first war—the first test for the survival of young America.

When the British troops left, Robert and the militia returned to

Washington where they comforted the wounded and buried the dead. Within two weeks, there were reports that the British would not return to Washington, but were likely to attack the city of Baltimore.

A call to arms was sent throughout the eastern states for additional troops to help defend Baltimore. Citizens from throughout the area responded, as well as additional militia members from Pennsylvania, Delaware, and Virginia. Robert and his comrades joined with the militia from Hartford, reporting to Captain Porter who was under the command of General Winder. They were instructed to set up their defense for the eastern side of the city, known as the Eastern Heights. The first line of defense was established at North Point, some fourteen miles from Eastern Heights.

By September 11, 1814, the American troops were in position in anticipation of the invasion. Again, Robert and his militia unit were prepared for the attack. The British troops were expected to attack from a position between the Patapsco River and Back Creek. In the early fighting on September 12th, several British soldiers were shot, including General Ross. Americans Daniel Wells and Henry McComas were credited with the shots that killed General Ross. It was rumored that the British troops had became demoralized. The American troops, under General Stricker, held their ground at North Point and put up a ferocious fight, inflicting many casualties on the British troops. When the ground fighting subsided, the Americans retreated to the area on the Eastern Heights, where Robert and the militia waited for the British assault. The British did not pursue the Americans, but held the ground at North Point waiting for further directions.

During the same period, a naval battle was underway at Ft. McHenry. The British warships battered Ft. McHenry on Whetstone Point with bombs and rockets. Under the command of Major Armistead, the fort withstood the constant bombing, and on the morning of September 14, 1814, the high flying American flag became the signal that told the world that the Americans had not only survived, but had turned the

British back, both on the sea and on the ground. Frances Scott Key, who had witnessed the battle as a prisoner from a ship in Chesapeake Bay, composed a poem entitled the "Defense of Ft. McHenry." The poem was printed, widely circulated, and eventually set to the music of a spirited English song. In 1931, the tune, along with the words of Frances Scott Keys would be acknowledged by the U.S. Congress as the national anthem.

Robert and his comrades celebrated the victory with the citizens of Baltimore. By the time the celebrations and mop-up operations were over, he and his childhood friends, Denny Wheeler and Peter Wells, were ready to go home. He was ready for a good rest and a change of pace after the war.

As Robert traveled home, he reflected on his childhood and his impulsive nature that seemed to crave action, adventure, and independence. Robert was born in Plainfield, Connecticut, the first child of Manuel and Lucy Park Kinne. He was a healthy baby with a slender, yet muscular physique. The rambunctious boy had some curly hair, a broad grin, and western teeth.

His father had been married before to Martha Gallup who had died several years earlier. His three half-brothers and four half-sisters were much older, ranging from eighteen to thirty-two years older than Robert. His father, a strong and energetic man, was fifty-eight years old when Robert was born. His younger sister, Ezra, would follow three years after his birth.

Robert had a special fondness for his mother, a slender and agile lady who was forty-one years old when Robert was born. When she saw how isolated Robert was from his older half-brothers and sisters, she showered him with affection and personal care. She often took Robert and his sister on visits to the Parks, the parents of her deceased first husband, including Henry Park, who Robert considered to be his grandfather.

Robert grew up on the family farm, just outside Plainfield, where he learned the fundamental tasks of living and working on a farm. He became a good worker and seemed to tolerate the strict instructions from his father. But in time, he rejected and rebelled against his father's strict discipline and authoritative manner.

At the primary school in Plainfield, Robert developed a competitive nature, which carried over into other activities. He was the fastest runner in his age group. He made a game of fishing and always wanted to catch the most fish. Same with hunting. When he reached nine, he had his first boxing match, after which his competitive nature expanded even more.

During a boxing match, he suffered his first injury, which was a broken finger on his left hand. He was going through a rapid growing period when he suffered a number of other injuries in rapid succession. When he was climbing a tree to retrieve some apples, he fell and broke his left arm. Even while he was nursing the broken arm, he tore the ligaments in his right knee when he was racing after some rabbits. Two months later, he fell off a horse and sustained lacerations across his forehead that left an ugly scar. His father accused him of living under a dark cloud. Robert shrugged it off as bad luck. Privately, he probably resented his father's lack of compassion. Nevertheless, he learned at an early age to deal with adversity and he rarely let an injury keep him from his important commitments or activities.

Holidays were filled with celebrations and family reunions, generally held at the Park's home or his parent's farm. His half-brothers and sisters would visit for special occasions and Robert traveled to visit them as he got older. His father's brothers, his uncles John and Spencer, told exciting stories about the American Revolution and how various members of the family had served during the Revolutionary War. Two of his cousins, Jacob and Ezra, served in the Continental Army. Uncle Jerome served under General Putnam and was wounded in the Battle of Long Island. Robert was entranced with the heroic stories and valor of General Putnam, who died in the nearby city of Brooklyn before Robert was born. In time, Robert inherited a strong patriotic spirit to go along with his youthful zeal for a military career, as so many of his relatives had accomplished.

Robert's mother died when he was eleven years old. It was a shocking and difficult time for Robert who had trusted and relied so heavily on his faithful mother. Privately, he blamed his father, becoming even more hurt when his father remarried within a year after his mother's death. He felt resentful toward his father, turning toward his close friends, Denny Wheeler and Peter Wells, for consolation.

During the next few years, he was steadfast in working on the farm and caring for his younger sister. He continued to gain valuable working experience, turning more attention toward his half-brothers, Merion and Isaac who owned neighboring farms. The strenuous work seemed to agree with him as he grew to become a strong and resourceful young man.

In 1810, the British Navy vessels were raiding American merchant ships and taking American seamen from their vessels. There were numerous reports of the British terrorizing the eastern seaports with unlawful conflagration of goods and routing of ships. Farmers were losing crops that were intended to be shipped abroad. There was a growing distrust among business men and overseas traders.

When Robert was twelve years old, his father announced that he would marry Edith Curtis, a young widow who would be a caring companion for his father and his younger sister. Shortly thereafter, his half-brother Isaac agreed to assist with the farming operations on his father's farm. Robert accepted that offer as good news because he could look outside for his own future without interrupting the operation of the family farm.

Not much later, President Madison declared war against Britain in June 1812. The Secretary of War, William Eustis, issued a plea for volunteers for the Federal Army. Robert attempted to sign up but he was rejected because he was too young.

The American military plan was to attack the British in Canada, where they had established their capitol at York. But the initial fighting went badly for the Americans and soon they retreated back to the south. By 1813, Secretary Eustis sent another directive requesting the states to organize, equip, and prepare their state militias for war. By law, no militia could be forced to serve outside its state. But under the difficult conditions of imminent danger from the British, the militia could volunteer for service if called to support the country. There were many young patriotic men, including Robert and his friends, Denny and Peter, who wanted to join the militia to fight the British.

When Robert was sixteen, he convinced his father that his time had come. As planned, Denny, Peter, and Robert together joined the Connecticut militia which was already preparing for the invasion of the British. Within three weeks, they rode to meet up with the Connecticut militia in the nation's capitol at Washington. But now, less than a year later, they were headed home after the unsuccessful defense of Washington and the successful battle to defend Baltimore.

After Robert returned to Connecticut, the American forces, led by Andrew Jackson, defeated the British in the Battle of New Orleans. Shortly thereafter, the Treaty of Ghent was signed, officially ending the war. As peace spread throughout the former colonies, the Connecticut militia was placed on a reserve status.

The experience Robert received in his initial military duty with the militia during the siege of Washington and Baltimore would serve him well in his future. Robert retained his reserve status in the militia and assumed a new position with the federal government to survey and map new territories. Denny Wheeler joined him, but Peter Wells stayed in Plainfield. It was a stimulating and exciting job, ideal for two young veterans of the War of 1812 who were eager for more adventure. They were sent on survey crews to western New York, Pennsylvania, and Ohio. The frontier was constantly moving west, and their surveys helped to identify where the roads, canals, and railroads would eventually be built.

Robert was helping to pave the way for the next generation. The spirit of westward expansion was captivating, giving him a proud sense of national pride and accomplishment. Between assignments, Robert and Denny often rode into the frontier territory to hunt, fish, and explore new regions. During their tenure with the surveying agency, they traveled as far west as Chicago and what would become St. Louis and as far south as Nashville and Atlanta.

Robert returned to Plainfield for Christmas in 1822. He had worked for the government about six years and was ready to settle down to manage a farm of his own. He paid his respects to his aging father with a visit, but stayed with his half-brothers until he settled on a new farming community near Tolland, Connecticut.

A few years after the Missouri Compromise was signed into law, Robert moved to his new farm where he began to clear the land and cultivate the grounds. In the summer, he married Clarissa Wilson, an amiable young lady he had known for many years. The wedding took place at the Congregational Church in Preston, about sixty miles from Tolland.

With the help of his half-brothers, neighbors, and other relatives, Robert and Clarissa built a small house and set out to establish their own farm. Using the agricultural knowledge and experience he gained from his youth, Robert planned an irrigational system for the crops in relation to the open lands and meadows identified as grazing lands for the cattle. The ground was rich with minerals, ideal for corn, hay, and alfalfa. With the population growth in nearby cities including Hartford and Manchester, they expected good markets for their products.

In 1825, Robert and Clarissa had a baby girl they named Lucy. Lucy was born premature and was too weak and frail to survive. She died when she was six weeks old. Another daughter, Emily, was born in 1826, and a boy, Charles, was born in 1830. While Emily and Charles were strong and healthy babies, Clarissa's health suffered during her last pregnancy. Although she worked hard to nurture and care for her children, her health declined and she died in January 1831. Friends and neighbors joined in support of Robert and his two young children, assisting him so that he could continue to work on the farm.

With the encouragement of several ladies from the church, Robert married Deborah Clark, a twenty-two year old lady from a farm south of Tolland. Deborah was eager to assume the role of a farmer's wife, including the care and related responsibilities for two small children. Their marriage got off to a difficult start when Deborah fell sick after encountering a torrential rainstorm when she was returning to the farm from a trip to the market in Tolland. She caught a terrible chill that turned into pneumonia. The doctors and Robert tried desperately to nurse her back to health, but her condition worsened, and she died in the fall just five months after their marriage.

Although Robert remembered the prophetic words of his father's prediction that he was "living under a dark cloud," he refused to believe such nonsense. He still had his successful farm and kindred responsibilities with two young children. He turned to his friends and to the Congregational Church for support. As always, he relied on his friends, Peter and Denny. He resigned himself not to act so impetuously, but to move on with his life.

In the spring 1833, Robert took his children on a trip to Plainfield where Peter Wells had organized a reunion for members of the Connecticut militia. To accommodate the children, they traveled in a covered wagon accompanied by several friends, including J.W. Skinner, a member of the militia. The trip took two days and on arrival, they were greeted by Peter and several members of his family. It was a harmonious reunion as well as a fortuitous introduction to meet Peter's niece, Louisa Wells.

It didn't take long for Robert and Louisa to get acquainted. Louisa took an immediate liking for Robert's children, Emily and Charles. They shared stories and danced with the children in the moonlight. When the time came for Robert to return home, he likely asked Louisa, "Would you like to come visit us in Tolland sometime?"

"Of course," replied Louisa. "I had such fun dancing with Emily and Charles. Perhaps they could teach both of us some new steps, and I would like to see your farm in Tolland."

"Right now our farm needs some repairs, but we'll practice our dancing and be ready for your visit whenever you can come," replied Robert.

Within a month, Louisa visited Robert's farm in Tolland and a romantic courtship continued during the summer. They were married in the fall 1833. Louisa joined Robert and the children on the farm in Tolland, adapting quickly to the rural lifestyle. Louisa blossomed in caring for the children and her presence created a new vitality and enthusiastic spirit for Robert.

Their romance flourished. They were blessed with a son, George Park, in 1834. George's middle name was made in honor of Robert's mother and her family that he grew to love as a young boy. The "Park" name has remained in the family for five succeeding generations. Another son, Robert Curtis, was born in 1837.

For the next twenty years, the farm proved to be successful in providing for the family's needs. Their valuable crops were sold to customers throughout the region. The children attended schools in Tolland and grew to be strong and healthy. Robert and Lucy kept focused on the needs of the family as their children grew to be self-sufficient, active, and adventuresome.

The country expanded with the conclusion of the war with Mexico, adding vast resources in the southwest and California. The movement west was escalating with pioneers seeking new fortunes. Robert, who never lost his zeal for adventure, followed the westward movement closely. He told stories and discussed some of the exciting new areas with his children. His sons, Charles and Robert Curtis, had a liking for the western frontier. They read stories about the expedition of Lewis and Clark and the opening of the Santa Fe Trail to California in 1821. They wanted to explore the western farmlands and the Rocky Mountains. His son, George, preferred the Ohio Valley and the glamour of business in the large, metropolitan cities along the east coast. A trip to Providence,

Rhode Island led George to vow to return some day.

Robert received discouraging news in 1858. A friend, Alfred Skinner, who was the son of J.W. Skinner, the comrade in the Connecticut militia, hurriedly rushed to Robert's home to tell him that the court in nearby Litchfield was looking for him. The authorities had issued a warrant for his arrest with charges of burglary and larceny. Robert was confused and uncertain as to why he was charged. He was innocent and unaware as to why he might be wanted by the court. He had visited a relative and friends in Litchfield over two years ago. Robert asked Al Skinner to return to the court to confirm the charges. Skinner obliged and upon his return, he told Robert that during Robert's stay in Litchfield, a thief had stolen valuable goods from two homes there and that Robert had been accused of the crime.

At that time, Robert was sixty years old. His children by his first wife were grown and married. His younger children were old enough to care for themselves. His beloved wife Louisa was dedicated and completely loyal to him and to the children. Robert was not about to subject his wife nor his children to the embarrassment and humiliation of a court trial, especially when he knew he was completely innocent.

He discussed his options with Louisa and his friend, Al Skinner. Skinner suggested they move quickly and quietly to the new territory. There were lots of new opportunities in the west. President Pierce had signed the Kansas-Nebraska Act in 1854 and there were rumors that someday a railroad would be built in the area. Several friends and a distant relative, Simon Kenny, were already living in the Nebraska territory. Skinner was aware of some survey work that the government wanted done. With their experience and their contacts through friends in the government, they might get survey jobs while establishing new homes in the Kansas-Nebraska territory.

Louisa reluctantly agreed. They gathered the children and some close friends to tell them of their plans. Their sons, Robert Curtis and George, would care for the farm until it was sold. Then, the young men would join them in the west when Robert and Louisa were settled in their new home. Quickly, they accumulated their savings, personal belongings, and family records. Al Skinner would travel with them, as well as a young family named Cady.

On September 9, 1858 they began their trip westward. Louisa made the following entries in her journal as they moved westward. The first entry came after they had been on the trail for about one week:

September 17. We camped near Scranton, Pennsylvania on a farm owned by the Godbey family. They were very kind and provided us with hay for the horses and coffee in the morning prior to our departure. It was difficult to leave our friends in Tolland, but once we were underway, we would pay attention to our travels and forget our good home behind us. Now our homes are our two wagons. There are seven of us, including my husband, Al Skinner, plus Lew Cady, his wife, Leslie, and their children, Susan and Jane.

September 26. Crossed the Susquehanna River and traveled about twenty-eight miles today. Yesterday a good many people passed along the road where we were camped, some appearing pretty weather beaten. We camped on a hill, cooked supper, and went to bed. The Cady's youngest, Susan, caught a cold, not used to sleeping outdoors. A medicine-man passing by, Dr. Philpott, gave her some strong medicine which seemed to work. So far we have stood our journey very well.

September 29. This day we came about twelve miles to the Fredrickson horse farm. Since our mare, Phoebbe, got sick and is having difficulty walking, Robert said if she doesn't improve, we'll have to put her down. The Fredericksons are a friendly family, and asked us to come inside their home for dinner.

October 3. Started again on our long journey. Bought a mare named Sky Rider from Farmer Frederickson where we stayed for the past two nights. Paid $15 for her, with hopes that she will be durable for the trip. I baked a lot of bread while we were there. We are getting appetites that take food pretty fast. I felt bad leaving the Fredericksons. They are such kind people. I hope we will meet again.

October 8. Traveled all day through woods and gullies. It was a dark and stormy night. When the rains finally stopped, the moon shown brightly and some coyotes started howling. Jane Cady has a special way with the animals. She gathered our dogs and kept them calm throughout the storm and the howling.

October 12. Had to cook supper after dark because of the bad weather. We can eat in the wagon when it rains. I fix our beds in the back part, and we sit on each side of the boards. We have to all keep our places in the wagon when we pass through rugged areas.

October 18. Another cold raw day, rained and the wind blew hard in the night. I could not sleep-thinking of Al, Lew and Robert who had to go out to check the horses occasionally. We put on flannel and wool today. The children don't seem to mind the wet and cold. I have not slept in a house since we left home.

October 23. We are traveling through Indiana and Illinois. The people are building beautiful farms. We camped on the farm of a wealthy farmer, who said he had only been there five years. Now he has plenty of vegetables and apple trees. The farmer and his wife were very kind to us. The farmer's wife sent us two bottles of milk for the children, and gave me some leaves and spice to make tea. Bought a basket of apples for a quarter. Apples are plentiful and I include them in many dishes.

October 26. Finally crossed the Illinois River after waiting several hours to take our turn. While waiting we visited with other travelers, some with heavy burdens who are ill-prepared for the long journey. We have the best wagons I have seen, making it possible to travel thirty miles on a good day.

October 29. We are taking the Burlington Road which leads to the Santa Fe Trail. I think it also can be connected on a northern route to part of the Oregon trail. The country is very hilly and it rained all day. Some places are so steep that I had to get out and walk. We had to let the horses rest several times today. We camped on the edge of a hickory nut grove, where we tried to gather some nuts. The men had to carry hay for the horses and water for cooking about half a mile. While they were walking, they came upon and shot a deer. After Robert and Al butchered it, we had a feast and shared it with other travelers.

November 2. The weather has turned so cold that I can hardly write. This morning I am sitting in the wagon with a heavy coat and a double shawl on my hands. We crossed Skunk River on a rope ferry and camped on the bank. I cooked supper (we usually ate a cold supper) and washed the children, and retired.

November 6. We started early and traveled most of the day. Ate dinner and laid in a new supply of provisions. We have huge appetites, can eat six times a day and still be hungry. We saw a light before we reached camp, and when we got there we found two men camped by the roadside. We warmed by their fire and cooked our supper. They were very sociable and seemed to travel a great deal. We did our work and went to bed.

November 7. Started early and reached the Wayne City Landing in preparation to cross the Missouri River on the steam ferry called the Irene. *The water looked deep and swift, but the campsite on the western shore was a welcome site with other travelers eager to visit. Tomorrow, we will begin early and move up the trail and westward toward our final destination.*

November 12. We have journeyed through hills, some gulches, and most all prairie. The land here seems poor and thin, mostly bush timber. The country is new and thinly settled. When we reached a campsite in a grove of trees, we had plenty of company. There were three other wagons in the camp. I cooked supper and went to bed. Slept warmly and comfortably.

Sunday (No date). We are still in camp and have just returned from Church. One of the visitors is a Methodist minister and he held services in a tree grove. I am not in the habit of doing much on the Sabbath, but I did listen to his sermon and was pleased to hear his comforting words. Yesterday, we stopped to buy some provisions. Fire wood is scarce, so we burn sunflowers and corn to keep warm.

November 19. We did not travel far today because Al wanted to stop and meet with government agents to discuss some surveying work in eastern Nebraska. Robert was pleased with the results and said that the agent would be in Fremont next month to make plans for the spring. The weather is turning cold and we are grateful to be getting close to our destination. We will stop early enough to have a good fire to cook supper and warm us before our night's rest.

November 24. We got started early and reached Schuyler about midday. The community was much smaller than I expected, but the gentle rolling hills were peaceful and beautiful. There were large cottonwood trees, some walnut, ash and box elders, and some fruit trees by the Elkhorn and Platte Rivers. The native Indians called it Rawhide Creek. The ground appeared to be rich loam and fertile, especially to the north where the ground had a deep color, almost black with a firm texture. Al Skinner knew the Hashberger family who came out to greet us. They were very kind and invited us to stay with them for awhile. We rested well that night and met most everyone in the town.

Sunday. We observed the Sabbath. Attended church services, which were held in the schoolhouse. We prayed long and hard, with special thanksgiving for our safe journey to our new home. We met our neighbors and new friends, and took stock of our journey. We left Tolland on September 9th and arrived in Schuyler on November 24th. We were all very grateful for the safe journey, and praised God for his guidance and safekeeping. It was a joyful day.

December 16. I did the wash and cleaning, then rested for several days while Al and Robert began exploring the area for a home site and possible farm. It did not take them long to identify a site southwest of town with adequate water and rich, fertile soil. There was a well protected hillside, where Robert wanted to build a temporary sod home. They found another site on the north side of town for the Cady family, who we have come to love as our own children.

January 17. It took Robert, Al, and a neighbor about a month to build our temporary sod houses. Our house is about fifteen feet wide and about twenty feet long, with two windows. Al's house is situated to the south about fifty yards from our home. We share a common storage area for perishable foods, and there is another building we share to house the chickens and farm animals. The house is well protected from the wind, the cold, and the rain. We all enjoy good health and are glad to live here.

In the spring, Robert went to work clearing the land and preparing the ground for planting. He planned to work on the farm and become self-sufficient as quickly as possible. Al Skinner met with the government agent in Fremont and made an agreement to begin mapping the area between Omaha and Council Bluffs. All agreements would be made in Al's name only, since Robert was taking steps to retain anonymity. He did not want government authorities nor the courthouse in Litchfield to know his whereabouts. While the Civil War raged in the east and the south, the federal government paid relatively little attention to likely fugitives in the west.

For the first three years after arriving in Schuyler, Robert and Louisa worked hard and enjoyed much success with their new home. The natural wildlife and fertile territory provided all the food and provisions they needed. In the first two years, Robert shot thirty-three deer and eight elk, sufficient game to feed his own family and many of the other residents in Schuyler. His farm grew steadily with abundant crops and cattle to supply buyers from Schuyler to Omaha.

In 1862, after the Homestead Act was passed and President Lincoln offered free land to settlers in the west, more pioneers began moving to Nebraska. The westward expansion accelerated even more after the Civil War. Robert and Louisa wrote to their sons and other family, extolling the grandeur of the Nebraska territory. They invited them to visit and hopefully live in Schuyler with them.

Their sons, George and Robert Curtis, both visited their parents, but chose to remain in the east. George had an entrepreneurial nature, leading him to travel extensively seeking new business and financial rewards. Robert Curtis deferred any visits while the country remained in such a turbulent time, absorbed with the Civil War.

Other family members and friends accepted their invitations and moved to neighboring areas in Nebraska. A nephew, J.L. Kinney and his wife Bettie lived about fifteen miles north of Schuyler on 200 acres of the best farming land in the region. Their son, Jesse Kinney, became a prominent member in the Nebraska legislature. When the Union Pacific Railroad was built through Schuyler, several families, including those of good friends, Charles Ferguson and Herman Anderson, moved into the territory. At one time, J.L. Kinney owned the Upton House Hotel, the premier hostelry in the area.

The town of Schuyler was named after former Vice President, Schuyler Colfax. When the county was divided from Platte County, the county was also named Colfax County to honor Vice President Colfax. The town was originally founded in 1856 by General Estabrook and Colonel Miller. The first deed was recorded in August 1860 from Abram Beeman to James Hashberger, with the first recorded homestead made in 1863 by Samuel Fowler.

There were very few recorded events until 1869 when the county selected its first county commissioners. The first meeting of the commission was held on March 20, 1869 with William Davis, Al Skinner, and Robert Kinney in attendance. Robert agreed to serve the county, but when he was elected later to be the county surveyor, he used his fictitious name, John Phinney. At the same time, Al Skinner was elected to serve as constable for the county.

Robert and Louisa moved to a home in southwest Schuyler located on 11th at Vine Street. Their house was located about three blocks from the Methodist Episcopal Church, which they attended regularly.

Shortly after Nebraska became a state in 1867, Robert received a letter from the court in Litchfield, Connecticut absolving him of all alleged crimes. The true thief confessed to the crime. Robert was grateful for being exonerated, but was happy and content with his home in Schuyler. Since he had lost contact with most of his family and friends in Connecticut, he had little interest in returning to the east.

Robert and Louisa spent their final days in quiet solitude with friends and neighbors. Without fanfare, Robert reassumed the family name, with the spelling of Kinney. Robert passed away quietly in 1870 when he was seventy-one years old.

Before Louisa died, her wish that her sons would come to live in Schuyler did come true. Robert Curtis moved to Nebraska soon after the Civil War ended. George Kinney arrived several years after that, planning to begin a new life on the property his father had left to him and his brother. But George only remained a few years. He would prove more than willing to move wherever he found suitable conditions to support his numerous entrepreneurial ideas.

Louisa stayed in Schuyler and lived peacefully until her death in 1873. She and several other Kinney family members are buried in the majestic Schuyler Memorial Cemetery, just six blocks from their original home. Her tombstone reads:

Louisa Wells Kinney
1805 – 1873
Safe in the Arms of Jesus

Robert and Louisa Kinney, circa 1860

Residence of George Park Kinney, Chicago, Illinois
circa 1894

Chapter 16

George Park Kinney
1834 – 1902
Entrepreneur, Traveler

MAKING THE BEST
OF CIVIL WAR ADVERSITY

George finished his tale, leaned back in his chair a bit, inhaled on his pipe, and looked directly at the young man sitting across the table from him. To his delight, congenial Tom Baker roared with laughter. The two of them had been telling "shaggy dog" stories in the past hour since their dinner plates had been removed. Baker had begun the evening a little stiff, but soon he was telling humorous Irish jokes and sharing his views on sports, literature, politics, and current events with this man twice his age. George's friendly demeanor, along with his soft spoken voice, seemed to make Baker forget it was a job interview.

After the laughter died down, George asked, "So tell me Bake, what happens when a potential customer says he doesn't want what you are selling?"

Baker leaned toward George and replied, "Why that's easy, George. I just let him know why he needs our product. A lot of times people just haven't heard that they're missing out on something good. Not only am I the guy to tell them, but I am also the guy who can solve their problems. And then I keep coming back to take care of what they need–and looking for any new opportunities along the way, of course."

"Bingo, young man! I like your spirit-especially your positive outlook. What say you join our company? Is it a deal?"

"Yes, sir. No doubt there are many folks out there that don't know they need our products and our services. But we can change that. Besides, it will be worth it to share some more good times with you."

They shook hands, George's firm grip indicative of his extraordinary strength in his six foot tall frame. Once an agreement was made, George moved quickly, demonstrating that he was decisive and ready to move on to other things.

George interviewed hundreds of similar young men over his lifetime, looking for new agents who could sell his products. He invited many to a comfortable dinner where he could better observe the man's true character. He often said, "There is an interesting relationship between a fellow's social graces, his conversation after two drinks, and his ability to be a successful businessman." His ultimate goals, both with customers and agents, were to create thriving business arrangements and to make long-lasting, personal friendships.

Not only could George sell his business prospectus to future agents, but he could also sell any number of products to anyone willing to listen. His friends said he could sell icicles and snow cones to Eskimos. He did sell hair lotion to bald men and orange scented perfume to cowgirls. Besides the concoctions he personally devised, he sold jewelry, fruit trees, chewing gum, perfume, and general hardware supplies over his lifetime. At one point he managed over sixty-five sales representatives in eight different states. But that had changed when the Civil War came along.

Andrew Jackson was President, Samuel Morse was working on the electric telegraph, and Texas was fighting for independence when George was born in Tolland, Connecticut in 1834. George was the first son of Robert and Louisa Wells Kinney. He had an older half-sister, Emily, and an older half-brother Charles. Another half-sister, Lucy, died in infancy. His brother Robert Curtis was three years younger.

At that time there was a steady stream of immigrants coming to the Northern Atlantic states. The immigrants were largely laboring people who went to work in the factories, new construction, and the railroads. They consistently moved westward with the expansion of the country. As construction of new canals and roads, including the Erie Canal in 1825, was completed, new business opportunities and prosperity followed. Life-changing inventions including the telegraph and the reaping machine were developed. Additional states were taken into the Union, including Arkansas in 1836, Michigan in 1837, Florida in 1845, and Texas in 1850. At the same time, there were also some dangerous signs hovering on the horizon, including the banking crash of 1837 and the question of slavery as it impacted the northern states in conflict with the southern states.

George grew up in a progressive environment with kind and caring parents. He had a constructive, formal education, whereby he learned to read and write at an early age, including a natural interest to write poetry. His father provided a basic library which included some biblical books, primers, and some adventure stories. As a studious child, he developed an early interest in science, geography, and mathematics. George's older half-brother and half-sister were good role models who paved the way for him to be a conscientious student.

When George was nine, he and a friend, Tom Appleton, were wandering along the Skungamaug River near the village of Moosup, when they found several arrowheads and a broken clay pot. They took them home and showed them to George's father who determined that they were likely from the Nipmucks or the Mohican tribes who had been known to live in the area prior to 1725. George and Tom returned to the area and found several other arrowheads. As George's father suggested, they took them to Preston Moore at his general store. Moore offered to sell the relics and divide any profits with the boys. The boys waited patiently and after about two weeks, Moore summoned the boys. He had sold three of the arrowheads giving each of the boys eighty-five cents. With the sale, George's merchandising career was underway.

George began his sales career working in Preston Moore's general store in Tolland when he was thirteen years old. He began doing routine chores, including housekeeping and cleanup, but quickly worked his way up to assisting customers as they selected their merchandise. Moore noticed how bright and energetic George seemed to be and that he had a natural inclination to speak with customers. Using his math skills, George would anticipate the total amount of a customer's bill prior to their checkout. In time, he also learned to anticipate the needs and additional expectations of the customers. Moore told him, "Just put yourself in the customer's position, and it's easy to determine what he might purchase next." George went a step further. He noticed that some customers were in a perpetual rut–they bought the same supplies, week after week, without knowing some of the new and potentially helpful products on the market. He reasoned that someone had to convince buyers to try new and improved products. This concept became a perpetual challenge to George for the rest of his life.

Another major break for George occurred when he entered the seventh grade and was assigned to John Brennan's science class. Brennan was a "hands on" kind of teacher, encouraging his students to get involved and to experiment with new ideas. For advanced students, including George, Brennan provided frogs to be dissected, miniature cranes and hoists for construction projects, and chemicals and other ingredients to mix and make various compounds. The serious and inquisitive students were quickly separated from the others. George thrived as he experimented and learned to mix various compounds. Chemistry became his favorite subject. At Mr. Brennan's suggestion, George kept precise records of his concoctions.

Mr. Brennan said that George had "a bit of the devil in him." As part of his experiments for chemistry class, he and his friend Tom Burke made stink bombs. At a time when the farmers were experimenting with sulfur and ammonia to improve their fertilizers, the young scientists took some ammonia sulfate and exposed it to some moisture. It hydrolyzed, giving out a putrid smell of rotten eggs.

"Perfect," said Tom, "Let's release some of this stuff by Patsy Bowman's house. That will drive her crazy." Patsy's mother and father were not pleased. It took three days for the odor to dissipate, but Tom and George were moving ahead with improved chemistry.

Mr. Brennan suggested the boys go a different direction and mix some chemicals to produce good fragrances, maybe even perfume. "I'll bet you could win Patsy's favorable attention, if you made her a rose-scented perfume."

The boys went to work. They tried rose petals and lemon, and orange peels, and they diluted the sulfur. Even though the aromas improved, they didn't have much use for them. They preferred something useful for their pranks, like a good stink bomb. They weren't that interested in impressing Patsy anyway.

Each spring, George's mother suffered from hives on her legs. The pollen from the weeds and flowers caused terrible discomfort. Consequently, she made a muddy mixture with straw and cow's dung to relieve the pain. It smelled horrible and caused everyone to avoid her during the pollen season. George felt sorry for his mother, so he decided to experiment and hopefully find an alternative remedy. He consulted with Mr. Higgins, the town's pharmacist, and Mr. Brennan, his chemistry teacher. He visited with Farmer McGregor who supplied some of his dairy products for his experiments. In attempt to find a soothing relief for irritated and chapped skin, he mixed various components, including calcium sulfate, alcohol, glycerin, boric acid, and honey with cream and milk. In the spring of 1850, his mother used George's lotion and the results were spectacular. The majority of the itching was gone, the odor was acceptable, and George's mother could join her family and friends for social occasions. "George's Salve" was born.

George enjoyed traveling with his father and older brother. By the time he was fourteen, he had visited eight states in New England and on the eastern seaboard. When he was fifteen, his father took him to

Chicago and Cleveland, traveling by the Erie Canal for a portion of
the trip. At that time, the Pony Express offered cross country mail
service and soon, the Illinois Central Railroad would be building tracks
westward. George would become fascinated with traveling on the trains.
Several railroad companies were already recruiting workers who would
be willing to relocate to lands along the new route of the railroad.

George's scholastic achievements earned him an opportunity to go
to college at Brown University. He returned to the campus at Providence, Rhode Island, just as he had vowed to do in speaking with his
father many years ago. He proved to be a good student, and to no one's
surprise, he became infatuated with the eastern establishment, including
the parties and friendly associations he enjoyed with his classmates. He
studied numerous business opportunities. As time passed, he planned
and calculated as to how he could establish his own business, possibly
using some of his scientific creations.

In 1854, George met Sarah Durfee, a petite, blue-eyed, and very
attractive young lady who attended some of the social events at school.
Her family lived in Warwick, Rhode Island, about eight miles south
of Providence near Greenwich Bay. They dated when George was in
school and spent time together during the summers on the shores of
Narragansett Bay. They were married in 1856 at her parent's home. The
happy couple moved to Ashford, Connecticut where George began his
business career.

George rented a small office and laboratory and began operations under the name of Durfee and Kinney. He sold two products,
"Dr. Weaver's Spanish Salve" and "Kinney's Washing Preparation." An
elaborate bonus system accompanied the sales, which provided gift-
incentives to both the salesmen and the customers for multiple sales.
George began traveling throughout the northeast selling his products,
securing sales agents, and seeking new opportunities. While he was
traveling, Caroline Ennis, an efficient secretary and office manager,
maintained the daily business operations.

In Boston George met Merle Stafford who was developing the hydrocarbon light. George was impressed with the potential for inexpensive illumination, and he offered Stafford $250, which was to be used for further research and a patent. They formed a partnership, Stafford and Kinney, and they operated from an office at 36 Washington Street in Boston.

Wherever George traveled, he recruited sales representatives, who would act as agents to sell his products. In Buffalo, George met Charles Allen, who was a distributor of fine watches and jewelry. Allen was a persuasive gentleman, who convinced George that they should have a jewelry store together. They opened a store at number 1 Niagara Street, and began additional sales of watches and jewelry. Within four years, George had established three different businesses and had nine representatives in nearby cities selling his products.

In the fall, 1858, George's parents would move west to Schuyler, Nebraska. But George had too many new opportunities in his own life to follow them. He chose to stay on the east coast.

George continued his exploration of new ideas and traveled westward to Ohio. At a time when Ohio was becoming a popular state, he established a general merchandise store with Leonard Dickson in Painesville, Ohio. The town was originally named Champion, but changed its name to honor Revolutionary War hero, General Edward Paine. The store, Dickson and Kinney, was located at a strategic, well traveled location near Lake Erie in Lake County along the Grand River. To the south was Cleveland and to the northeast were Erie, Buffalo, Rochester, and numerous other cities in Pennsylvania and New York. Business in Ohio was growing rapidly and several friends and sales representatives advised George and Sarah to move to Ohio, which they did in 1859.

At that time, James Buchanan was president and he anticipated a heated reelection campaign in 1860. But trouble was on the horizon. If compromises could not be reached regarding the slavery issue, several of the southern states threatened to secede from the Union. George was hopeful for a peaceful solution and he continued working with ongoing intentions to expand his business ventures.

He developed more products, including "Dime Glue" and "Dr. Park's Adhesive." The adhesive would "cure burns, corns and flesh wounds, or give your money back." In addition, he created a new product, calling it "Alaska Chewing Gum," for which he obtained a U. S. patent. He embarked on an elaborate advertising campaign using billboards, colorful brochures, and large printed posters. To promote a new concentrated ink compound, he offered free samples with the notion that satisfied customers would share the products with other people. To expand his sales, he hired new representatives. But times became increasingly difficult with the grim reality of a civil war approaching.

In 1861, two important things happened that changed George and Sarah's direction. In March they had their first child, a girl they named Annie Josephine who they called "Josie." Josie was a small, yet active baby and she quickly captured their adulation. The delivery of the baby was difficult for Sarah. Consequently, she was slow to regain her normal strength and endurance.

The second important event occurred on April 12th when the Confederates opened fire on Ft. Sumter in the harbor of South Carolina. This marked the beginning of the Civil War. President Lincoln issued a proclamation calling for 75,000 volunteers. Initially, George and Sarah didn't think the war would last long. As George attempted to maintain his business activities, it became apparent that the impact of the war would dramatically affect his business. Many of his agents left their homes and joined the Union Army. It became increasingly difficult to travel and coordinate business operations. Sales of his products, including lotions, adhesives, the ink compounds, lights, and jewelry came to a standstill. Customers were not interested in purchasing luxury items, but directed their efforts to the war and their money to purchasing the bare necessities.

The Dickson and Kinney General Store at Painesville, Ohio became a supply warehouse and distribution center for the Union troops. Leonard Dickson and George set to work coordinating the purchase of foodstuffs from the farmers and supplying armaments and food to the troops. Working with government authorities, they created a transportation network to move supplies to the troops. As the fighting intensified, it became more difficult to accumulate sufficient supplies. The logistics involved in transporting and safely delivering the goods became more dangerous and problematic as the battlegrounds moved about the country.

In the spring of 1862, shortly after the Battle of Shiloh, a plea for additional troops came from the Ohio Army. George volunteered and reported to Fort Dennison near Cincinnati. Most likely, because of his past experience, George was ordered to continue working with officials to coordinate the movement of food, supplies, and arms for the multiple regiments of the Ohio troops.

The state of Ohio played a key role in providing troops to the Union Army. Ohio raised twenty-three volunteer regiments, including 310,000 men, more than any other state except New York. Arming and feeding the troops was an enormous task.

George traveled with supply wagons to several battle zones, including taking supplies to the Ohio Eighth Regiment under Colonel Samuel Carroll. The Ohio Eighth Regiment was involved in several skirmishes, but their first major battle occurred at Gettysburg in July 1863. The regiment was under heavy fire but withstood the Confederate attack known as "Pickett's Charge." The fighting was intense, and after a long siege, the Confederate attack was repulsed. According to the monument which stands at the site, there were originally 209 men from the Ohio Eighth that went into the battle, 18 were killed, 83 wounded, and 1 was reported as missing. Much of the credit for the victory of the Union troops at Gettysburg went to the tenacity of the fighting men and the leadership of the officers. In addition to Colonel Carroll, special recognition was given to Lieutenant Frank Sawyer and Captain George B.

Kenny, a nephew of George Park Kinney.

George continued his service with the supply corps throughout the war. Shortly after it ended in 1865, he returned to Painesville, Ohio.

Business in Painesville was slow to recover and likely insufficient to support the families of Leonard Dickson and George Kinney. The country was torn apart and would take considerable time for recovery and reconstruction. For several years George attempted to revive his businesses, but was barely able to provide a suitable income for his family. In addition, George's wife Sarah had contracted pneumonia during the winter of 1868 and her health was suffering. It was a difficult time when George realized that he would need to make major changes for his family to meet the challenges of the times.

In 1870 George received news that his father died and had left the family farm in Nebraska to him and his brother. He knew that Schuyler was a small agricultural town, located on the new railroad line going to Cheyenne and eventually to California. Farming conditions around Schuyler were considered to be good with rich, fertile dirt and abundant water primarily from the Platte River and its tributaries.

In late 1871, shortly after the Chicago fire, George made an important decision to move to Schuyler. He would leave in the spring of 1872. With rejuvenated expectations, George prepared to make a fresh start in Nebraska. As he traveled across the plains, he made a mental note of the areas where there was lush and colorful vegetation. When he was a boy in New England, he grew to appreciate the beautiful trees, especially during the fall when the vibrant colors covered the landscape. As he crossed the plains, he was surprised to see some areas where there was little or no vegetation. George concluded that there was an opportunity there, and that he might be the first to introduce some new plants, bushes, and fruit trees to the western plains. Rather than grow corn, hay, or alfalfa as did most of the farmers in Colfax County, Nebraska, George decided to create a nursery farm.

He contacted Leonard Dickson in Ohio and George Allen in Buffalo with urgent requests to send him a wide variety of seeds and bulbs for spring planting. He tilled the ground in preparation for planting and built a greenhouse with a small laboratory for his new experiments. With the railroad running through Schuyler, he planned to ship his fruit and small plants eastward to Chicago and the Midwest, and westward toward Denver. To evaluate his new markets, he traveled to Denver and Chicago where he resorted to his old manner of salesmanship. He met several new friends and cultivated several business associates.

But more trouble was brewing on the horizon for his family. The Nebraska winters were more severe than Sarah and George had anticipated. Sarah and Josie suffered from the cold and the biting north winds. George's mother died in 1873 shortly after passing the family records to George. The winter of 1874-75 was exceptionally cold and snowy. Sarah and Josie became deathly ill after they both were stricken again with pneumonia. Sarah died in February and Josie succumbed in early July. Their deaths were a severe blow to George who had struggled and tried desperately to comfort and save them. Sarah and Josie were both buried in the Memorial Cemetery in Schuyler.

By the following spring, George was still mourning, but ready for another change. He likely stood at the gate of the cemetery, reluctant to say goodbye. All around him the grasses were growing long and green, a miracle in light of the harsh winter. A miracle too that he had survived this past winter without Sarah and Josie. All the poetry he could write wasn't going to bring them back to him. He spent long hours thinking about his family-the importance of kinship—and what to do next. George had brought his family to Schuyler with such great hopes that his wife and little girl would grow healthy in the wide open spaces. Winters in Ohio were cold too, but the family had not accounted for the biting north winds that blew through Nebraska with little to stop them. And now, already the grass was growing over their graves.

At forty-one, George had already lived a lot of life. He had survived the Civil War when nearly 7,000 Ohio soldiers had not. He lost many friends on those battlefields and others had been scarred for life. Still, he had many loyal friends from his business enterprises and comrades in the supply corps.

Despite creating and losing eight different business ventures, he knew that many of those ideas were sound. Maybe he was just ahead of his day, a victim of poor timing. After dealing with the war and family illnesses, he felt confident that one of these days, with his innovation and work ethic, he was going to be in the right place at the right time. And so he decided to move to Chicago, a city knee deep in the rebuilding after the war and the Great Fire of 1871. Business was good at the Chicago Stock Yards and passenger traffic through Grand Central Station was setting records.

George stayed at the Sherman Hotel for a short time and then settled into a rented apartment on Clark Street. He opened an office and created a laboratory for making perfumes and other concoctions at 39 Dearborn Avenue. During leisure times, George enjoyed walking around Chicago, often spending Saturdays and Sunday afternoons in local parks and along Lake Michigan. When summer musical programs began in Grant Park, he attended the outdoor concerts.

At one such concert in 1876, George found himself watching a group of young ladies who were singing and dancing as the Theodore Thompson Orchestra played. One in particular stood out for her energy and vivacious personality. George likely walked over to her during a break from the musical sets.

"Good afternoon, miss. Lovely afternoon for a concert, isn't it?"

"Indeed it is. How do you do?"

"Fine, it seems. My name is George Kinney. And yours?"

"Emeline. Emeline Kelley. Pleased to meet you, George. Would you like to join our little group? That is as long as you don't mind if we sing off-key from time to time."

"Yes, I'd like to join you and, no Emeline, I won't mind. I think that's pretty much the way the rest of the crowd here sings. It's a beautiful Chicago summer day and no one seems to have a care."

George joined in. Once the concert was over, the two shared ice cream before they parted. And so, George was pulled back into the springtime of his life more than able to keep up with a young woman less than half his age.

Emeline was born in 1858 in Racine, Wisconsin, where her family lived west of Racine near the Wisconsin River. Her parents were Irish. Her grandparents came from County Cork in Ireland. They had arrived in America in 1784. Her father, Raymond Kelley, was a dairy farmer who specialized in raising purebred Guernsey cattle. They produced dairy products, including a large variety of Wisconsin cheeses. Emeline's mother was a strong and vibrant lady who assisted her husband in all aspects of running the farm. She managed the family's household and reared the children, including Emeline's brother and three sisters.

Over the period of their courtship, Emeline restored the gregarious spirit and vitality of George. Together they enjoyed music and the stage shows and often attended the McVicker Theater to see various musical and theatrical productions. George's work took on new meaning and he developed several new products. After extensive experimentation, he introduced a variety of perfumes with distinct fragrances. He opened a new and larger laboratory at 48 State Street. He improved the "Dime Glue" and updated the printing ink compound.

In the spring of 1878, Emeline invited George to visit her family in Racine. Since there were about twenty years difference in their ages, there was some concern from Emeline's parents about George. But the meeting and friendship that followed between George and Emeline's parents dissolved any doubts about the couple. They were passionately in love, marrying in Racine on July 9, 1878.

George and Emeline went on an extended honeymoon, traveling to Boston, New York, and Washington, then south to Florida before returning to Chicago. They spent several extra days in central Florida exploring the citrus gardens. George took some samples of the seedlings and rose petals with the intention of creating new fragrances for his perfumes.

About the time that Alexander Graham Bell made a patent for the telephone and Mark Twain published *Tom Sawyer*, George and Emeline returned to Chicago and purchased a home at 835 North Clark Street. It was an ideal location, about three miles from downtown Chicago and within walking distance to George's office. It was a happy time for the newlyweds. Emeline set up housekeeping and furnished the home with classic American furniture. George engulfed himself in business and rapidly attracted several sales representatives throughout the Midwest. By Christmas, Emeline announced that she was pregnant. Their first son, Raymond Park was born in the later part of the summer of 1879.

On a business trip to Unionville, Ohio, George was confronted with several friends, including some members of the Ohio Supply Corps. They were working in support of their friend, former neighbor, and military comrade, James Garfield, now campaigning for the presidency of the United States. They convinced George that he must join the campaign and help convince voters in Illinois to vote for Garfield. George liked Garfield and remembered him as a personal friend from his training days at Ft. Dennison. When Garfield went to Chicago to campaign, George helped organize several pep rallies and a speech at the Palmer House Hotel to wealthy business supporters. There was a big celebration when Garfield won the election, including the Illinois vote.

While George campaigned for Garfield, Emeline spent the majority of her time caring for their baby. But she did find time to follow the women's suffrage movement and support Clara Barton, who was spreading the good work of the American Red Cross. Emeline volunteered as a Red Cross worker at the children's ward of the Chicago General Hospital.

Emeline's older sister Ellen and her husband Allan Howard moved to Sioux City, Iowa. In the summer of 1882, George and Emeline went on a vacation to visit the Howards. Allan and George shared many interests, including a natural inclination to start-up new businesses. Allan convinced George that a new, first class restaurant would be successful in Sioux City. With an initial investment and substantial advice from George, the Howardon House Restaurant opened its doors in 1883. After the opening, it was difficult for George to participate because he was living in Chicago and managing his own business. But he tried to keep in contact with Allan, who successfully operated the restaurant for many years.

George then corresponded with his nephew, Albert Kinney, who lived in Hartford, Connecticut. Albert served in the Union Navy during the war, and he had kept in good correspondence with the Kinney relatives throughout the Northeast. He informed George of plans to incorporate the Kinney Historical Foundation in the Connecticut State Legislature. Basically the purpose was to preserve the family history, promote kinship within the family, and protect the sacred burial grounds of the Kinneys and their ancestors. Albert invited George to attend an organizational meeting which was held March 26, 1884 in Hartford, Connecticut. George attended the meeting and was awestruck by the number of family members attending, some from great distances.

Henry Keney was eulogized as the progenitor of the family which, by 1884, had members living in at least ten states from Maine and New York in the north, to the Carolinas in the south, and Illinois in the west. One representative, reportedly made a statement, (later, a similar quotation was attributed to Spencer Penrose) which read, "The fact is one great man (Henry) opened and prepared the way for many others. We are his beneficiaries. Thus the influence of a great man is constantly multiplied and increased."

The Kinne (Kinney) Historical and Genealogical Society was officially organized on June 9, 1884. The incorporation papers were filed with the General Assembly of the State of Connecticut. William Kinne of Ithaca, New York was elected President, Herbert E. Kinney of New York was elected Secretary, and Archibald Kinney was elected Treasurer. George Kinney was elected to serve on the Board of Directors.

The second meeting of the society was held the next year on June 8,

1885 in Norwich, Connecticut. George actually missed the second
meeting of the Society because he was still in Chicago helping to care
for their second son who was born earlier in the year. They named him,
Osgood Roland, commonly called Roland.

Roland was a husky, strong baby weighing six pounds, 10 ounces.
Emeline and George celebrated with great excitement the birth of
Roland. They took great pains to care for both boys, as they paraded
throughout Chicago and the lakefront to display their happiness.

In the later part of the century, Chicago was preparing for the World's
Fair, called the Columbian Exposition in celebration of the 400th
anniversary of Christopher Columbus's discovery of the new world. In
time, there were dazzling new buildings led by architect Louis Sullivan
and his understudy, Frank Lloyd Wright. They brought new designs and
stunning perspectives for new buildings along the Chicago River. The
Chicago Board of Trade and the Chicago Auditorium attracted new
business, with numerous conventions and tourists. Along State Street,
major shopping developed with Marshall Field & Co., C.D. Peacock,
and the Emporium of the West.

As the boys grew up, George and Emeline continued to travel, often
combining business trips with pleasure for the family. They frequently
visited the Kelleys in Wisconsin. The boys learned to fish on the lakes
in Wisconsin. In 1888, they traveled to Gettysburg, Pennsylvania for a
reunion of the Union troops who had fought there in the war. Two years
later, they visited central Florida, where George renewed his interest
in a citrus plantation. In 1892, the family took the train to Denver and
surveyed the mining camps in Cripple Creek, Leadville, and Georgetown. George was intrigued with the mining industry and vowed to
return to Colorado someday.

George showered his boys with affection and attention. Emeline
was an outstanding teacher and she supervised their early education
with meticulous care for their elementary lessons. Like their father,
Raymond and Roland were good readers at an early age. Their early

religious education came from Sunday School at Grace Episcopal Church under the direction of Reverend Clinton Locke.

Roland grew to be large and physically active for his age. He excelled in kickball and he showed signs of leadership in the team sports. He related well to his mother and she constantly encouraged him to improve his educational skills. Raymond was slight in appearance and somewhat restrained with a slight case of asthma. He favored his father and his protective nature. He developed an interest in printing with plans for a business career out west.

The Columbian Exposition opened in 1893 when George's business was losing representation throughout the country. The majority of sales orders came by mail to the office, where a staff of three people managed the daily operations. Although the company produced twelve different products, the majority of the sales were for various perfumes including twenty-eight standard fragrances. As time passed, the operations became fairly routine and gradually George's time was directed elsewhere. He enjoyed traveling and socializing with his friends, allowing the business to operate on its own. Unfortunately, the business, including its profits, began to decline.

In the summer of 1894, George traveled to Colorado on an exploratory trip. He made friends with Bishop J.F. Spaulding, superintendant for the Jarvis Military Academy. The academy specialized in studies for young men, including some boys with breathing disorders. George was concerned about his son Raymond's health and after previewing the school, he decided to enroll him in school at the academy.

About the time that Henry Ford produced the first petro driven car and William McKinley, a favorite son of Ohio, was elected president, George purchased a citrus farm in Leland, Florida. A friend, Dr. Dennie Dorrall, convinced George that life on the citrus farm, moderate exercise, and Florida sunshine would improve his health.

George hired a local farmer, Ben Duran, to plant the citrus crops and care for the property. In addition to selling the citrus fruit, George would use the lemons and oranges for his perfumes, possibly some new fragrant products. With hopes that Florida would be healthy for George, they planned to spend several months there in the winter and return to Chicago for the summers. Unfortunately, it became more difficult for him to travel as he approached his sixty-sixth birthday.

Shortly after President McKinley was shot in September 1901 and Teddy Roosevelt became President, George and Emeline were invited to Hartford Connecticut for a reunion of the Kinney Historical Society. George planned the trip so that he could visit some sales representative along the way, then they could attend the reunion and travel south to the citrus farm. They encountered some bad weather along the way and the trip became exhausting for George.

By the time they reached Florida, he was deathly sick with a high fever. Emeline comforted George as he struggled, but shortly after the first of the year, he died peacefully in his sleep at their farmhouse in Pierson, Florida. Emeline returned to Chicago where funeral services were held for George at Grace Episcopal Church.

At the funeral services, George was eulogized as a man driven to be successful with his many business ventures, as well as his zest for the good life. A reflection of what success meant to George was summarized by his favorite author, Ralph Waldo Emerson, as follows:

To laugh often and love much,
To win the respect of intelligent people and the affection of the children,
To earn the appreciation of honest critics and
endure the betrayal of false friends,
To appreciate beauty,
To find the best in others,
To leave the world a bit better whether by a healthy child,
A garden patch, or a redeemed social condition,
To know even one life has breathed easier because you have lived.
This is to have succeeded.

About five years after George's passing, Emeline moved to Colorado to live with her son, Roland and his wife, Annabelle. Emeline brought a small trunk filled with family records and relics which she gave to Annabelle for safekeeping. Roland and Annabelle had a special affection for Emeline and, in turn, she brought a caring and loving nature to their home. Roland became a successful agent for the Prudential Insurance Company. Together, they shared many good times with their grandchildren and other relatives.

Emeline died of natural causes in 1928 and is buried at the Crown Hill Cemetery, west of Denver.

George Park Kinney, circa 1875

Raymond Park Kinney, circa 1885

Chapter 17

Raymond Park Kinney
1879 – 1932
Printer, Indian Curio Trader

IN SEARCH OF NEW BEGINNINGS
IN COLORADO

Ray sat in the waiting area, watching as the secretary entered Merlin William's office. She quickly turned and nodded to him.

"Mr. Williams is ready to see you Mr. Kinney."

Ray likely jumped from his chair, walking as quickly as he could to greet Mr. Williams who was now standing in the door with his hand outstretched, but without a smile upon his face. Williams was the trust officer for the Illinois Trust Company, the firm administering George Kinney's will. Several months had passed since his father died this past winter. Williams had told him in the beginning that an estate the size of his father's could take considerable time to permit creditors to submit their outstanding bills and for their firm to finalize the reports for the bank and the state. The bitter Chicago winter had not improved Ray's growing sense of impatience.

"Mr. Kinney, please have a seat. I'm afraid you aren't going to like what I have to tell you. Several creditors claimed abnormally large amounts of money due to them, and the survey of assets revealed far less than anticipated. Here, have a look."

Willams handed over the papers. Ray saw that after the payment of the debts, most of the remaining assets would pass directly to his mother Emeline. Neither Ray nor his brother Roland would receive large distributions.

Somewhat stunned, Ray eventually regained his voice. "Are you sure these are correct?"

"Quite correct, Mr. Kinney," came the reply.

"But that's not fair!" responded Ray.

"Unfortunately, Mr. Kinney, life is not fair. The sooner you learn that, the better off you will be," replied Mr. Williams.

Ray regained his composure and Mr. Williams continued, "We will proceed with the final distributions and file a report for the state. Thank you so much for having Illinois Trust serve you during these difficult times. Please call us if we can be of further assistance."

Ray stood, shook William's hand and braced himself, not only for the cold wind outside, but also for going home to face his wife. What would she think? What would she do? She expected a large inheritance that would provide for them well into this new century. Would there be no end to her verbal abuse, ranting, and raving about her no good in-laws and her inadequate husband who could not provide for her in a manner that she expected?

Privately, Ray was not afraid to face the world without his father's money nor his protective image. He was ready for a fresh start, even though he would not have the inheritance he expected.

His father George had been his guiding light, his protector, and his constant advisor for every major decision he had faced thus far in his life. He had a deep respect for his father and he appreciated everything he tried to do for him. But now, it was time to contemplate his own family's future and pursue some of his own dreams.

Ray knew better than anyone that his father's business had suffered in the later years. Profits had steadily declined and his father was forced to discontinue business with some of his marginal traders. Promotional efforts and campaigns to attract new business were slowly discontinued.

Even though the business was considerably smaller after the Sherman Silver Purchasing Act was passed in 1890, the economy continued to falter. His father continued to be optimistic that higher profits would return and the business would prosper after the act was repealed in 1893.

Ray's father had continued to give the appearance of wealth and social prominence, even though Ray sensed that it caused emotional stress and strain to him. Ray wondered why people put up a false front, knowing that in the end, everyone, including the members of one's family – his kin – would know the truth anyway. With time, the truth tended to be exposed.

Other than his mother, Ray was the only relative living in Chicago at the time of his father's passing. His Uncle Charles Kinney had moved to Denver, Colorado and his brother Roland stayed there after attending the Jarvis Military Academy. Ray planned to stay in Chicago for the time being, primarily to care for his mother, and to settle the business affairs of his father.

Since his father's death, Ray had plenty of time to think about his childhood, his family, and what important events had brought him to this juncture in his life.

Raymond was the first son of Emeline and George Park Kinney, born in 1879 when his father was forty-five and his mother was twenty-four. Almost five and a half years later, his younger brother Roland followed on February 16, 1885.

As a child, Ray was eager to participate, but he lacked the physical size and endurance, primarily because of some restricted breathing. When he exerted himself, he always seemed to be out of breath. The doctors felt that he had a mild case of asthma. Consequently, his mother was protective for Ray, yet caring and sensitive to his particular needs.

When his father returned from business trips, he showered Ray and Roland with gifts and affection. But there were long periods when

George was gone and, consequently, Ray developed signs of independence and some irresponsibility. He rejected some of the discipline his mother attempted, especially when he was expected to share his mother's attention with his younger brother.

As Ray began to play with other children, he learned to tell humorous stories and perform as a comedian. When he was given a lead role in the class play at school, he liked the attention and laughter that accompanied his role. He became a leader within his small group of friends, and they would mingle and share times together before and after school.

Summer was a favorite season for Ray because he loved the outdoors. The family enjoyed picnics at the beach on Lake Michigan and they occasionally traveled north to Wisconsin to visit his mother's family and other friends in the Lake Country. As they grew older, Ray and Roland fished on the Wisconsin lakes, hiked in the woods, and often joined their friends for camping excursions.

When Ray entered the eighth grade, he was in a crafts shop that had a small printing press. His teacher took a special interest in Ray, teaching him to print notices for the lunch room and some school bulletins. Ray brought home some examples of his printing which pleased his father. Attempting to cultivate his interest, George took Ray to visit other printing facilities, including a visit to the *Chicago Tribune* newspaper.

Wherever Ray's father traveled, he looked for opportunities for his boys to obtain good training for their futures. On a trip to Grand Rapids, Iowa, he made friends with Thomas Spindell, who owned a successful printing company. Since Ray had shown a special interest in printing, George arranged for him to have a summer job with the Spindells. Setting type and running the press became more than a hobby for Ray. He developed some artistic creativity and combined it with his journalistic writing to produce his first printed records. He was proud of his work and he convinced his father that he should have a printing press of his own.

He wrote to his father to announce his accomplishments:

July 29, 1891

Dear Papa,

I received your letter, with clippings. I have ordered some (printing) things with a press and everything. The complete outfit will cost about $85.00. With a new press, I will print many wonderful things. P.S. I am getting very anxious to come home.

Your loving son,

Raymond

When Ray returned to Chicago, he set up a printing shop and began printing business cards and sales flyers. To earn additional money, he had a newspaper route and he worked part-time in the neighborhood grocery store. Ray became a good worker, but he always seemed to have some spare time to socialize and have fun with his school friends.

On an exploratory sales trip to Colorado in 1894, George established accounts in Manitou Springs, Leadville, and Denver. During his stay in Colorado, he met several important business leaders. About twelve years earlier, the owner of Denver's Windsor Hotel, James Duff, recruited employees from Chicago, including Henry Tammen to come to Denver. In addition to tending bar at the Windsor, Henry Tammen founded a mercantile and curio store, and partnered with Frederick Bonfils to create *The Denver Post*.

While in Denver in 1894, Ray's father arranged another important opportunity for his sons Raymond and Roland. After meeting Reverend J. F. Spaulding, the principal of the Jarvis Military Academy, George decided to enroll his son Ray in the school. If successful, Roland would also enroll when he reached the proper age. George hoped that the high altitude in Denver would improve Ray's health. In addition, his father was convinced that the academy would offer a sound academic and military training program for both boys.

In 1895, Ray traveled with his father on the train to Cheyenne, then southward to Denver. From the train station, they took a horsedrawn wagon to the campus in Montclair where Ray would live in the boys dormitory at the academy. Within a short time, he became good friends with some of the other students as they were immersed in a stringent military routine.

The thin air in Colorado was good for Ray's health. He thrived in the Colorado sunshine. His breathing improved, allowing him to play baseball and football on the school teams.

Compared to Chicago, Denver was much smaller with a population of about 185,000 people. Ray traveled throughout the Denver area and often visited his Uncle Charles who lived in the Highlands area, just west of town. Ray grew to understand and respect the rigid military system. With new confidence and a solid academic foundation, Ray graduated in 1898. His brother Roland followed Ray to the academy and remained in Denver after graduation, never returning to live in Chicago.

When Ray moved back to Chicago, he found that the city was growing rapidly with massive projects downtown and along the Chicago River. The stockyards were booming and the Midwest Stock Exchange and Grain Market was attracting major financial markets to the region.

Chicago was destined to become the second largest city in the country. The world's first skyscraper was erected in Chicago for the Home Insurance Company. It was an exciting period. President McKinley was beginning his second term as president. Thomas Edison had submitted a patent for the phonograph and the microphone. New forms of printing presses, with high speed capabilities for daily newspapers had been developed. *The Chicago Tribune* became the dominant paper for Chicago, with a distribution exceeding 100,000 daily circulation.

Meanwhile, Ray's father, George, continued his explorations and frequent business trips across the country. In Florida, he purchased an orange grove on twenty acres of ground with plans to sell citrus and build a perfume factory.

On a trip to Buffalo and New York City, he met a merchant named Harry Stevens. Stevens sold various food products in Brooklyn, Long Island, and Manhattan. The Stevens family was well known throughout the northeast as respectable, hard working, and energetic. A distant uncle, John Stevens was to gain fame as one of the most experienced railroad engineers in the country. Later, he would be named by President Teddy Roosevelt to be the chief engineer for the Panama Canal.

George Kinney took an immediate liking to Harry Stevens, and after dinner one evening, they began discussing their families.

Stevens likely said, "Now take my older girl, Sally. She is the practical one. Why she took on several jobs so that she could attend Columbia University, majored in interior design and home economics. Oh, she's a beauty, too. She got her degree and then married a tennis star. They live in New Haven these days. Got me a grandson named Scott, and another one on the way. How about you?"

George responded, "Well, believe it or not, but this old dog still has a couple kids–boys. My younger, Roland, he's still in school, but the older, Ray, just graduated from military school in Denver and is back home in Chicago. Say, if you've got an older girl, does that mean you have a younger one, too?"

Harry's face lit up. "Oh, indeed, I do. Ethel's her name and she just graduated from Barbara McCarthy's Finishing School for Girls. Nineteen and her friends describe her as 'cute as a button,' which she is. Tell you what, she's lively, loves to go to parties, and have a good time. I guess she's a bit carefree and spoiled, probably my fault, you know what I mean?"

"Oh, indeed. You want them to have a good life."

"When she was young, I used to boost her on my shoulders. We'd parade around the neighborhood, her whistling and singing with delight while I smoked my stubby cigar and skipped along the sidewalk. Nothing was too good for her and her sister. Expensive clothes, the finest schools. Honestly, though, I think her mother spoiled her even worse."

"Yes, daughters are special," George paused for a moment, reflecting on the wife and daughter he lost before he'd met Ray's mother.

"One time Ethel missed out on signing up for a Girl Scout troop. My wife went straight to headquarters to plead her case. Caused quite a public display—even the girls were embarrassed, but Ethel got to join that troop. Over the past few years, her social calendar has been swimming with opportunities. Why her mother even finished her homework and completed her term papers when Ethel was too busy."

George chuckled. "My Ray is very social, too. Sure would like to see him settle down with a good woman. Hmm, so has Ethel settled on any suitor yet?"

"No, despite all those earnest young men calling on her. Many of her friends are already married. Wouldn't be upset if she met a fun-loving, good looking fellow—as long as he was ready to give her the support and lifestyle she is used to. What's your son up to these days?" asked Harry.

"He does a pretty fair turn with a printing press. Plus, he's begun to manage different aspects of the business while I'm on the road—which is often."

"So, do you think he might need to accompany you on a trip to New York in the near future?"

"Starting to sound necessary, isn't it? Oh, I think your girl would like my boy. Does she listen to what you and your wife say?"

"Yes, she relies on us quite a bit and in turn we can rely on her to be obedient to us. So, how soon do you think the two of you can return? We'll be happy to host a little dinner party while you are visiting."

The two men set to working on the details. Ray and Ethel had no idea their lives were being drawn together, but soon they would. Less than a month later, George and Raymond were ushered into the Stevens home where Ray instantly spied the vivacious Ethel walking down the staircase. Upon setting her eyes on Ray, Ethel figured out that her father's hand probably had something to do with the visit–and that this explained why her mother had been so insistent on helping her find just the right new dress for tonight. Still, the young man did look as if he were worth getting to know. She smiled and walked toward the guests.

When Ray's proposal came, Ethel happily accepted it. Saint Timothy's Church in New York was the setting for their wedding in July 1900, ushering in both their life together and a whole new century. After a honeymoon to Niagara Falls and the Catskill Mountains, the newlyweds traveled to Chicago to establish their new home, staying at the Kinney family home on Clark Street until they could find suitable quarters on their own.

As they settled into their new lives in Chicago, Ray continued to assist with his father's business affairs and he took a job as a printer and part-time bookkeeper with the *Daily Calumet* Publishing Company. The job looked promising and things were going well when Ray's father unexpectedly died in the winter of 1902. Ray and his brother Roland consoled their mother and made all the proper arrangements for their father's funeral, including submitting his estate to the Illinois Trust Bank.

In October 1902, soon after George's death, Ethel and Ray had their first child, a son they named Stevens Park, a fitting name combination representing both families. Three other boys would follow, Robert in 1903, Floyd in 1905, and Curtis in 1908. Floyd would be the first Kinney child born in Colorado.

In the spring of 1904, Ethel and Ray, with sons Stevens and Robert made a trip to Denver to visit his brother Roland. Ray had a rousing reunion with some former classmates and friends from the Jarvis Academy. They had a wild party at the Windsor Hotel, which lasted all night. Ray's ability to tell good stories made him the center of attention. As Ray described the party, "One thing led to another, and before we knew it, the morning sun was shining through the window."

Ethel and the babies stayed with Roland at his home in south Denver.

Two days later, Ray paid his respects and visited with his father's friend, Henry H. Tammen. Although he had met Tammen when he was a student at the Jarvis Academy, now things were different. He wanted to talk about the possibility of a new job. Tammen was wildly enthusiastic about the future prospects for Colorado and he encouraged Ray to move to Denver. He assured Ray that he could have a job as a printer and bookkeeper at his mercantile company.

It didn't take long for Ray to make up his mind. The climate in Denver was good for his health. With some good drinking friends and, now, a good opportunity for an entry level job, he was ready to move. He returned to Chicago to complete his affairs and prepare to move to Denver.

With some reluctance, Ethel agreed to move to Denver. She argued that it was so far west that her family in New York would rarely get to visit. The move westward precipitated an ongoing barrage of criticism from Ethel, primarily toward Ray, but also encompassing the uncivilized way of life in the west. That different way of life with new opportunities seemed to appeal to Ray, but for Ethel, it was a long way from the glamour and high society she left in New York. Her deep-seated air of east coast sophistication would haunt her and cloud the family's compatibility for the rest of their lives.

Ray and Ethel bought a home at 509 South Ogden Street, within a short walk to shopping on south Broadway. Steele Elementary School was only two blocks away and Washington Park was three blocks east. The park was the largest designated recreation area in the city, with over 465 acres. There were two natural lakes, with a beautiful stream meandering southward through the park. Originally, the ground was rather barren, but plans were underway to plant many different kinds of trees with sprawling lawns and picnic areas. There was a horse path that later, turned into a bicycle and a walking trail. In time, there would be facilities for tennis and lawn bowling. In a large open area near south Downing Street, there were three baseball fields which were converted to football and soccer fields in the fall.

At a time when leisure sports were available to the working class and especially young people, their home was located in an ideal location. Since the Kinney boys had a unbounded amount of physical energy and were naturally competitive, they used all the facilities at Washington Park and considered the playing fields to be an extension of their home. They made life-long friends with many other children in the area including Doug Morrison, Claire Henderson, Eric Puterbaugh, and Robert McWilliams.

Ethel appreciated having a place where her boys could be boys, play with the neighborhood children, and grow strong and independent. Ray and his brother Roland encouraged the boys by providing their equipment and teaching them the basic skills for baseball, football, and tennis.

In 1912, Ray and Ethel planned a summer vacation trip to Chicago and New York. The night before their planned departure, Ray attended a party after work with some of his friends. They first met at the Tivoli Bar for drinks and then walked to Delmonico's for dinner. For a night-cap, they headed over to John Gahans, a thriving saloon on Ninth Street. The party lasted well into the night with games of pool, poker, and dancing. Ray, as a general rule, did not participate in card games. But on this occasion, he agreed to play some poker. The game ended in an argument after one of the players was accused of cheating. Ray lost about $60.00, including some of the money he had planned to use on the trip. Feeling discouraged, he had a few more drinks and was escorted out of the saloon as the sun was rising in the east.

Ethel, Ray, and the boys missed their scheduled train the next day. They waited two days while Ray recovered, then rescheduled their departure. Their stay in Chicago was shortened by two days and now they would stay with Ethel's family in Brooklyn, rather than in a hotel.

Ethel did not take kindly to Ray's drinking and parties with his friends. She scolded him and admonished him to be a better example for the children. Besides, the family was on a tight budget. Ray was not making enough money to provide for her in a manner she expected. Without an occasional gift of cash from Ethel's father, it was difficult to cover her needs and the costs of raising four boys. In Brooklyn, Ethel confided to her father about her growing problems with Ray. Harry Stevens was sympathetic and compassionate. He would help, especially with the four boys who were growing up rapidly in a home gradually being torn apart by bickering and contentious parents.

In the course of their stay in Brooklyn, Harry Stevens developed a warm and caring relationship with Stevens Park, his oldest grandson. He sensed a bright and aspiring intellect in him, which was consistent with the school reports as described by his mother. After discussing the situation with his wife, Harry decided to invite Stevens Park to come live with them and attend school in Brooklyn.

Shortly after Ray and Ethel returned to Denver, Harry sent a letter to Stevens Park and his parents confirming the arrangements. Stevens Park was jubilant as he opened and read the letter.

"Look, the letter arrived from Grandpa. He and Granma want me to live with them and go to school in Brooklyn. He says not to worry–he will even pay for the train ride."

Ethel sighed. Her father was ever so helpful when she was growing up. And now, he was more than helpful–he was a lifesaver. She said, "Oh Stevens, you are so young to go so far. Brooklyn is a long way from Denver. Is that what you really want?'

"Yes, Mom. My history teacher told me it would be the opportunity of a lifetime. Besides, I want to see the Dodgers play the Giants at the new Ebbets Field. I don't want to leave my family, but I am willing to go if it will help in the long run."

Ethel hugged him quickly, then let go. "All right, then. Let me see the letter. Your father and I will make arrangements and I'll contact your grandfather."

Stevens lived with Ethel's parents from fifth through eighth grade. When he returned to Denver, he found his parents still struggling with inadequate income to support Ethel's spending habits and Ray's propensity to enjoy socializing with his friends. Arguments over family finances, social status, women's rights, and the futility of Prohibition seemed to be the main subjects for family bickering.

With Ray's job in jeopardy due to the uncertain times surrounding the war in Europe and whether or not the United States would join the fray, the tension was intense. Prior to the national election in 1916, Americans were firmly neutral. But as Americans were killed as a result of the U-boat attacks, the pressure to support the allies increased. On April 6, 1917, President Wilson declared war on Germany.

Ray was thirty-eight, too old to enlist in the army, while Stevens at fifteen, was too young. Still, Ray started to worry about having his boys prepared for war. Thus, using tactics he learned at the Jarvis Military School, he began incorporating daily military training in their lives. The boys must be punctual and obedient, adhering precisely to all rules set forth by their parents. He insisted they join the ROTC programs at their schools. The younger boys grew to accept their father's military style, but the oldest son, Stevens, rebelled. Against his father's wishes, he announced that he would attend North High School, and, hopefully, study at the University of Colorado in Boulder.

Shortly after the Volstead Act was passed in 1919, when Prohibition was spreading across the country, Ray made a renewed and deliberate effort to improve his work habits and provide a steady income for his family. He liked his job and was devoutly loyal to his boss Henry Tammen. Sharing a mutual respect, Tammen liked Ray and repeatedly encouraged his good workmanship. In the early twenties their business was profitable and rewarding. Consequently Ray was promoted to be the sales manager. He was asked to increase sales and supervise all printing.

Ray bought a Model T Ford and began a family tradition of taking the family on Sunday excursions. The Sunday trips often included Ray's mother, Emeline, who moved to Denver and resided with Roland and his wife. For business, Ray traveled to Georgetown, Leadville, and Pueblo to attract new accounts. His favorite trips were to Santa Fe and Gallup, New Mexico, where he purchased blankets, jewelry, moccasins, and other merchandise from the Navajo Indians. The authentic Indian curios sold well in Denver, and they became a specialty of the Tammen Company. To publicize the Indian mystique, Henry Tammen placed a mummified Indian princess near the entrance of the store for all the tourists to see.

Ray's son Floyd, who was nicknamed "Piggy" was a star athlete at South High School. He was very popular and selected class president for his junior year. But at the beginning of his senior year, he was struck with a rare bone cancer, dying suddenly just before Christmas. Doctors reported that Floyd received an unsuspected attack that could not be anticipated nor prevented. With the many friends and classmates of Floyd, the family gathered to pay their respects to Floyd. Floyd's death was a tragic blow to the family. Ethel resumed her verbal attacks against her in-laws and Ray began drinking again.

When the stock market crash of October 1929 reached Denver, the ripple effect reached all the major businesses in the area. Several banks and brokerage firms closed. The tourism business, including the sale of Indian goods became stagnant. Ray's brother Roland, who worked for Prudential Insurance Company, lost his job. The Sullivans, neighbors on Ogden Street, lost their home and had to move into an apartment building. The H.H. Tammen Company dismissed employees for the first time in its history. Ray was asked to reduce his working hours and take a pay cut. Upon hearing the news shortly after Christmas, Ethel opened with new verbal attacks about Ray's worthless character. When Ethel didn't get the Christmas presents she expected, the verbal abuse was followed by her smashing and breaking the glass coffee pot on the counter and throwing leftovers from dinner at Ray. It would take awhile for things to settle down.

As the Depression took hold in 1930s, driving the Model T Ford was reduced to only special occasions. Everyone looked for ways to economize. Friends and neighbors tended to help each other, often sharing children's clothes and toys. The Kinney boys took on new jobs to help pay for the family's needs.

Ray spent more time with his wooly friends. He frequented the Criterion Saloon and the Broadwell Hotel where they had a pet monkey named Jerry. Ray and the other patrons used to give drinks to Jerry-and together, Jerry and the patrons would get drunk. Getting home safely after drinking with Jerry became a difficult task for Ray. One night, after a lengthy session at the Broadwell, Ray stumbled home, entering in the dark so as not to wake Ethel. But unknowingly, he entered the wrong house. Ray later told the police, "It looked just like my house." The homeowner pulled out a pistol and began firing when Ray stumbled through the doorway. The sirens were blaring as police officers jumped from their cars and ran to the open doorway. Luckily, Ray fell down and wasn't shot before the police arrived.

Fortunately, police officer Thomas McGoo recognized Ray as one of the jovial friends he often drank with at the Broadwell Hotel. McGoo, a senior officer on the police force, interrupted the interrogation by the young patrolmen and said, "Let me handle this. I believe I know this man. I have always liked taking a long shot and I can solve this."

McGoo took Ray aside, gave him time to sober up and regain his composure before taking him to his rightful home. Ray was forever grateful, and told McGoo, "If there is anything I can do to repay you, let me know and I will do it."

Ethel was disgusted. She confronted Ray with a barrage of verbal criticism, something like this, "Your mother and your family are responsible for this outrageous behavior. If I had known how irresponsible you are and where you came from, I never would have set foot in your house, let alone married you."

"Now Ethel," George tried to explain. Life had not been exactly what he expected either. "Let's look at the good side of things, not always the bad. You have a nice home, three great kids, you have everything you want and spend money as if it grows on trees."

"It's all your mother's fault," shouted Ethel.

"No, that's absurd. Between your financial requirements and your unrealistic desires to be socially acceptable, you have thwarted any desire I have to be financially successful. Unfortunately, you have been the biggest detriment to my business career."

So the arguments and bickering continued, without any resolution. Ethel appealed to her family and friends, including Pastor George Van Ardel at Central Christian Church for help. Gathering her three boys, she admonished them to dismiss the disreputable ways of their father.

The boys took their father's blemished condition in stride. They had ambitious goals of their own and they were not to be diverted. Stevens Park was already an aspiring lawyer. Robert developed a growing interest in aviation and planned to become a pilot. Curtis was interested in mining and engineering. He planned to attend the Colorado School of Mines.

Ray was repentant. He continued to work part-time at the Tammen Company, but was discouraged and nearly broke. He was restricted from driving, so he was confined to the printing shop and sales work within the store. Gradually, he withdrew from many of his favorite activities and spent more time with his friends. Occasionally, he would wander down to the Broadwell Hotel for a friendly chat with his loyal friend Jerry. While he and Ethel had tried to give the pretence of social respectability, he knew that his life in the west had brought some unexpected difficulties, including leading Ethel to become a demanding and unforgiving wife.

In May 1932, Ray suffered a heart attack. He was rushed to Denver General Hospital, but died prior to receiving any medical treatment. Stevens, his oldest son, returned to Denver from Boulder to be with his mother and his brothers. As the eldest son, Stevens made arrangements for the funeral and paid for the burial plot. In addition, he retrieved a brown rectangular trunk with some antique possessions and the family's historical records which he decided to keep in his own possession.

Harry Litzenberger, a friend who worked with Ray at the H.H. Tammen Company, gave a stirring eulogy commending Ray for his loyalty as a business associate. Many of Ray's social friends attended the funeral. Some of them told memorable stories about Ray and his unique ability to tell jokes and help others have a good time.

Ray's sons, Stevens, Robert, and Curtis consoled their mother as she mourned for her husband with whom life had been so different than her expectations. As Ethel aged, her hostility and animosity grew to encompass most everyone near to her. She blamed her husband and relatives for a lack of adequate income and wealth, leaving a bitter swath of resentment and scorn in her twilight years. Ethel continued to live in Denver under the guardianship of her oldest son Stevens Park. Not only would Stevens Park care for his mother and his own family, but also he would become a positive force in the Denver community.

Ray was buried at Crown Hill Cemetery, northwest of Denver. When Ethel died in 1962, she was buried at Fairmount Cemetery, east of Denver.

A Family Picnic
Top row – left to right: Gib Frye, Hallie Springsteen, Roger Kinney
Front row – left to right: Dennis Samson, Dick Frye, Robert Frye, Steve Kinney, circa 1939

Stevens Park Kinney, circa 1927

Chapter 18

Stevens Park Kinney
1902 – 1963
Lawyer, Businessman

FULFILLING
FAMILY RESPONSIBILITIES

When the building committee for the new fraternity house ran into an impasse because of a disagreement with Boulder city building department, the chairman suggested they call Park Kinney because he would know what to do. When Coach Harry Carlsen considered what to do to build teamwork and inspire his players to play their best for the coming season, he appointed Park Kinney to be the captain of the team. And when Ray Kinney unexpectedly died, his widow told her other two sons to call Park, because he would know what to do, including making proper arrangements and caring for the family. Park was always the "go to" guy. He seemed to have a special calling to be the provider, caretaker, and guardian, a role he assumed with a deep sense of kinship and personal responsibilities. From his earliest days, he prepared himself for that role.

The prophecy for the University of Colorado, Class of 1928, identified Stevens Park Kinney as the "most likely graduate to succeed." Indeed, his record as an underclassman was impressive. He graduated with honors with three degrees, one in Arts and Science, another in Journalism, and a third from the Law School.

During his college years, he was invited into membership of several honorary societies, including Torch and Shield, his sophomore year, Sumalia, his junior year, and Heart and Dagger, his senior year. Sigma Phi Epsilon was his social fraternity. Other honorary fraternities included Sigma Delta Chi for journalism, Delta Sigma Pi for business, and Phi Delta Phi for law. He lettered in baseball four years and was captain of the team during his junior and senior years. During his undergraduate days at CU he was a member of the C Club, Student Council, the Athletic Board, and the Boosters Club. He was a frequent contributor to the CU newspaper and was a member of the Board of Publications.

Yet Park didn't just excel in academic and extracurricular endeavors. He also earned more than enough money with numerous jobs and his own creative business to pay his way through college. Possibly, the most rewarding job started as house manager of the Sigma Phi Epsilon house. He directed the business operations, including buying the food, hiring the cook and staff, keeping the records, and maintaining the physical property. He became so proficient at the job that he created his own management services company and offered similar services to the other fraternities and sororities.

In the summers, he worked for the H. H. Tammen Company, a mercantile department store. As a sideline, he created a fireworks stand to sell fireworks for the annual celebrations of the Fourth of July. During the same period, he played with the Boulder Collegians baseball team who played their games on Sundays, in preparation for *The Denver Post* Tournament which was played in late August each summer.

Stevens Park Kinney was a very busy young man and that's just the way he wanted it when he graduated from the University of Colorado. He was goal-oriented, with many objectives and dreams on his mind. He had deep-seated incentives, largely fostered by his compassionate and caring Grandfather Stevens. He could foresee opportunities in many areas and was ready to move into the competitive world with determination and a clear vision for the future.

Stevens Park Kinney, or Park as he came to be known, was born in 1902, a time of great changes for the United States. At a time when Orville and Wilbur Wright made their first flight and when construction work was beginning on the Panama Canal, the pervasive spirit of the country called for widespread expansion and commercial development. The country was emerging as an international power. President Teddy Roosevelt, who had assumed office the previous year after the assassination of President McKinley, declared, "We stand on the threshold of a new century, big with fate of the great nations of the earth. A man who wanted to get ahead could work ten hours a day, six days a week and achieve remarkable success." Park's Grandfathers George Kinney and Harry Stevens were such men, and Park prepared himself to follow in their footsteps.

Park, a strong, healthy baby of six pounds, two ounces, made his entrance in Chicago, not long after his Grandfather Kinney had died. He was the firstborn son of Raymond and Ethel Kinney. He would later be followed by brothers Bob in 1903, Floyd in 1905, and Curtis in 1908. Although Park's grandparents on both sides were considered wealthy for the times, Park's parents were closer to middle class status with their modest wealth. When he was born, his family lived in a four-story walk-up residence at 835 North Clark Street, about one and a half miles from the downtown Loop district. The family moved to Denver in 1905 where they resided at 509 South Ogden Street.

For the first ten years of Park's life, the Kinney family provided all the educational and social advantages a young boy could assimilate. Park learned to do the very basics-to read, to write, to calculate arithmetic problems, and to use proper English. Park grew to be physically strong. A fast runner, he was athletic and liked to play games with older children. He had many friends and showed early signs of leadership with his playmates. In time he would develop a paternal instinct for caring and sheltering his younger brothers. He was taught to be polite and he was instructed to use proper manners. Occasionally he attended

Central Christian Church where he received some fundamental religious training.

When Park was nine, while playing ball in the back yard with some other boys, the ball went astray and landed on top of an ash pit, a common way of burning and disposing of the trash. He took it upon himself to retrieve the ball and climbed quickly on top of the ash pit. As he lost his balance and fell into the fire, he screamed for help. His friends ran to the nearest house. When two adult neighbors arrived, they pulled him out of the fire, but not before he suffered second degree burns to his legs, primarily to his right thigh and both calves. Some of his skin had to be grafted to cover the burned areas. He recovered with full use of his legs, but would have unsightly scars on his legs for the rest of his life.

When Park was recovering from his burns, he spent many hours reading, and he developed a keen interest in the stories of Mark Twain, Robert Louis Stevenson, Nathaniel Hawthorne, and the historical novels of William Hubbard. His interest in academics escalated during this period. When he was in the fourth grade, his teachers recommended him for advanced studies.

At that time, his parents had limited resources. Park's mother appealed to her parents, Mr. and Mrs. Harry Stevens for help. On a vacation visit to the Stevens family, she described Park's advanced abilities, including his teacher's recommendations.

The Stevens, who lived in Brooklyn, New York offered for Park to live with them, where he would have the benefit of an outstanding educational opportunity with the Brooklyn Public Schools. After due consideration, his parents agreed that Park could move to Brooklyn where he would begin fifth grade at the Brooklyn Public School #139.

The train trip to New York was a marvelous experience for Park. The train moved across the country with rapid speed giving such beautiful views of the country side. He wondered at the grandeur of the skyscrapers and the multitude of people in New York. Harry Stevens picked him up and took him to Brooklyn where Park would spend the next three years.

His athletic prowess helped him make friends with many of the boys in the neighborhood. He adapted well in the Flatbush area of town, once he learned the major streets and intersections. He continued to get exceptional grades, especially since he had a new incentive to study and perform well. At P.S. #139, all students who made straight A's received free tickets to the Brooklyn Dodgers baseball games. That was sufficient incentive for Park, who saw lots of baseball games during the next three years.

His interest and love for the game of baseball grew rapidly. He could tell anyone about all his favorite players, including their batting averages and fielding percentages. His all time All-Star lineup included Tris Speaker batting first, then Eddie Collins, followed by Ty Cobb, George Sisler, Babe Ruth, Home Run Baker, and Lou Gehrig. He chose Roger Peckinpaugh of the Yankees as his idol at short stop. His favorite pitchers were Walter Johnson, Cy Young, and Christy Mathewson. By studying the habits of all the players and following their examples, he developed his own batting stance and fielding techniques.

His grandfather, Harry Stevens, often took Park to the Polo Grounds to watch the Giants play the Brooklyn Dodgers. The rivalry between the Giants, Dodgers, and, eventually the Yankees, infatuated Park. He loved to play the game with his playmates, but he also began to develop and an interest in the dynamics of the game, including the fans' participation, the ballparks, and the operations of the leagues. He watched closely as Ebbets Field was built in Brooklyn in 1913. He followed the career of Branch Richey, who played and then became instrumental in creating a farm system to spread baseball throughout the county with the additional benefit of developing young players.

Harry Stevens was in the baseball business in an unusual way. He owned a wholesale food company, which included the sale of meats, poultry, and bakery goods. In his prosperous business, he distributed his products throughout Manhattan, the Bronx, Long Island, and Brooklyn. When his friend, Harry Magely, the catering director at the Polo Grounds, asked him for new ideas to attract fans, Harry suggested that they sell "red hots," a product that another friend, Charles Feltman, created for patrons at Coney Island.

When "red hots" were introduced at the Polo Grounds, sports cartoonist, T.A. "Tad" Dorgan called them "hot dogs." The fans gradually grew to like them. Hot dogs became so popular that similar products were introduced at Ebbets Field and in baseball stadiums throughout the country.

Park's years in Brooklyn made a great impression on him. The combination of a challenging scholastic education, the rigors of competitive athletics, and living with kind and caring grandparents was invaluable for his development and maturity. The setting allowed him to make big dreams about his future. He perfected his academic skills and gained confidence in his own abilities.

Grandfather Stevens was a strong and dominating influence, as he talked about current events with Park. Together they discussed politics, the revolution in Mexico, the opening of the Panama Canal, and the election of Woodrow Wilson in 1912. Park watched as the world powers engaged in what would be known as World War I. He became an avid observer, watching his grandfather negotiate business deals and discuss the pros and cons of the government's involvement with big business and the labor unions. During this time, Park became aware of other exciting events including the emergence of autos and the assembly-line production of Ford automobiles. Airplanes were gaining acceptance, including some scheduled flights to California.

In 1916, Park moved back to Denver to live with his family. His brothers attended Steele School and would go to South Denver High School nearby. Park chose to attend North High School because it was new and reportedly offered some specialized training classes. With the solid background from school in Brooklyn, Park excelled in his class work at North. He advanced his athletic endeavors by playing football, basketball, and his favorite, baseball. He was well-liked by his class-mates and was active in several other activities, including the Hi-Y Club and the school newspaper.

As Park and his brothers grew, there were financial strains for the family causing all of the boys to work part-time jobs. They sold newspa-pers, delivered groceries, cleaned sidewalks, and worked in nearby restaurants.

In 1919, Article Eighteen to the U.S. Constitution prohibited alcoholic beverages and the reaction across the country was calami-tous. Park's father Raymond liked to drink occasionally and he objected strenuously to the new law. This caused considerable unrest and some arguments within the family. His father argued that many people, including waiters, bartenders, and distillers would lose their jobs. Park had seen the results of excessive drinking when he walked by some slums and bars, including those in Brooklyn. He remembered the damage it had caused his friend, Ted Daniels, whose parents had divorced because his father became a helpless alcoholic. Park watched with alarm as the arguments escalated and family and friends were torn apart. All the tensions affected him emotionally. Consequently, he vowed never to drink alcohol nor to be a party to its destructive forces which became a vow he held throughout his life.

By the time Park was a senior in high school, it was easy for him to choose his next school, the University of Colorado. The baseball coach, Harry Carlsen wrote to Park and invited him to attend CU, where he could play on the baseball team and get a superior education. Although a scholarship was not available, it was common for students to work while they were in school. Park was confident he could accomplish both objectives. In addition, Park had several older friends attending school there and they joined the rush to urge him to join their social fraternity, Sigma Phi Epsilon. Park left Denver and began his college education in the fall of 1921.

Since Boulder was about thirty-five miles from Denver, it took Park about two hours by bus to travel from home to school. Park visited home occasionally and he stayed in contact by corresponding with his parents and brothers. He felt especially close and committed to his brothers, who were following his footsteps in many ways. He taught them to play baseball. He tutored them in various subjects and encouraged them to be good students. His brothers Floyd and Bob showed promise as baseball players and both would make the varsity team at Denver South. Floyd had assumed the nickname of "Piggy," and Curt's moniker was "Jiggs." Bob was interested in flying and he joined a local aviation club.

When Floyd was a senior at South Denver High School, he was struck with a rare bone disease, which was preliminarily diagnosed as a form of cancer. His physical condition deteriorated and within several months, he died. It happened so quickly that the family was in complete shock. Floyd had been very popular at school and many of his friends grieved with the family upon his passing. Park was stunned and greatly saddened. He resolved to do his best to provide comfort and guidance to his younger brothers, Bob and Curt, with hopes that they would build a stronger kinship. When he returned to school in Boulder, he promised to correspond with them. Park's support would help Bob, who was a student at Denver University, and Curt, who had yet to finish high school.

Shortly after Charles Lindbergh flew the Spirit of St. Louis non-stop from New York to Paris in 1928, Park opened an office for the practice of law in downtown Boulder. To maintain an adequate income, he continued to operate management services for the fraternities and sororities on the Boulder campus.

In addition, he was courting a charming and attractive young coed, Mary Louise Springsteen, called Mimi by many friends. He had dated her older sister, Martha, and when Martha's younger sister arrived on the campus in Boulder, Park's full attention turned to Mary Lou. She was from east Denver and a member of Kappa Alpha Theta Sorority. Park's fraternity brothers voted her the prettiest freshman on the campus and told Park he better grab her before she went astray. He quickly followed their advice.

Mary Louise and Park made plans to marry, and after he raised sufficient money with the fireworks stand in June and early July, they were married on July 16, 1929. They drove their new Buick on an extended honeymoon, first to Chicago, then to Niagara Falls and Brooklyn to visit with family and friends. Mary Louise didn't know much about baseball, but she quickly learned a great deal about Park's priorities. Upon their arrival in New York, they checked in at the Astor Hotel, then left within minutes for a Dodgers baseball game at Ebbets Field.

They had a wonderful time in Brooklyn. Park had a joyful reunion with the Harry Stevens family. They reminisced about Park's adventures in Brooklyn and Harry gave Park some fatherly advice for a successful marriage. It was a sad parting as both men expressed their mutual respect and appreciation for bygone memories.

When they arrived back in Boulder, Park began his law practice in earnest. He joined the Colorado Bar Association and became active in the Boulder Chamber of Commerce. However, business throughout the country soon became difficult. When the stock market crashed in October, economic panic spread throughout the country. Many men lost their jobs. The young couple heard reports of long soup lines and rioting in the east. Some farmers gave up and deserted their properties. In Denver, some banks and insurance companies closed. Investors were devastated and reports of stockbrokers committing suicide were not uncommon.

Park was frugal and basically conservative with financial matters. He decided to continue his management services to provide for a basic cash income. He would preserve his modest assets and continue gradually to build his legal practice. That seemed to be the prudent decision under the circumstances, especially when he and Mary Louise were getting established and planning their family.

They liked Boulder and business there seemed to be somewhat secluded from the depressing state of business in Denver and other larger cities in the country. They enjoyed the nearby mountains, with short trips for picnics to Left Hand Canyon and to Estes Park. They used their meager resources well to make the most of what they enjoyed. Park worked long hours and worked tirelessly to represent his clients in the most professional manner. His legal business was growing nicely. Several of his college friends, including Louie Telk, Ray Morris, and Brian Miller secured his legal services. His legal practice expanded to include business law and real estate.

In May 1932, Park's father died. Park returned quickly to Denver to console his mother. He purchased a burial site at the Crown Hill Cemetery, west of town and arranged for the funeral to be held at Olingers Mortuary. Park had an ongoing sense of his personal responsibility to care for his mother and to assist his younger brothers. Kinship to Park meant caring, providing, and, if necessary a guardianship, no matter what the personal sacrifice might be for himself.

His younger brother Curt was enrolled at the Colorado School of Mines, and his brother Bob was working part time and attending the University of Denver. It would be very challenging to keep them in school and provide for his mother. He made arrangements for his mother to live in an apartment at 1805 Pennsylvania Street, and he began sending her monthly checks.

On a snowy, wintry day, the first baby for Park and Mary Lou arrived. Stevens Park Kinney II was born on January 24, 1933 at Boulder Community Hospital. Baby Steve was a healthy, lean baby weighing 5 pounds, 8 ounces. He grew rapidly in the warmth and comfort of the couple's loving care. Mary Lou and Park would have two more children. Roger was born in 1937 and a daughter, Barbara Louise, in 1939.

Within two years after Steve's birth, Park decided to move his office and residence to Denver. A friend, Milton Sweeney offered to form a legal partnership and they established an office at 1710 Welton Street in the Patterson Building. It proved to be a good location, just four blocks from the Denver Court House. Park and Mary Lou purchased a brick, two bedroom home at 635 Dexter Street, in the Colorado General Hospital area.

The business economy in Denver consistently improved and Denver itself was growing rapidly. Park engulfed himself in his legal work and became active in numerous civic activities. He joined the Denver Lions Club, the Masonic Lodge, and the Denver Chamber of Commerce. For the next ten years, his legal practice flourished, and his list of prominent clients steadily increased.

At that time, municipal judges were elected by popular vote, similar to other government officials. Park offered to help several friends, including Henry Lindsey, Robert McWilliams, and Phil Gilliam, who were subsequently elected to their respective courts. With success in several elections, Park became a popular political advisor and a valued manager for other elections. He began to take additional interest in national elections and began correspondence with national officials, including former President Herbert Hoover. As a representative of the Colorado Republican party, Park traveled to Cheyenne, Wyoming to meet with Hoover when he visited there.

Many friends, fraternity brothers, judges, and other lawyers were exceptionally loyal to Park. They came to him for legal advice and counseling. And he often offered political comments and advice. A friend, Ray Morris, who lived in Little Rock, Arkansas, called Park after most major elections to review the results.

When Judge Neil Horan was asked by another lawyer who he would hire if he needed a lawyer, he replied, "Park Kinney, he's the best lawyer, and best friend any lawyer could have." Some people referred to Park as "a lawyer's lawyer" after that. When asked about it, Park replied, "Thank goodness. There were not many lawyers that needed outside counsel, but I appreciate the nice compliment."

As their family grew, Park and Mary Lou needed additional space. They purchased a four bedroom, brick home in the Park Hill area at 1736 Grape Street. The new home was about three miles from downtown

Denver, which could easily be reached by taking the #15 street car on
Colfax Avenue. The Park Hill neighborhood was the most fashionable,
upper middle class section of town. It had wide boulevards and beautiful
parkways, lined with evergreen and elm trees. Bountiful flower gardens
lined the streets during the summers. The schools, Park Hill Elementary, Smiley Junior High, and East Denver High were considered the best
schools in the district. The Denver Zoo and the Natural History Museum
were located in City Park, about twelve blocks west of their home.

Mary Lou and Park chose the perfect area for raising children,
especially since it included the presence of numerous kind and consider-
ate neighbors. Within two blocks of their home, there were twenty-eight
children of similar ages. The summers were filled with games of "Kick
the Can," "Tug of War," and "Cops and Robbers." In the winters, kids
made snow forts and there were sleigh rides and sled runs. The vacant lot
on the corner hosted casual games of football and baseball. A common
trait in this time period, neighborhood families took a personal interest
in each other and, collectively, they helped raise all the children.

As the 1940s approached, Park and Mary Lou heard ominous
reports from Europe after Germany's invasions of Poland, Belgium,
and Italy. No doubt the country would be called into the war at some
point. As the danger increased, Park's brother Bob Kinney enlisted in
the Army Air Corps. He was sent to California for training.

On an unseasonably warm Sunday morning, December 7, 1941,
Park and Mary Lou were planning an outing to Evergreen and Bergen
Park for a family picnic. Radio reports announced that Pearl Harbor
had been attacked by the Japanese and President Franklin Roosevelt
responded with a declaration of war. The family changed plans and
gathered with loved ones.

Family, friends, and neighbors responded by signing up for military
service. Park's brother-in-law, Jerry Samson, joined the Navy and was
assigned to the Seabees. A neighbor, Harold Tague, joined the Army,
and a nephew, Gilbert Frye, enlisted in the Army and was assigned to

the First Combat Division. Park was thirty-nine years old-too old for active duty, but he volunteered for service with the Denver Selective Service Office. Mary Lou, along with her sisters Martha and Sylvia, volunteered and worked for the local branch of the USO and the American Red Cross.

The war changed everything. Gas and many products were rationed. Victory gardens appeared everywhere, including one located on the neighborhood vacant lot. Tin can and rubber tires were recycled. Families were separated and women replaced men in labor jobs. The war caused major adjustments, but people everywhere were willing to sacrifice and unite for the defense of the country.

While people were making the best of dangerous conditions, Park received the devastating news that his brother Bob had been killed in a plane crash in California. Bob was married and had one small child at the time of his death. His body was returned to Colorado, where he was buried at Fairmount Cemetery, east of Denver. Park felt crushed by Bob's death and he suffered with grief and depression for several months.

The war raged on for four more long years. People in Denver pulled together, learning to live with rationing, air raid drills, and restricted travel. Park kept his focus on his law practice, supporting his family, and caring for his mother. Mary Lou was the homemaker, concentrating on the steady growth and development of their children in unsteady times.

When the war ended in 1945 and troops began coming home, the Denver economy rapidly expanded. Many of the service men who trained prior to the war at Lowry Air Force Base returned to live in Denver.

The post-war years saw remarkable growth in the greater Denver area. Park envisioned many business opportunities, and he made ambitious plans to start several new ventures. Acting like Grandfather George Kinney, Park entered the real estate business, creating the Park Realty Company. He also began building homes with the Stevens Construction Company. After conferring with his friend Sam Russell, he created the Stevens Investment Company. He also built a lumber yard in Derby, Colorado.

As the multiple businesses expanded, Park became active in local politics. In time, he agreed to serve as the Campaign Manager for a friend Dick Batterton who ran for Mayor of Denver. Batterton was a Republican, which meant it would be a difficult campaign since Denver was largely controlled by the Democrats. The campaign was strenuous and exhausting for Park. The contest against a popular opponent Sonny Mapelli was close, but Park showed a unique ability to estimate the "vote count" accurately in decisive areas. He particularly focused the campaign in those areas and Batterton was elected mayor.

The election had been successful, but the victory led to a devastating period for Park. He was spread too thin to oversee and manage all his investments. Henry Triple and several other trusted employees had misdirected funds, causing substantial losses. The financial problems from the construction company had a domino effect on the other businesses. To determine the extent of the misallocation of funds, Park worked long hours and hired independent auditors to identify the problems. It was a long and expensive process. The physical and emotional strain showed in Park's physical condition.

In the fall of 1953, Park suffered a heart attack. He was overweight, discouraged, and physically exhausted. It was fortunate that he was close to a hospital when the attack occurred. In the following days, Park had extensive tests and he received extensive medical care. Dr. Ken Sawyer and Dr. Franklin Ebaugh explained that his recovery could likely take a lengthy time. A good friend, George Bakkee, assumed some of his legal work while he recovered.

By the spring of 1955, Park's health had improved to the extent that he could return to work. Many of his outside business interests were gone, so he concentrated on his law practice, primarily his established clients. He formed a law partnership with Governor John Vivian and a long-time friend, Henry Sherman. During the next four years, the firm of Vivian, Sherman and Kinney attracted some notable clients including The Fox Sheet Metal Company, the local professional Denver Bears Baseball Club, the Rio Grande Railway, and the Weaver Construction Company. Several close friends, including Jim Burris and Dr. Henry Kafka, retained his firm for their legal work.

Park was learning to live with his physical limitations. He tried hard to dismiss some fretful memories by turning his attention to other happier endeavors. He and Mary Lou built a mountain home in Estes Park where he planned to retire. He was elected state president of the Old Timers Baseball Association, an organization that provided a summer baseball program for children. He corresponded with some of his political friends, including Mayor Dick Batterton, Senator Gordon Allott, and politicians Richard Nixon and Lyndon Johnson.

The next five to six years were filled with periods of jubilation and happiness for the family's successes which were offset with periods of depression and disappointment. Regarding Park's medical condition, the doctors identified two distinct and different ailments. The first was heart disease. At that time, doctors were limited with their procedures for treatment of clogged arteries and veins. Preliminary testing was under-way using various drugs to thin the blood and prevent blockage of arter-ies. Some other research was underway involving the use of stents to open blood passages. But neither of these procedures was available for Park.

The second medical ailment pertained to preliminary signs of diabetes, accompanied with periodic depression and emotional distress. Friends said Park suffered from "a broken heart" caused by his business setbacks and other physical restrictions on his health. Again doctors were limited with their treatment. When Mary Lou requested medical procedures to address both problems, the response was to treat each ailment separately and there was no comprehensive plan for recovery.

It was a time that tested the faith and durability of both Mary Lou and Park. She was the primary caregiver and she needed strength and courage to care for Park without impairing the growth and development of their children, a concern they both shared. They resolved to make the best of a difficult situation and move ahead as best they could. Mary Lou and Park watched with pride as their children grew to be adults.

The children flourished, with oldest son Steve graduating from law school and joining Park in the law firm of Vivian, Sherman and Kinney. Roger excelled in sports and played baseball at the University of Colorado. Barbara was selected to be the Head Girl, co-president of the student council, at East High School. She attended the University of Colorado where she received Phi Beta Kappa honors and was elected president of her sorority, Kappa Alpha Theta. She married a brilliant young man, Charles Kall, who would become an outstanding lawyer, bound for success with the law firm of Holme, Roberts and Owen.

During these same years, Park lost his brother Curtis when he died from heart failure in 1958. Curt was survived by his wife Margaret and son, Richard. Curt, commonly called Jiggs, was very popular and had many friends. Park reminisced about how he, Curt, Freddy Leonard, and Reverend Edwin Thayer enjoyed the DU football games on many brisk, fall afternoons. Curt's infectious laugh and pleasant personality showed how much he loved to have a good time. Park had a special camaraderie with his brother Curt and his passing left another painful loss in his life.

Park's mother died from diabetes in 1962, after a lengthy stay in the Westminster Nursing Home. Park had carried the primary financial burden of supporting his mother since 1932 when his father died. Her passing left Park as the sole survivor of a once healthy and prominent family with four gifted sons.

Park was filled with grief and discouragement. He battled his physical ailments including diabetes and heart disease. The mental anguish was devastating to him and it took its toll on Mary Lou and the children as they tried valiantly to comfort him.

Park suffered a second heart attack in July and died on August 13, 1963. His funeral was held at Olinger's Mortuary, where the Mackey Chapter of the Masonry, Rose Croix Number One, officiated at the services. Honorary escorts included Judge Phillip Gilliam, Judge Neil Horan, Robert Howsam, Jim Burris, T. Mitchel Burns, and Willard Moore.

Park was laid to rest at the Fairmount Cemetery Mausoleum in east Denver.

Oldest son Steve (II) assumed the family's paternal leadership with careful consolidation of the family's resources. He followed his father's path with widespread community involvement, accompanied with a deep and abiding religious commitment.

After a period of mourning, Mary Lou renewed her interest in ballroom dancing and taught lessons with her sister, Martha Frye Macomber. They directed a popular cotillion dance program for children. Mary Lou also renewed her interest in painting, specializing in watercolor pictures of regional landscapes.

Within a year she moved to Oceanside, California to be near her daughter and some other favorite relatives who lived in southern California. In time she regained her youthful enthusiasm and sparkle.

A friend and distant cousin, Jim Moorehead, renewed a friendship with Mary Lou. Before long, they decided to marry. They had many common interests and delighted in traveling together and exploring many areas and events, including Disneyland and the Hawaiian Islands. But unfortunately after a short time, Jim suffered what was believed to be a stroke and died unexpectedly in December 1965.

Mary Lou returned to Denver, where she rejoined her social friends and the families of her sons and daughter. She spent much of her time in the summers at the family home in Estes Park, Colorado.

Judson Slater Hubbard, a long-time friend of the family escorted Mary Lou on family outings and social events. It is believed that the ancestors of the Hubbards and Kinneys had been casual friends as far back as 1650 when both families were living near Salem, Massachusetts. Mary Lou and Slater Hubbard enjoyed each other's company and after a delightful courtship, they were married in April 1970 in Denver. Their friendship expanded as they traveled with Dr. Doug Macomber and his wife Martha-Mary Lou's sister-on some adventuresome trips throughout the world. They had a happy union and spent many memorable times together with their extended families.

After Slater Hubbard's passing in 1981, Mary Lou remained in Denver and resided in apartments at Cherry Creek Towers and the Park Lane, just blocks away from Roland and Annabelle Kinney's first home in Denver in the early 1900s.

Wherever Mary Lou resided she brought a cheerful and happy countenance to those around her. When she moved to the Heritage complex for retirement living, she quickly became a popular resident with the staff and other residents. Within her private diary, she kept a favorite poem, *Afterglow* which was written by Helen Lowrie Marshall:

I'd like the memory of me
To be a happy one.
I'd like to leave an afterglow
Of smiles when day is done.
I'd like to leave an echo
Whispering softly down the ways.
Of happy times, and laughing times
And bright and sunny days.
I'd like the tears of those who grieve
To dry before the sun
Of happy memories I leave
Behind—when day is done.

She celebrated her glorious ninety-fifth birthday with her extended family on April 15, 2005.

Stevens Park Kinney &
Mary Louise Springsteen Kinney Descendants

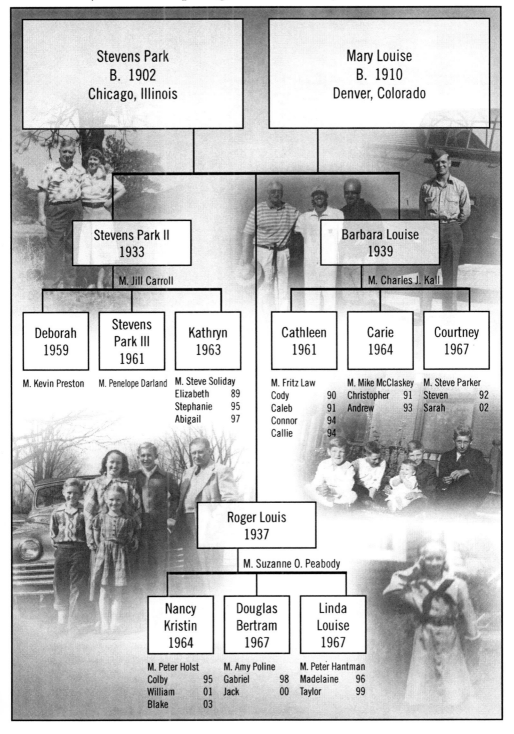

| Stevens Park
B. 1902
Chicago, Illinois | Mary Louise
B. 1910
Denver, Colorado |

Stevens Park II
1933

M. Jill Carroll

Barbara Louise
1939

M. Charles J. Kall

Deborah
1959

M. Kevin Preston

Stevens Park III
1961

M. Penelope Darland

Kathryn
1963

M. Steve Soliday
Elizabeth	89
Stephanie	95
Abigail	97

Cathleen
1961

M. Fritz Law
Cody	90
Caleb	91
Connor	94
Callie	94

Carie
1964

M. Mike McClaskey
| Christopher | 91 |
| Andrew | 93 |

Courtney
1967

M. Steve Parker
| Steven | 92 |
| Sarah | 02 |

Roger Louis
1937

M. Suzanne O. Peabody

Nancy Kristin
1964

M. Peter Holst
Colby	95
William	01
Blake	03

Douglas Bertram
1967

M. Amy Poline
| Gabriel | 98 |
| Jack | 00 |

Linda Louise
1967

M. Peter Hantman
| Madelaine | 96 |
| Taylor | 99 |

April 15, 2005, Upon the occasion of "Mimi's" 95th Birthday

Standing – left to right: Fritz Law, Cathy Kall Law, Cody Law, Bob Frye, Chris Frye, Deb Frye, Chip Frye, Sherrie Frye, Gib Frye, Debbie Kinney, Chuck Kall, Steve Parker, Courtney Kall Parker, Roger Kinney, Mike McClaskey, Katie Kinney Soliday, Carie Kall McClaskey, Pete Holst, Nancy Kinney Holst, Pete Hantman, Linda Kinney Hantman, Del Lebsack, Darell Brown, Mike Lebsack, Suzanne McNitt, Dick Frye, Sheryl Lebsack, Christopher McClaskey

Seated in chairs – left to right: Mary Krane, Liz Frye, Shirley Frye, Freddie Hubbard Brown, Babs Kinney Kall, "Mimi" - Mary Louise Springsteen Kinney Moorehead Hubbard, Sue Kinney, Marcia Frye, Marcia Moorehead Gaudet, Judy Samson Lebsack

Seated on the ground – left to right: Caleb Law, Connor Law, Andy McClaskey, Stephanie Soliday, Abbie Soliday, Will Holst, Gabby Kinney, Taylor Hantman, Blake Holst, Maddie Hantman, Sarah Parker, Callie Law, Steven Parker, Colby White, Doug Kinney

Stevens Park Kinney II, circa 1946

Chapter 19

Stevens Park Kinney II
1933 – 1993
Colonel, Judge

HERE COMES THE JUDGE

"You're out!" came the call from the umpire, following a vicious collision at home plate. The jubilant winners exploded into a wild celebration.

No one thought the small, skinny catcher named Steve Kinney could possibly hold the ball when the big, husky runner, Jack Girtin, slammed into him. But he did and that was the final out. Now the baseball game was over. The Park Hill Pirates beat the Barnum Wolf Pack six to five, and the Pirates were City Champions of the Junior Division, ages twelve and thirteen, of the Young American League.

The Pirates team celebrated by all the team members jumping into a pile by home plate with little Steve Kinney and the winning pitcher, Don Carlsen, on the bottom of the pile. As they crawled away from the other players, Steve said, "Congratulations, Don, you pitched a great game."

"Thanks, Steve," replied Don. "I never thought we could get them out, especially when they had the bases loaded in the fifth inning. Thank goodness Harry (Lewis, the third baseman) made a perfect throw to you for the final out."

Harry, who was considerable taller than Steve–but everyone on the

team was taller than Steve–came over to join in the replay of the final
out. He said, "Man, that runner must have weighed 140 pounds. Steve,
why did you block the plate?"

"I had to," was Steve's reply. "If he slid around me, I never could
have tagged him."

Harry continued, "It's a good thing you had it figured out before
it happened, 'cause that meant the game and now we have our first
championship."

Steve tended to figure out a lot of things before they happened.
Even as a young athlete, he would learn the rules of the game, and then
anticipate the important moves that might decide the outcome long
before they happened.

Steve was born January 24, 1933 in Boulder, Colorado, first son of
Park and Mary Louise Kinney. Within two years, his parents moved to
Denver where they purchased a small two bedroom, brick bungalow at
635 Dexter Street. Steve was an active and rambunctious child, often
wandering independently about his yard and his neighborhood. He
was slender, yet agile, ambidextrous, and a fast runner. He had a wide,
bright smile, with western teeth showing a pleasant disposition. He
had an inquisitive nature and liked to play games with his friends and
playmates, including his cousins Denny Samson and Gilbert, Robert,
and Dick Frye. Dick occasionally called Steve "kins" as a friendly
reminder of their family relationship. Julius Berger was his best friend
when he started school at Steck Elementary in east Denver.

Steve was naturally athletic and he showed signs of leadership when
playing with other children. He organized neighborhood activities
including camping excursions and swimming parties. With his neighborhood friends, he led bicycle trips out to Stapleton Airport to hunt
rabbits in the nearby fields. When the weather kept him indoors, he
became creative with other activities. He carved model airplanes out of
balsa wood and fashioned some of the best flying kites in the area. Just
for fun, he made a bow and arrow set, which he used at a practice facility

he built in a nearby vacant lot.

Steve's parents had experienced the stock market crash in October 1929 and they worked hard to overcome the lingering aftermath of the Depression. As a child growing up during the Depression, Steve developed personal habits reflecting careful and prudent use of his meager, yet valuable resources. He learned to be thrifty, to eat everything on his plate, and to share his clothes, including the "hand me downs" with his cousins and brother Roger, born in 1937.

When his younger sister Barbara was born in 1939, the family moved to 1736 Grape Street in the Park Hill neighborhood. During this time, Denver was emerging as the "Queen City of the West." With abundant water supplies from the mountains west of Denver, the arid plains were turning into green lawns and colorful summer gardens. With the growth of several large businesses including the Gates Rubber Company, Samsonite Luggage, and the Martin Marietta Company, Denver's economy was moving away from its long dependence on its agricultural base.

When World War II began in 1941, several government facilities, including the Federal Arms Plant and the Federal Finance Center, were activated. The federal facilities helped the Denver economy, as all Denver residents adjusted their lives to meet the needs of the war effort. Everyone saved tin cans and rubber products and learned to move quickly to safety when practice bombing raid alarms were sounded.

Steve and his family, like others, lived simply and enjoyed even the most common experiences. They visited City Park for family picnics. By the time he was eight years old, he loved to visit Merchants Park, home of the professional baseball team, or go downtown. Sometimes those trips became all day adventures. At the height of war years, gas was rationed. Consequently, automobiles were scarce and street cars, commonly called trolley cars, were the popular means of transportation. Number 15 trolley left the substation at nearby Quebec Street, and headed straight down Colfax (Fifteenth Street) with the downtown loop as its destination. Soldiers from Lowry Air Force Base were the first to board the trolley at Quebec and their presence was a constant reminder of the times.

Steve's parents generally handled the preparations, but the children were expected to put on their best clothes and were on notice to behave properly. Just the excitement of getting to meander down Colfax was enough to keep Steve from causing trouble, especially with the opportunity to see the city come alive with the strange and fascinating characters who frequented Colfax Avenue and downtown Denver. It was a three block walk for Steve, his young brother, sister, and mother to reach the Grape Street pickup location.

Once aboard the trolley and after receiving some friendly greetings from the soldiers, Steve settled in as the rickety old streetcars rattled and rolled by the infamous Bluebird and Aladdin Theaters, then by Mammoth Gardens, where a person could roller skate or watch George Zarahias wrestle with a mad bull. With the State Capitol in sight, the tramway would roll down the snow sledding run from Grant Street to Broadway. Lots of folks, including many soldiers, departed at Broadway, probably to go to the Broadway Theater or the famous Blue Parrot Restaurant. A glance south and Steve could see the original site of the Mountain and Plains Festival and the spacious Civic Center Park.

The trolley seemed to crawl across Broadway, past the Denver Public Library, the Gas and Light Building, and around the corner to the Loop Market-crossroads for all travelers. At that point, people appeared to go in all directions as they scurried about the Loop. Travelers could also transfer to other trolleys. The number 3 went south to Denver University (why they called it Tramway Tech). The number 14 went west to Golden and Lookout Mountain and the number 7 would go north all the way to Mary Elitch's Gardens. Walking west four blocks would take travelers to the Denver Union Train Station and destinations throughout the country. Steve believed the downtown loop was the hub for all pathways to the world and the Loop Market had the biggest and best variety of food in the region. The aromas from the market were unavoidable, with the combination of fresh produce, a variety of flowers, freshly baked bread, exotic fish, and butchered meat, combined with steaming hot dogs and a smoking bar-b-que stand.

A visit to H.H. Tammens Merchandise Store for a friendly visit was always first on the agenda. That's because Steve's grandfather used to work there and the Tammens were good and generous folks. Mr. Litzenberger, the general manager used to always say to Steve, "Denver is growing, you better be ready, because you cannot stop progress."

Steve would lead the family on a short walk to Daniels and Fishers for shopping and a chance to see the seven foot doorman. While his mother shopped, Steve liked to take his little brother and wander down to Curtis and Larimer Streets to see Burlesque Row and the Windsor Hotel. He liked to meander through Dave Cook's Sporting Goods Store to inspect the latest baseball gloves or wander over to the Gart Brother's Store in the middle of the block on Larimer Street. Inside Gart's, you could hear Nate Gart, the senior member of the famous family, greeting all the customers while shouting instructions to everyone on his staff. Steve also liked to meander over to Curtis Street where there was a cavalcade of movie theaters, bars, and pool halls. Some strange characters and movie stars like Buffalo Bill, Mae West, and Charley Chaplin could be found on the billboards in front of the theaters.

By three o clock, it was generally time to head home. A walk back to the Loop for some grocery shopping and then a ride on the number 15 trolley going east on Colfax led to the Grape Street exit. The soldiers liked to sing on their way home, which always made a joyful ending to a memorable day.

As Steve grew older, he developed a close friendship with a unique group of classmates. They shared common experiences from grade school through high school. Together, they attended school, played sports, enrolled in Aunt Martha Frye's dancing classes, built floats for the parades, shared picnics and bonfires, and pulled together in the annual tug-of-war games. They were Boy Scouts together in Troop 28.

Steve's junior high school basketball team, named the Panthers, included Harry Lewis, Dick Frye, Rod Johnson, Bob Webb, Chuck Froese, John Siple, and Willie Stewert. One of their most memorable games, which was played for the eighth grade championship at Smiley Junior High School against Tom Carey's Educated Five, was won by the Panthers by the score of three to two. The teams practiced at the Park Hill Methodist Church, a holy venue that produced some of the most valuable Christian fellowship anyone could imagine.

Not that Steve's life was all play-he learned to work at an early age. If he wanted spending money, his father suggested he earn it. Over the years, he had several part-time jobs, including cutting lawns, shoveling snow, and performing summer work at the Stevens Lumber Company. He learned to scoop ice cream and to mix malts and shakes when he worked at the Dolly Madison Dairy. His newspaper route for *The Rocky Mountain News* was east on Hudson and Ivy Streets, next to the routes of his family's friends, Tom and Al Seawell. During the summer recess from school, he became a carpenter and painter, working for the Denver Public Schools. As Steve gained valuable experience with his youthful employment, his father watched with admiring parental approval. He was very proud of Steve and, without fanfare, he took pride in knowing that his son had developed good work habits and could work well with other people.

In 1952, the U.S. Geological Service announced plans to survey and explore some remote areas in Wyoming, Colorado, and New Mexico. Because Steve loved outdoor work, he applied for a summer job. With his experience in camping as a Boy Scout, after careful review, he got the job. He was assigned to a mountainous area in northern Wyoming. He tended to the horses, cooked the meals, and learned to survey the mountainous terrain. This city boy grew to love the job and he especially liked to meet his friends who were working in other parts of Wyoming. They often gathered for weekend rodeos in Dubois, Cody, and Jackson

Hole. His friend Bill Zimmerman taught Steve how to fish and another friend, Tom O'Brien, taught Steve how to manage and judge cattle.

Steve worked three summers on the geological survey and, throughout his life, he declared it was the best job he ever had. One favorite summer he was assigned to a remote wilderness area in southwest Colorado, near Silverton. He loved the beautiful country and he enjoyed the fun and excitement of the rodeos. He was a cowboy at heart, and for many years even after college, he would put on his Levis and cowboy outfit to attend the National Western Stock Show in Denver. With his friends, Bob Wilder and Tom O'Brien, Steve would wander into a cowboy bar for a cool beer prior to sitting on the interior fence to watch the steer wrestling and bronco rides. If their favorite won, they were likely to celebrate with another cool beer prior to heading home.

Steve had a lot of fun with his friends who were very loyal to him. He liked to double date with Rod Johnson and Willie Stewert. Willie's dry sense of humor especially captivated Steve. Steve tried to tell funny stories about Willie, but in the process, he would laugh so profusely that he could not finish the story. His mother used to say that she never knew the complete story, but it was always fun to visualize Willie's antics and to see Steve laugh so hard.

In college, Steve continued his close and endearing friendship with many of his neighborhood friends. He pledged Chi Psi Fraternity, which turned out to be a good fit. But his passion and personal ties were with his friends from the S.P.A.D. organization. The Society for the Preservation of Alcoholic Dissipation was a group of friends from many different fraternities who simply liked each other and who enjoyed getting together occasionally to share stories and libations. The SPADs offered a casual way to relax and have a good time and Steve fit right into their spirit of kinship, camaraderie, and friendship.

In spring of 1953, Steve drove to Arizona for spring training camp to see his favorite team, the New York Yankees. He traveled with three of his pals, Bob Webb, Deane Writer, and Jim Bob Day in a flashy 1948

Ford sedan owned by Jim. According to Steve's letters, they laughed all the way, played in the sun, and saw Mickey Mantle and Gil McDougal hit home runs. Upon their return, they announced that the Yankees were a shoo-in for the pennant in '53, and at the end of the season, they were proven to be right.

As time passed, Steve became more serious with his studies as he became interested in a professional career. He worked at the Kappa Kappa Gamma sorority house as a hasher where he became a favorite of the cook and the housemother. Some of his friends from the SPADs also worked there and they extended their fun and merriment to the kitchen, the dining room, and some wonderful parties with the Kappas. Yet Steve also knew how to settle down to do school work, especially after making his decision to go to law school. He joined his close friends Ron Loser, Bill Shade, and Jerry Winters and went on to graduate from the University of Colorado Law School in 1958.

Shortly after President Eisenhower was reelected and Congress passed legislation for the nation's first interstate highway system, Steve began dating Jill Carroll, a popular Kappa coed from Denver. Jill shared Steve's love of the mountains and their courtship often involved hiking and picnicking in the Rockies. They dated while Jill finished her studies and Steve completed law school. Their mutual affection and respect was recognized by their friends and they became known as the "sweeties" around the Kappa house. What Steve didn't know he was looking for, he soon found in Jill's strong Christian faith.

Steve and Jill were married on September 20, 1958, just prior to Steve reporting for active duty with the U.S. Army. Since Steve had completed the ROTC Officers Program at the University of Colorado, he entered the Army as a second lieutenant, assigned to command a training unit of new recruits at Ft. Leonard Wood, Missouri. His leadership training became evident as Steve quickly distinguished himself and his company with several training awards for superior performance. He served his initial active duty at Ft. Leonard Wood and traveled to numerous Army bases, including the Presidio in California and Ft. Carson in Colorado for duty as a reserve officer in the Judge Advocate Corps.

At that time, Nikita Khrushchev was proclaiming that Russia "will bury you." Many people were concerned about the nuclear arms race and the Cold War. The Russians had put the first rockets and men into space. It was an anxious period for America as the country entered the 1960s. After John Kennedy was elected president in 1960, Steve and Jill followed closely his response to the Cuban Missile Crisis. Steve's military unit and all servicemen were on alert, with several warning signs to be prepared for war.

As a devoted student of history, Steve was practical and judicious in his feelings about war. He understood that ongoing battles and wars have been a constant peril throughout history, consistent with human nature and the rightful incentives for free people. Recognizing the proud history of many generations of the Kinney family in various roles of military service, Steve was a proud soldier. He subscribed to the belief, originally attributed to the ancient philosopher Vegetius, "Let him who desires peace, prepare for war."

In President Kennedy's inauguration address, he said "Ask not what your country can do for you-ask what you can do for your country." The message struck a vital chord for Steve and Jill who were deeply patriotic. They had a mutual commitment to serve God and their country. Kennedy's invitation had solidified their common philosophy to live in harmony with their strong religious faith, to live in service to their country, and to strengthen the wonderful institutions and the dedicated people who shared their commitment.

The threat of war subsided and when Steve's tour of active duty was completed in 1961, they settled in the suburbs, like many in their generation. They moved to Arvada, a suburb west of Denver, where they purchased a home at 6051 Pierson Court. Steve began practicing law with his father in the firm of Vivian, Sherman and Kinney.

Jill and Steve joined the Arvada Presbyterian Church, where Jill became active in the ladies auxiliary and their Bible study group. Jill was raised in a family with a long and dedicated commitment to the Presbyterian Church. They attended church on a regular basis. Jill was an avid student of church history and she loved to sing their favorite hymns. It was a joy to sit within three rows of Jill in church because she was a marvelous singer, and it was awe-inspiring to listen to her remarkable gusto and enthusiasm with every song.

Steve was raised in a family governed by strong Christian values, but the family rarely attended church on Sundays. His father's family had a historical tradition with the Episcopal Church, which his Uncle Curtis and Grandmother Kinney followed. Steve's mother's family followed the teaching of Hallie and Louis Springsteen which was a philosophy based on the personal history and observations of several noted scholars. Steve's family assimilated the religious teachings of both parents into a workable Christian practice. They respected the religious rights and preferences of their neighbors and they observed the Christian holy days and traditions. The more Steve learned from Jill and the more he attended services with her, the deeper he was drawn into the Christian faith and into the Presbyterian Church.

As time passed, Steve and Jill embraced the Arvada Presbyterian Church. They taught Sunday school classes and both participated as lay readers in the church programs. Jill continued to head the Bible study group and Steve became the president of the Board of Trustees. Steve and Jill used scripture to reflect their devotion to their faith. They modeled their lives upon one of their favorites, Rom. 14:17-18 as follows:

> *For the Kingdom of God does not mean food and drink, but righteousness and peace and joy in the holy spirit. He who thus serves Christ is acceptable to God and approved by men.*

Their strong faith became the guiding force for their family. They raised their three children with a comprehensive Christian education. Debbie, the oldest was born in 1959, when they were stationed at Ft.

Leonard Wood. A son, Stevens Park Kinney III, was born in 1961 and another daughter, Katie, was born in 1963.

Steve and Jill liked Arvada where they had many friends. In time, they immersed themselves in their favorite community activities. However, they enjoyed activities elsewhere, too. Steve became active in the Colorado Bar Association and he joined the Denver Lions Club. He became president of the Denver Old Timers Baseball Association and would serve as president of the Denver Junior Golf Association. Jill joined the I.P.O. Ladies Club. She volunteered at the Molly Brown House and she became the president of the volunteers at the Colorado History Museum. With her comprehensive background in Colorado history, Jill was also an outstanding guide at the Evans Mansion.

Within several years, the family moved to a new house located at 12465 West Sixty-Sixth Street in Arvada. Their home was located about twelve miles downstream from the water drainage path of the Rocky Flats Plant, close to the Rocky Mountain Arsenal. For many years, Rocky Flats was the site for experimentation and the factory for nuclear arms. Although contested for numerous years, many people believed that there were excessive amounts of chlorine and a compound of THM in the wastewater and that the contaminated water was accidently combined with the public water supply for the city of Arvada. The federal government performed numerous studies, some which conflicted with conclusions from other independent studies.

Over the years, an abnormal number of Arvada residents contracted various forms of cancer. In addition, an abnormal number of the dogs and cats in the neighborhood, including Steve's dog, were diagnosed with cancer. Cattle were forbidden to graze on the fields surrounding the plant. Other precautions were added as the years passed. The damage caused by contamination was difficult to identify and would not be totally known for many years. Nonetheless, many people believed that the consumption of the water over a period of time would likely cause medical problems in the long run.

In 1969 Steve was selected to be the Arvada Municipal Judge and he served in that capacity until 1988. As judge, he took a special interest in the Arvada citizens who came to his court. He developed a reputation for his fairness in dealing with offenders, regardless of their status or wealth in the community.

On one occasion, the popular quarterback of the Denver Broncos, Craig Morton, stood in front of Judge Kinney after being summoned for a speeding violation. Oh, Steve loved his Broncos, but he was mighty tired of how many drivers who lived in Arvada didn't seem to care about the town's speed limits. The police officers knew that when Coach John Ralston would call for an 8:00 a.m. practice at the Broncos north Denver practice field, they could expect many players to race through their town. Yes, many of the players drove with the kind of speed that scored touchdowns, but didn't do much for the safety of the community. The conversation went something like this.

"Good morning, Mr. Morton. I'm Judge Kinney and I see that you've been summoned here for going 52 miles an hour in a 35 mile zone. Could you tell me why?"

Morton replied, "Sir, I'm sorry, but I was running late for a Bronco team practice. I knew if I didn't get there on time, Coach Ralston was going to fine me $50.00."

"Ah, well that's too bad because in this case, you will be paying the city of Arvada $100.00, double Coach Ralston's fine."

Morton froze, as if he didn't quite believe what he had heard. Steve continued to gaze at the football player until he finally sensed that the judgment was understood. Then he smiled and said, "If you stop at the counter outside of this room, you will be able to pay the fine. If you would like to help out our court system further, the clerk will be able to give you information about our youth advocacy program. I believe that if Craig Morton helps our young people, we'll stand a better chance of reaching some of our more challenging young offenders—and Arvada will be a much better place for both you and me to raise our families."

Morton replied, "Let me think about it."

"Fine," said Judge Kinney. "Give me a call when you decide. And good luck on Sunday. I'll be sitting in the east stands on the forty-five yard line, rooting for you and your teammates. Your passing looks really strong this season and I think you will beat the Raiders in the next game."

Steve watched the star quarterback walk out of the courtroom, not knowing if he'd made an enemy or a friend. But not long after that, Morton called to accept his invitation to work with young offenders. Craig Morton became a strong advocate for the Arvada Courts, and, undoubtedly, made a valuable impression on many young people. Plus, he learned to leave a little earlier for the Broncos practice. Once in front of Judge Kinney was enough.

Steve excelled in dealing with juveniles who were brought into his court. He took special care to determine not only the charges, but also the underlying causes and nature of the offense. Rather than attach harsh sentences, he often created unique terms calling for appropriate recompense and community service. Sometimes, children were required to write a paper dealing with the role of government and the reasons for fair and just laws. Such sentences became standard procedure in the Arvada court and Steve developed a reputation for fair punishment and positive learning experiences for the children.

Steve shared his experiences on the bench with other municipal judges and over a period of time, that led to the formation of the Colorado Municipal Judges Association. For his leadership in the legal field and the innovative program he installed at the Arvada Court, Steve was honored as one of the Outstanding Young Men in Colorado by the Colorado Junior Chamber of Commerce in 1973. He was nominated for the award by his good friend, Judge Sherman Finesilver.

While serving the Arvada Court, Steve was also an active reservist with the Army Reserve Judge Advocate General Corp. He commanded the 126th Judge Advocate Guard for Colorado, serving as a military judge and practicing before the U.S. Court of Military Appeals. After serving in the Army Reserves for twenty-eight years, he retired with the rank of colonel.

Steve combined some of the resources from the Arvada Court with some resources from the Army Reserves and other resources from the Denver Bar Association to create a unique program called "Law Day." The program was a statewide celebration highlighting the history, legal system, and heritage of the country. Special emphasis and recognition was given for the rights and accompanying responsibilities of all citizens. The annual event was originally held in early May 1975 and it successfully grew within a few years to be called "Citizenship Day." Eventually the date and the accompanying festivities were moved to coincide with the celebration held when new citizens of the United States are officially awarded their citizenship.

While Steve was involved with legal activities, church work, and community organizations, he never lost sight of his sports connections and his loyalty for the home teams. He envisioned great value in athletics for children. Working with John Laskey and Bob Mantooth, he served as the chairman of the Denver Junior Golf Program and later, he joined forces with John Dikeou, Caroline Writer, and Don Hinchey to serve as the Board Chairman of the 1990 Denver NCAA Final Four Basketball Tournament. Irv Moss and Dick Connor provided media coverage in *The Denver Post*. President Jerry Ford was the Honorary Chairman.

He continued to encourage his own children and other relatives to train and compete. His son, Steve III, became a champion distance runner and later, a pilot with Delta Airlines. His daughter, Katie, enjoyed hiking and his daughter Debbie was a varsity cheerleader at the University of Colorado. His nieces, Cathy, Carie, and Courtney Kall, excelled in swimming and enjoyed mountain hiking.

When the Denver Broncos were created, Steve was one of the first season ticketholders. He joined the Broncos Boosters Club and assisted the president, Mark Freeman, and the team's broadcaster, Bob Martin. In the early days, he organized a group of friends to attend the Broncos first games, including a historic preseason game against the Detroit Lions in 1963 when the Broncos defeated the Lions, 23-17. In 1968, when the first Super Bowl was played in Los Angeles, Steve and Jill attended the game. They rooted for the Kansas City Chiefs, the champions of the American Conference, even though the team was ultimately defeated by the Baltimore Colts.

One of Steve's good friends was Jim Burris, the president and general manager of the Denver Bears Baseball team, and past general manager of the Denver Broncos. Steve provided legal work for Jim and some of the other sports professionals in the area, including the Bear's Manager, Tony LaRussa. To expand his legal practice, including his sports connections, Steve formed a law firm with his friends, Alan Woods, Dick Breithaupt, and Hal Torgan. They opened an office in the Denver Tech Center, a newly developed business area in southeast Denver.

As Steve's family grew older, he had more time to enjoy the fellowship and social activities of the Denver Lions Club, including a term as president. He volunteered and served as treasurer at the Savio House, a shelter for needy families. In 1988, he became president of the Rocky Mountain Lions Eye Institute where he worked in partnership with the University of Colorado Health Sciences Center. Together with Bob Litchhard and Bob Frye, he created an ambitious plan to raise six million dollars for the construction and establishment of the Eye Institute on the new Fitzsimons Medical Campus. The campaign was a magnificent success with the institute being completed in 1994. In recognition of his leadership for the project, the grand hall of the Rocky Mountain Eye Institute was named in Steve's honor.

Early in 1991, Jill was diagnosed with breast cancer. The medical diagnosis was identified early enough to establish a chemo program to stop the spread of the cancer. Jill entered a rehab program and faithfully adhered to the treatments. Steve became the caregiver and he devoted his full time and compassionate care to comfort Jill. She responded well and, together, they savored their joyful moments, together with their children and their families.

In one of the family's Christmas newsletters which Jill composed, she reflected on her family observations and her faith.

My life has been one of watching the changes in my children's lives and the changes in the lives in many of you. Change is good when it brings new vitality and a renewed sense of purpose. I rejoice when I hear about new beginnings, new direction, retirements and all that goes with this. It saddens me to see dear friends move away, but I am overjoyed at the prospect of 'new life.' I above all, should understand the necessity at times of laying the old life down and embarking on a new adventure with the Lord....Living through Him means accepting who he is and appreciating each thing that he brings into our lives. He has a special plan in mind for each of us and all he wants to do is have us be willing to have him implement it. It's wonderful to know that he controls all of life and that he is faithful and worthy of our trust.

Steve was stricken with liver cancer in 1992. Their roles were reversed and Jill became the caregiver during an extended period for his treatments. She tried valiantly to comfort him, staying with him night and day on one occasion at his bedside for seventeen days in the hospital. She constantly worked with the doctors, reviewing his case and searching for answers and remedies for his cancer. When the doctors told her that his death was imminent, Jill prayed to comfort Steve and the children. She said how thankful she was that God had given Steve to her for this life and that together they would receive the ultimate reward of eternal life together.

Steve died peacefully on November 29, 1993. He was buried at Ft. Logan National Cemetery with full military honors. Services were held at Cherry Hills Community Church. One of his friends, Tom O'Brien, sent a sympathy note, along with excerpts from the poem about death, written by Henry Scott Holland in 1847. It was one of Steve and Tom's favorite poems, and one they had read together on one of their cowboy camping trips in the Colorado back country.

Steve's outlook on the nature of death:

Death is nothing at all.... I have only slipped into the next room.

I am I, and you are you.... Whatever we were to each other that we are still.

Call me by my old familiar name.

Speak to me in the easy way which you always used.

Laugh as we always laughed at the little jokes that we enjoyed together.

Play, smile, think of me, pray for me.

Let my name be ever the household word that it always was.

Let it be spoken without effort, without the ghost of a shadow on it.

Life means all that it ever meant. It is the same as it always was.

There is an absolute and unbroken continuity (of kinship).

What is this death but a negligible accident?

Why should I be out of mind because I am out of sight?

I am but waiting for you, for an interval, somewhere very near,
*   just around the corner.*

All is well.

Stevens Park Kinney II with his wife Jill and daughter Debra, circa 1960

Gabriel "Gabby" Kinney, circa 2000

Chapter 20

Douglas Bertram Kinney
1967 –
Businessman, Adventurer

DREAMING ABOUT THE FUTURE

———— ✺ ————

About 5:00 A.M. on April 16, 2000, not long before the dawning of a bright and beautiful new day, Doug Kinney started the car in preparation for a short trip to St. Joseph's Hospital. His now overly pregnant wife, Amy, scurried about as best she could with only last minute details. Her bags had been carefully packed several nights earlier, ready for an urgent departure whenever the time came. Doug and Amy had expected the baby to arrive several days before and if the baby didn't come soon, Dr. Zarlengo was considering birth by caesarian section. Well, the baby seemed to be following his own plan after all.

Amy felt well prepared. She had delivered their first child Gabriel, a bright and energetic girl about two years earlier, so she anticipated a similar experience. This night, Gabby had gone on a sleepover with her grandparents. Dr. Zarlengo, recognized as one of the best female obstetricians in Colorado, had cautioned Amy that the second child often came much quicker. Although her contractions and the dilation had only begun about 4:00 A.M., by 4:30 A.M., her contractions were coming about every fifteen to twenty minutes. Remembering Dr. Zarlengo's advice, Doug encouraged Amy, "Move quickly, it's time to go." Rolling her eyes before smiling, Amy got into the car, ready for the next adventure on their family's journey.

St. Joseph's Hospital had an extensive maternity department, with competent staff and excellent facilities. Amy and Doug attended the preparatory classes, so they were confident, yet as anxious and nervous as any expectant parents.

As they drove north on University Boulevard, Doug attempted to divert Amy's attention by talking about the amazing story of his own birth. Just minutes before delivery, a bright and attentive nurse asked Doug's mother, "Would you go for two?"

"Two what?" came her answer, as she was completely unaware there was a chance for twins. Sure enough, Doug was born first, before his sister, Linda, followed three minutes later. He and his twin sister were born in March 1967 when doctors sometimes did not identify multiple births during pregnancy. Surely, that would not happen again with all the modern medical tests and procedures. And wasn't there a general rule that twins skipped a generation?

Doug turned his Honda sedan left onto Eighteenth Street. They headed west just as the sun began to shine, sending its brilliant red glow onto the majestic mountains and to the top of Denver's skyline. Amy said, "I haven't seen such a brilliant sunrise since we went to Easter sunrise services at Red Rocks. I can't remember much about the sermon, but I think I will always remember the chill in the air and the glorious view of the sunrise. What a fabulous way to start the day."

Doug replied, "Sure, I remember Red Rocks, how could I forget? I carried all those blankets to keep warm, not only for the sunrise, but some of the sunsets there were pretty good too. Willie Nelson's performance at Red Rocks was almost as good as mine."

"Right," answered Amy.

Ever since that morning several years ago, Easter had been a favorite holiday for Amy and Doug. They decorated their home and held an annual Easter egg hunt in their spacious backyard for their children and all their cousins. Following church, a lavish brunch, and the Easter egg hunt, then came the highlight of the morning-a raw egg toss, with the participants gradually extending the distance for tossing the eggs. Of course, the objective was to win the contest, but the most fun was to watch the eggs break and splatter, sometimes over clean Easter outfits. The children loved to compete against the adults, especially since they knew they would not possibly be punished for their childish behavior when the adults were acting just as carefree, rowdy, and childish as the children were.

By 5:15 A.M., the contractions were coming every eight to ten minutes. Doug drove by Presbyterian/St. Luke's Hospital (PSL) where many relatives were born. From Doug and Linda's grandmother who was born there in 1910 to his aunt Barbara in 1939, more than twelve relatives had been born at PSL.

Doug glanced at PSL before returning to concentrate on the road. He said, "It's amazing that most of the family was born in this area and even though we have been spread out across the country from time to time, we still get together for annual events. Just think about the annual football game at Estes Park for Thanksgiving or the family softball games."

Amy said, "Yeah, the softball game in Tucson at Randolph Park was one of the best. What an unusual way to celebrate yours and Linda's birthday. It had all the excitement of opening day at Yankee Stadium, and I remember the birthday dinner the night before in Tucson when the teams were formally introduced." Linda, Doug's sister, who was captain of the home team "Linda's Lizards," announced her starting lineup:

"Batting first will be Taylor Hantman who will play second base." Taylor is Linda's youngest daughter. She is naturally enthusiastic and vocal. She is a gifted actress, a very fast runner, and likes to be in the midst of all the action.

Linda continued, "Batting second is Colby White who will play short stop." Colby is older sister Nancy's oldest son. He has the natural ability to be a super athlete, already a smooth and graceful skier. He has traveled to most every state in the union and has played more sports than most people twice his age.

"The next batter for the Lizards is Maddie Hantman." She is Linda's oldest daughter and is "cute as a button," and stars in school at St. Anne's and on the soccer field. She really prefers dancing and the piano, but in the softball game she will play left field.

"Batting cleanup is Peter Hantman." Pete is Linda's handsome husband and he is not only very handy with numerous projects around the house, but also swings a ferocious bat. Of course, while playing softball, he has to be careful not to damage his Blackberry computer and telephone which is normally situated in his side pocket.

Linda continued, "The fifth batter is Nancy Holst." Nancy is Linda's older sister who is a ski instructor in Vail in the winter and a leader in Denver's Devonshire neighborhood throughout the year. She hits home runs with tennis balls, golf balls, and charity balls. In this softball game, she will play third base and, likely call for the infield fly rule whenever pop-ups come her way.

"I am going to bat sixth," touted Linda, who seemed to be gaining confidence in her team. As captain, she called the plays for the Lizards. Linda stays in great shape, preferring running, playing tennis, or being Mom to playing softball, but as Doug's twin, she was a good sport for organizing and playing this important game.

"The final batter will be Roger." He is Linda's father who thinks he knows the "ins and outs" of the game, but is likely to tire if the game goes into extra innings. He wanders about the field, often cheering for one of the heavy hitters to hit it over the opposition's head. Doug just smiled as he remembered his father reduced speed after tearing his Achilles tendon several years ago when he was running to first base after a perfect bunt.

That night, Doug's brotherly love allowed Linda to finish her introductions before he announced the lineup for his team, "Doug's Dragons":

"Batting first for the Dragons will be Gabby." Amy broke into Doug's thoughts as she mimicked his voice. "Gabby the wonder woman." Doug and Amy had no idea that one day Gabby would be the one playing on a boy's baseball team as well as playing soccer and skiing at Cooper Hill. Gabby learned early to be competitive and was ready to play any game at most any time.

"The second batter will be Blake Holst, playing second base." He is Nancy and Pete's youngest and he is so quick he is likely to steal first base. He tends to make things happen, so look out if he is rounding third and coming home with the winning run.

"Batting third will be Sue." She is Linda and Doug's mother who would rather be a cheerleader than a player. Consequently, she lead questionable cheers like, "Go team go, hit em where they ain't." When she really wanted to rattle the opposition, she screamed, "You ain't going nowhere, nowhere." No doubt people walking by questioned her grammar and intelligence.

"Batting cleanup for the Dragons will be Will Holst." He is Nancy and Pete's second son and this kid is tough. When he was five years old he skied all the way down Riva's Ridge, a black diamond run when it was minus ten degrees and the wind was blowing thirty miles per hour. No wonder he is the cleanup hitter.

Doug continued, "Batting sixth will be Pete Holst." He is Nancy's husband, who is known to be a "big hitter" with men on base and conferencing calls on the line. If called upon, he could rattle any of the fences, but normally he would prefer to walk softly and carry a big stick.

Doug said, "I will bat next because I want to come up with lots of runners on base."

Amy replied, "As I remember, once the game starts, the batting order doesn't mean much because you always bat with runners on base." Everyone knew Doug would find a way to win the game.

The softball game was a good memory for Amy and Doug. They knew it was fun and simply a good way to work up a healthy thirst. As they finished reminiscing about the lineups, they arrived and pulled into the hospital entrance.

By now it was almost 6:00 A.M., and the contractions were coming every seven to ten minutes. Doug parked in the car loading zone, hurrying inside to get some help. Amy, true to her independent style, got out of the car on her own before Doug and the attending staff returned. She rebuffed the offered wheelchair and walked into the reception area. As Doug followed her inside, he felt the crisp, refreshing morning air suddenly change to the sterile, placid air in the hospital. Once Amy was settled, Doug retreated to the car, where he telephoned both sets of parents to notify them of their arrival at the hospital.

Amy was deliberate and direct as she answered the nurse's questions. She came by her independence honestly because her family moved often when she was a teenager. She learned to adapt to changing neighborhoods and different schools. She attended Smoky Hill High School in Aurora and later she went to college at Colorado State University in Ft. Collins. There, she developed close friendships with Tina Beckman, Jeanie Small, and Katy McDonald. She adored her father and stepmother, Don and Gail Poline. And she kept in good contact with her kind and gracious mother, Cheryl, who lived in Miami, Florida. Amy matured quickly and after college, she worked in sales for a computer supply company. Amy was very capable of taking care of herself. Even now, as she entered the hospital, she felt ready physically and mentally to deliver their baby.

Doug also inherited his own healthy dose of independence. During high school, he rebelled with school chums to form the "Fun and Games" club. Sure, it got him into trouble with the school authorities, but on a positive note, it cultivated some loyal friends with Butz, Benes, and Perlov for a lifetime and sparked some wild musical numbers he will never forget. One of his favorites was a ditty they called "Wild Thing" which combined their singing and dancing abilities for the school's talent show.

Doug also excelled in sports, skiing and playing football, baseball, and golf. His favorite sport was lacrosse, where he once set a record by scoring five goals in one game.

After graduating from the University of Colorado in Boulder, Doug struck another blow for independence when he began his working career. He began as a carpenter building homes for Henry Van Doren, but soon moved to Washington D.C. to serve as a legislative aid for Congressman Dan Schaeffer. Next on his working path, he moved to Boston where he worked for CIGNA and Sun Life Assurance Company. Thereafter, he returned to Colorado. After a stint with the Oral Labs Company, he created a sales company called Bridgeway. Independence and small business was fine, but Doug began to find his corporate passion in the combined fields of sales, communications, and education. He was always fascinated with changing technology, especially the science dealing with the Internet and new opportunities to learn and to teach others. He gained valuable experience with the Raindance Company and Fast Tracks for Kids, before joining the professional staff of the E College Company as a Senior Account Executive. As his friend Eric Butts said, "If experience is the best teacher, then Doug has had a fabulous education".

By 6:30 A.M. the contractions were coming every four to six minutes, and Amy's dilation had expanded accordingly. The attending nurses gave Amy some medications and prepared the room. Dr. Zarlengo arrived with a cheerful greeting and a cursory examination. Both Amy and Doug's anticipation was growing. This time, Doug would be in the room and share the birth with Amy.

"Do you remember the first time?" Amy asked Doug.

"Sure, I remember that I had to stay in the waiting room, and I remember a lot of other special firsts too," Doug said trying to keep Amy calm. "I remember our first date at the Washington Park Grille, and the engagement date at the Chart House, the seafood cafe on Lookout Mountain, and our first house at 1531 South York Street."

With other things on her mind, Amy began pacing herself as Doug continued to ramble. "I remember our first car, the white '79 Honda.

And how about our first big trip to the Caribbean and St. Bart's Island when it rained all the time? That trip wasn't as much fun as our trip to Europe when I was working for Oral Labs, was it? But the trips to Aspen and Vail to see our college friends, Rob and Jeanie and John Lindner were the best."

Doug's voice trailed off as the contractions were coming every three to four minutes. Dr. Zarlengo shouted directions and the nurses moved into supporting positions. A messenger appeared to give notice that the family members had arrived and were in the waiting room. Amy reacted with each contraction while Doug held Amy tight with every movement.

At 7:24 A.M., the baby arrived. He was a good size, weighing seven pounds, four ounces with light brown hair and golden brown eyes. He stretched vigorously and cried for a few minutes, as the nurses cleaned him and wrapped him in a white nursery blanket while Dr. Zarlengo cared for Amy.

Amy was exhilarated, tired, relieved, and so happy, all at the same time. Doug, with tears in his eyes said a prayer of thankfulness and a blessing for the baby. It was one of those rare and special moments that parents cherish for a lifetime—a time when parents feel touched by God and eternity.

As the nurses recorded the vital information and rearranged the room, Dr. Zarlengo came out to visit with the family in the waiting room. After about fifteen minutes, the family came into the delivery room to congratulate Amy and Doug and, of course, to see the baby. Nancy took several pictures while Pete opened some champagne for a toast. Doug announced that the baby's name would be Jack Douglas and, everybody, including the nurses, swooned with adoration.

Amy, Doug, and Jack spent a quiet afternoon on April 16th at St. Joseph's Hospital. In the evening, they had dinner in Amy's room while Jack rested in the nursery down the hall. Their daughter Gabby was spending the day with Linda's family. It had been an exhilarating day. As they talked they counted their blessings and began to talk about their future. They were so grateful for their good health and the extraordinary support from their family and friends.

They thought about their minister Tom Melton and their friends at the Cherry Hills Community Church where Amy and Doug taught Sunday school classes. Several years ago, they had volunteered once a week to assist underprivileged children with their school work. Both Amy and Doug were committed to the Christian articles of faith and shared a personal philosophy to share their talents and to serve others. With a grateful heart, Doug left the hospital at closing time, with hopes that Amy would get a good night's rest.

And rest she did, even though Jack was brought from the nursery to see Amy about every four hours. He was breathing well and the nurses were pleased with his progress.

Doug returned shortly after breakfast with the morning newspapers and a pocket full of M & O cigars.

"What's in the paper, Doug?" offered Amy.

He replied, "Not much, but the Rockies won yesterday – maybe this will be their year."

"Sure, dream on," replied Amy.

"Well," said Doug, "I did dream that the Rockies will play in the World Series, Barack Obama will succeed George W. Bush as President, and that someday the Winter Olympics will be staged in Colorado."

"That would give the politicians plenty to work on," Amy responded.

Doug continued, "And how about Scott McIinnis. Maybe he will run for the U.S. Senate. He was a terrific friend to work for during his first campaign, so I hope he will run again. Oh, don't let me forget the conference call I have scheduled at ten o'clock. I have arranged a meeting with six department heads and I can attend by calling directly from the hospital."

Amy shook her head. She knew his Blackberry would sound the alarm.

When Dr. Zarlengo came into the room for a morning checkup, Doug took one of the cigars out to give to her.

Amy said, "Surely you are not going to light that in here—it must be against the rules, and besides, that's an old and outdated tradition."

"Oh, I don't know," replied Doug. "Some old traditions still work. When I called my mom last night, she told me that she still plants pennies in the ground for good luck, just like her grandparents used to do. She has already planted some money for Jack."

"Why, that's archaic and old fashioned. Jack is going to have to grow up in a new era, without voodoo and ancient superstitions."

Dr. Zarlengo seemed to agree. "You know it's hard to know what is right for raising children these days. It's certainly a lot different today than it was when I was younger, or when I was raising children. When I was young, I saved money for my kids' college education, and possibly medical school if they were so inclined. I planned to give them a trust fund if there was anything left. Neither of my kids had any interest in medical school. My son was interested in computer science and my daughter studied Chinese history and graphic design. I can understand their lack of interest in today's medicine—it has changed so much in the last two generations. It costs over $125,000 per year for insurance and other costs just to open the doors. With new research, any practicing doctor has to spend a substantial amount of time in class or studying just to keep up. I believe that the trend of medicine will be toward preventive care, with individuals taking personal responsibility for their own care."

Dr. Zarlengo continued, "That's not to say that there aren't some exciting new things happening in medicine. With substitute parts and heart transplants, people are bound to live much longer."

Doug interjected, "I understand that the DNA tests can trace a family's roots."

"That's substantially right," replied the doctor. "If you want, we can get a sample of Jack's DNA and possibly identify his ancestors for the past ten generations."

"Wow!" said Doug. "That's one way to find your kinfolk. But maybe it's better not to know your ancestors. Then children cannot blame their parents and they will take a personal responsibility for their own future."

Dr. Zarlengo replied, "In today's world, it's very hard to know how kids are going to act in most any situation, including their future."

Amy asked, "And how do your kids feel about the trust fund?"

"Oh, that's changed dramatically too. My children laugh at the kids they grew up with who were reliant on trust funds. It seems that most of them were lazy, ambivalent, and rarely amounted to anything. To be successful, children seem to need to be hungry and ideally curious and inquisitive about whatever is important to them. They need a burning desire to be successful."

"The kids in the future, including Jack, won't likely work for one employer for thirty years and receive a gold watch upon their retirement. He will likely have many different jobs, perhaps many of his own business ventures. He will need to have a high level of varied skills just to adapt and move to attractive opportunities. He will need a healthy passion 'to continue learning' and to take personal responsibility. There are likely to be financial bumps along the way and a sound financial support system would be nice to carry him through rough times."

Dr. Zarlengo continued, "You know I meet a lot of anxious parents and they all want to do what is best for their children. All parents have a kinship of some kind with their children. As a society, we are still learning how to pass along knowledge and virtue from one generation to another. But the answers as to 'what is best' keep changing. I don't think there are any hard and fast rules, because times change quickly and people must change and adapt to meet the times. The only ingredients that don't change are the qualities that build character and skills that endure for generations. To find those qualities, I believe that parental kinship involves an unconditional love that knows no boundary and that lives forever. Parents can't give children enough love and support to build their confidence for the challenges, opportunities, and yes, unfortunately, some adversity that they are likely to encounter."

Amy asked, "What is the best training for kids today?'

Dr. Zarlengo replied, "While they build their character, I believe children should be exposed to a varied curriculum with as many different and valuable experiences as possible. Just think, Jack is likely to grow up in a new world with space travel, daily communication with anyone in the world, and an educational system that provides instant information on most any subject in the universe. With a solid foundation, children can specialize later."

"Well, Amy," said Dr. Zarlengo, with a smile, "I had better finish your examination before we settle Jack's future."

Amy agreed. Doug said goodbye and excused himself to find a quiet place for his conference call. Amy's examination went well. Dr. Zarlengo told her to rest for one more day and prepare to go home the next day.

Doug wandered down the hall and settled into the hospital library, where he dialed his office in anticipation of the meeting with the other department heads at the E College Company. He was glad that he did not have to drive back to the office and that he, just like the other department heads, could exchange current information. He found a space on a table for his small laptop computer, checked in, and maneuvered his browser to find the sales report he had prepared in anticipation of the meeting. After all the participants came online, the meeting began with a birthday congratulatory message for Doug and Amy. Doug responded with the announcement that the baby's name was Jack Douglas Kinney and that he would provide cigars and birthday cake when he returned to the office. In the course of the meeting, he took a few notes from the other department reports and noted several important sales contacts and visits he would need to schedule with his staff. The meeting lasted about forty-five minutes, with a minimum of lost time. After the meeting was adjourned, Doug checked for other messages and called his assistant with instructions to update the department sales report. As Doug finished the meeting and walked down the hall toward Amy's room, he thought about Dr. Zarlengo's comments. The business world is changing rapidly. Business meetings like this, with conference calling and interchangeable reports for all participants, could not have happened just a few years ago. Doug wondered what the future held for Jack.

It was time for an early lunch when Doug entered Amy's room and saw Armanda, the nurse, preparing some space for Amy's tray.

Armanda said, "Doctor's orders–after lunch, Amy is scheduled for some physical therapy–that means a walk around this place and a good nap this afternoon. I've ordered a special treat for Amy and you, Mr. Doug, so plan on dinner here at six o'clock."

Doug hardly had time to reply, but thought, isn't it amazing how most everyone takes charge of their own territory. This place and whatever happens here belongs to Nurse Armanda, and she is not about to let anyone interfere. Doug kind of liked that.

Doug had a busy afternoon. After picking up a list of baby supplies, he went to his office and to the grocery store. Then he took Gabby to his sister's house, where she would stay for the evening while Doug returned to the hospital. He arrived back at the hospital just in time for a gala entrance by Armanda with the birthday celebration dinner.

Since Amy and Doug were celebrating Jack's birth and since this was the last night at the hospital for Amy, the hospital chef had prepared a special meal. Armanda turned the lights down low before she maneuvered the serving cart into the room. Bright yellow and red roses graced the centerpiece while the makeshift table was bedecked with a linen table cloth, napkins, and formal silverware. As Armanda removed the silver warming covers, Doug and Amy saw a beautiful presentation of filet mignon, baked potato, and garden vegetables. For dessert, they had chocolate mousse with a touch of whipped cream. It was a marvelous dinner, reminiscent of the impeccable room service at the famous Brown Palace Hotel in Denver.

When Doug and Amy finished their delicious dinner and were enjoying a quiet moment, Amy said, "I have been thinking about what

Dr. Zarlengo said this morning. Doug, what do you think we need to do for Jack?"

"Nothing right now," said Doug, in a carefree and joking mood. "I'm still celebrating the fact that he was born healthy and that you came through it in great shape. I'll deal with his education later."

Amy persisted, "But what is the right thing for parents to do for their children?"

Doug tried again, after realizing that Amy wanted a more substantive answer. "All we can do for our kids is to give them unconditional love and provide them with the support and encouragement that will give them the best chance for success. I hope we can teach him to see, that is to envision a plan for the future, to feel and learn from experience, and to trust in himself as he discovers each important milestone in his life."

Amy asked, "And what do you think he will find when he searches for those things that are truly important?"

Doug replied, "Well, my friend, David Cook, once described the ultimate significance—what is truly important in life—to involve qualities like '(family) relationships, values, virtues, and faith.' I believe it is important to remain steadfast with these traditional qualities."

Just then, there was a knock on the door and Doug's sisters, Nancy and Linda, came in with a bouquet of spring flowers.

Amy said, "Linda, what do you think about 'unconditional love' for children?"

"Whoa," said Linda, "That's a bit heavy for me. I just came by to see baby Jack and to see how you two are doing."

Amy continued, "Well, Doug and I have just been talking, and we would like to know what you think about the beginning of life and preparing children for what looks like a pretty frightening and awesome future. Nancy, what do you think?"

Nancy responded, "The answer isn't easy. Some wise person said, 'Life is a continuous, unbroken thread of kinship connecting each generation to the next.' And with things changing as fast as they are right now, I think kids need to have the confidence necessary to move through the mine fields. As for me, I always say, go for it, be all you can be! Live up to your greatest expectations! Remember Christ admonished us to 'live abundantly.' To do that, every child needs to know that their parents are there, and that with God's grace and compassion, they will be there continuously, no matter what happens along the road. If a child has a strong moral foundation, I believe his character will emerge and grow favorably as he encounters new experiences and opportunities."

Just then, Armanda, with Jack in her arms, entered the room and announced, "Time for Jack's dinner, Miss Amy." She squeezed by the table to get closer to Amy.

Nancy said, "That means it's time for us to run. I have to help Colby with his homework, so I'm out of here. Just let me see Jack, our newest celebrity before I go." After some goodbye hugs and kisses, Nancy and Linda left for home. Doug stayed until Jack finished his dinner and returned to the nursery. Amy and Doug agreed that it was important for everyone to get one more good night's rest, so he left shortly after Armanda turned down the hall lights signaling visiting time was over.

As the morning of the eighteenth dawned, Amy and Jack were up early preparing to go home. By eight o'clock, Amy had eaten breakfast, showered, and packed her belongings. She was waiting for a final checkup from Dr. Zarlengo. She expected to be discharged before ten o'clock and home for lunch.

Nurse Frances was on duty and getting Jack ready for a big day. "He is going to be a fighter," she said. "Look at the way he wiggles and squirms. He already knows how to scream when he gets hungry." She put a clean diaper on him, wrapped him in a new blue blanket, and handed him to Amy.

It was 8:30 A.M. when Dr. Zarlengo entered Amy's room with a cheerful greeting for the day. "It's a beautiful day, Amy, perfect to take Jack home. How are you feeling?"

Amy replied, "I slept well, but now I am ready to test the comforts of our own home."

Dr. Zarlengo said, "I wish all mothers and fathers were like you and Doug. Babies need so much initial care these days. Without a healthy start, it's almost impossible to catch up later. Can you imagine what the future holds for Jack? The AMA just released a report that says many babies born today have a life expectancy of ninety-five years. That means Jack, with good health, has a good chance of seeing the clock strike one in the year 2100. Can you imagine that? How many changes can we expect in the next one hundred years?"

Dr. Zarlengo caught herself pondering about other future things. It almost seemed like an afterthought for her to give Amy an examination as she settled down from the excitement she held for future generations. Soon she gave Amy a clean bill of health, declaring that she and Jack were ready to go home.

When Doug arrived, it was about 9:00 A. M. After passing out a few more cigars, he loaded the car and politely bid adieu to Dr. Zarlengo, Nurse Frances, and the other staff members in the maternity work station. By 9:15 A.M. Doug pulled away from the hospital loading zone, with the car carefully loaded with Amy, Jack, their personal belongings, and a back seat full of beautiful spring flowers. The car smelled so heavenly, Doug said, "the birds and the bees will follow us all the way home."

As they drove east on Eighteenth Street, Doug said, "Jack is already known throughout the world. I downloaded his pictures and sent copies to my friends, Leonard in Ft. Worth, Roel in Holland, and Paul in Norway. All the department heads at work and our distributors got his picture in my e-mail yesterday."

Amy said, "I'm sure your Blackberry is working overtime. I'm surprised you haven't taught Jack how to operate it yet."

It was 9:30 A.M. when they turned south on University Boulevard, passing City Park, the band shelter, and Bromwell School. The students in gym classes were out on the playground where some students were engaged in a softball game.

Doug noted, "Rockies won again last night, maybe this really will be their year."

"Right, Doug, dream on," retorted Amy. As they drove by the Denver Botanic Gardens, they compared the flowers in their car with the display of flowers on sales stand along the entrance to the gardens.

Doug said, "You know I did have a strange dream last night. The whole family was in Aspen for Thanksgiving. But we didn't ski. It was snowing and we were playing football at beautiful Paepcke Park, a fitting venue, named after Chicago industrialist Walter Paepcke. Maddie and Gabby were the captains of the teams. One team was called Maddie's Munchkins and the other was Gabby's Goblins. Taylor kicked a field goal and I had a vision that Jack scored five touchdowns in one game. Will and Blake just laid in the snow and made angels by waving their arms in the snow. Is that weird or what? Why would anyone go to Aspen and not go skiing?"

Amy replied, "That is a bit strange. But I had a dream–mine was about Jack. He turned six years old and on his first day in school he went to Cherry Hills Village Elementary School. Mrs. Thomas was his teacher and he was beginning to read and manipulate your Blackberry computer. And, oh yes, he was singing in the school choir at a performance for all the parents."

Doug said, "I hope he wasn't singing the song entitled 'Wild Thing.' But who knows, we're likely to have many dreams about his future, and a few nightmares too."

As they turned east on Hampden and headed toward home, Doug asked, "What do you think we should get Jack for his first birthday?"

Amy replied, "Are you really thinking about that already? How about some play clothes or some furniture for his room?"

Doug replied, "I was hoping to get something that he really might use–like a PC, a world globe, or a set of golf clubs."

Amy started laughing, "Sure, something useful! This kid is in for a frightening ride."

It was 9:45 A.M. as the car turned right onto Elm Street heading toward home. The sun was high in the sky and spring appeared to be busting out everywhere. The cherry trees were in full bloom at the Ferguson's house and the crocus flowers were peeking through the grass on the Woodward's lawn. Even the Metz's snowball bush was beginning to bloom. Life had renewed itself, and yes, that wise person was right:

"Life is a continuous thread connecting one generation to the next."

Doug Kinney and his son, Jack, April 16, 2002

2007
The Softball Team

Top row – left to right: Douglas, Amy, Sue, Linda, Colby, Nancy, Pete (Holst), Pete (Hantman), Roger
Bottom row – left to right: Maddie, Blake, Will, Jack, Taylor, and Gabby

2006
The Grandchildren – *left to right:* Taylor Hantman, Maddie Hantman,
Will Holst, Blake Holst, Colby White, Gabby Kinney, Jack Kinney

2007
The Kinney Ski Team

2007
The Kinney Family

Standing – left to right: Colby White, Nancy Holst, Roger Kinney, Pete Hantman, Doug Kinney, Amy Kinney *Middle Row – left to right:* Gabby Kinney, Sue Kinney, Mary Louise Hubbard, Linda Hantman *Seated on the ground – left to right:* Maddie Hantman, Blake Holst, Pete Holst, Taylor Hantman, Will Holst, Jack Kinney

Epilogue

Not long ago the mail carrier delivered the results of my DNA test. I had anticipated the arrival of that package as if it were a long-awaited Christmas gift. Inside I received an official certificate, looking a great deal like a college diploma, with my own "Y-Chromosome Allele" and "Loci Designation DYS" numbers. In addition I received a colorful map showing the human migration (Haplogroups) as the first natives moved about the world. With my limited knowledge of genetics, I was especially pleased to have a four page explanation of the results.

So now, armed with an explanation and help from experts, I could proceed to compare my bloodlines with my ancestors. Geneticists are eager to point out that the results will "most likely estimate" the result when describing "a match." Accordingly, I proceeded with caution to match my markers with good results and growing confidence, confirming blood lines with my "Most Recent Common Ancestors."

A friend asked me what I was going to do with the test results. At that moment, his question rather startled me because I really hadn't thought much about it. There would be no life changing decisions based upon the test results. My quest for kinship didn't need scientific proof to be valid, but the results were worth knowing, nonetheless.

I already shared kinship with those relatives I had known in my lifetime and had felt it with those tales I'd heard over the years. For me, this newest certificate was just another artifact to place in my new storage chest where it would be available for another generation of Kinney family researchers, who might be more scientific-minded or who might even be able to use the knowledge to aid other Kinney kin in some sort of health-related matter long after the kin I know are gone.

That reminds me of a discussion I recently had with my grand-daughter, Maddie, when she and her sister, Taylor, had a sleepover at our house. Maddie came into my office and noticed a manuscript that I was preparing.

"What's that Grandpa?" was her inquiry.

"That's a chapter of our family's history; would you like to read it?" I replied.

"No thanks," said Maddie. "I can hardly read your writing, and besides, I'd rather go outside and play basketball with you and Taylor. Maybe I'll read it some other time."

After checking my damaged ego, I felt all right with Maddie's reaction. As a matter of fact, as I thought about it, the more I liked it. I have a natural respect for any person, especially young people, who have a reasonable set of priorities and stick with them. This book isn't going to cause any life-changing decisions nor impact her right now. It's more important for her to shoot some hoops and I'm pleased she wanted to do it with Taylor and me.

But someday, sometime, the grandchildren may want to read it—maybe use it for a reference or hopefully, share it with their grand-children. In the end, it's nice to know that it is here and will be available whenever the time is right. This book tells just a few tales of some of their kin—many more stories remain to be written, as their descendants will have their own "once upon a time" tales to tell, adding to the chapters of our family's kinship that began long ago.

Desiderata

The Desiderata has been used over the years as a means for an author to express his "desires" and "final will" for a concluding message to his family and, if appropriate, to his readers. John Kynne wrote his final will in 1572. Benjamin Kinnie wrote an extensive Desiderata in the later years of his life, about 1645. Deacon Thomas Keney gave his Desiderata to his children in 1755.

The Apologia of Robert Keayne was written as his last will and testament and published as a chapter in Publications of the Colonial Society of Massachusetts in 1952-56. It was considered to be so important (and popular) that it was reprinted as a separate text in 1964.

The following Desiderata has been assembled as an expression of advice from the works of many authors, and, summarized by the lives and works of various members of the Kinney family. Over the years, many family members have enhanced these principles, practiced them, and handed them forward to the next generation. These principles are offered with hopes that they will be preserved and shared with others in the years ahead.

❧ DESIDERATA ❧

❧ Respect the miracle of life. Protect, care for, and nurture your mind, body, and soul as your sacred temple. ❧ Be true to yourself. Share the joy and magnificence of friendship, love, and affection as precious gifts. ❧ Take personal responsibility for your actions. Enjoy your achievements, as well as your plans and expectations. ❧ Exercise caution in your business affairs, for the world is full of trickery and deception. ❧ Heed the lessons of time, family, and friends. Beyond a wholesome discipline and diversity, be gentle with yourself. Enjoy the humorous side of things. ❧ Embrace change and associate with those who live in harmony with science, nature, and new technology. ❧ Be kind and helpful to your children. Habits are likely to pass to other generations. ❧ Be at peace with God, whatever you conceive him to be. Whatever your happenstance, keep peace with your soul. ❧ With all its shams, drudgery, and broken dreams, it is still a beautiful world and every day, you have a fresh start. ❧ Be careful. Strive to be happy. ❧

Nancy (Kinney) Holst, Kate Hanley, and Linda (Kinney) Hantman, circa 1998

Credits & Acknowledgements

The author would like to thank the following people, institutions, and other resources for their support and generous assistance with the research for this project.

Personal collections:

The Genealogy works of Florence Keeney Robertson, M.A., 1947,
   Los Angeles, California.

The Kinne Historical and Genealogical Society, William Kinne, President,
   June 9, 1884, New York, New York.

The family records recorded by Manuel Kinne, 1820, Windham County, Connecticut.

The family records and correspondence of Julia Sayles Kinnie Giest, 1968,
   Griswold, Connecticut.

The family records and papers of Annabelle and Roland Kinney, Denver, Colorado.

The census data and family records of Rose Kinney, Colfax, Louisiana.

The family records of Stevens Park Kinney, Estes Park, Colorado.

Individual Contributors:

Trina Lambert, research, editing, and coaching, Englewood, Colorado.

Judith Evans Hanhisalo, historical research, Duxbury Massachusetts.

Beverly Raymond and Marilyn Dunham Labbe, genealogical research,
    Norwich, Connecticut.

Barbara and Charles J. Kall, historical research, Denver, Colorado.

Tony Verba, geographic research, Schuyler, Nebraska.

Lew Cady, literary assistance, Denver, Colorado.

Susan Maddock, historical research, Principal Archivist, King's Lynn, Norwich, England.

Mike McIntosh, document services, Denver, Colorado.

Ryan McKee, photography, General Manager, Rich Clarkson and Associates, LLC,
    Denver, Colorado.

Illustrations:

INDEPENDENCE Wayne City Landing, "Start of the Santa Fe Trail" in 1842
    by John Stobart, Image @1977 courtesy of Maritime Heritage Prints,
    100 Cummings Center, Suite 3351, Beverly, Massachusetts 1-800-989-3513
    www.Stobart.com

Family Birthday Party for Mary Lou, 2005, courtesy of Fritz Law, Denver, Colorado.

FRONTIER HOME, by Dan Paxton, circa 1978, courtesy of the Paxton family,
    Denver, Colorado.

The Kinney Family pictures archives, Estes Park, Colorado.

Libraries and Historical Institutions:

The Archive Center at the Town Hall, Susan Maddock, Principal Archivist,
    King's Lynn, England.

The Church of Jesus Christ of Latter Day Saints, The International
    Genealogical Department.

The Colorado History Museum, Stephen H. Hart Library, Rebecca Lintz, Director,
    Judith Steiner, Assistant Curator of Photography, Denver, Colorado.

The Denver Public Library, Western History Department, Shirley Amore, Librarian, James Jeffrey, Genealogy, Jim Kroll, References, Denver, Colorado.

The Englewood Public Library, Hank Long, Director, Carol Wilbur, History Department, Englewood, Colorado.

Family Tree, DNA Testing, Houston, Texas.

The Institute for Heraldic and Genealogical Studies, Cecil R. Humphery-Smith, OBE,FSA. and Dr. Richard C.F. Baker, FHG, Vice Principal, Canterbury, England.

The Killingly Historical Society, Marilyn Durham Labbe, Danielson, Connecticut.

The Koelbel Public Library, Lourie Christensen, Manager, Centennial, Colorado.

The Lighthouse Writers Workshop, Michael J. Henry, Executive Director, Andrea Dupree and Shari Cauldron, Denver, Colorado.

The Lynn Museums and Custom's House, Alison Gifford.

The Lynn Public Library of Andrew Carnegie, Linda Tree, Librarian.

The Lynn Town Hall, The Worshipful Mayor, Mrs. Ann Clery-Fox.

The New York Public Library, Geneology, Milstein Division, Paul LeClerc, President.

Norfolk Family History Society, Mrs. Rhona Kerswell, Director, Norwich, Connecticut.

The Peabody Essex Museum and the Phillips Library, Kathy Flynn, Salem, Massachusetts.

St. Elizabeth's and St. Nicholas Church, Reverend Christopher Ivory, Vicar, and Reverend Christopher Wood, Assistant Vicar. King's Lynn, England.

The Salem, Massachusetts Public Library, Loraine Jackson, Director.

The Schuyler Nebraska Museum, Nadine Bern, Director.

The Schuyler Nebraska Public Library, MeMe Smith, Director.

True's Yard, The North End Trust, Joanna Barrett, Manager, King's Lynn, England.

The University of Denver, Viva Program, Vonnie Wheeler, Director, Jean McGinnis and Lois Munson, Professors.

The Voluntown, Connecticut Historical Society, Judy Harpin, Author.

The Voluntown, Connecticut Public Library, Debra Fleet, Director.

References and Resources

Aiken, J.W. *Reminiscences of Lynn*. King's Lynn, England, 1865.

Andrews, A.T. *History of Nebraska*. Schuyler, NE: Schuyler Nebraska Museum, 1982.

Arlott, John and others. *Illustrated Guide to Britain*. London: Drive Publications, Limited, 1971.

Bailyn, Bernard. *The Apologia of Robert Keayne*. Gloucester, Massachusetts: Harper and Row, Reprinted 1970.

Barry, J.S. *History of Massachusetts*. Boston: Barton, Phillips, Sampson & Co., 1855.

Battley, Susan. *Mayors of Lynn*. State University of New York, 1981.

Bell, Mrs. N.S. *Pathways of the Puritans*. Norwood, Massachusetts: Old America Company, 1930.

Bickford, Christopher P. *Plainfield Transformed 1699-1999*. Plainfield Historical Society, 1999.

Black, Jeremy. *Historical Atlas of Britain*. Gloucestershire, England: Sutton Publishing, 2000.

Bodge, George Madison. *Soldiers in King Philip's War*. Boston: Rockwell and Churchill Press, 1906.

Bonfanti, Leo. *New England Indians*. Salem, Massachusetts: Old Saltbox Publisher, 1939.

Brinkley, Douglas. *History of the United States*. New York: Penguin Group, 1998.

Brown, Rev. Charles E. *Personal Reminiscences*. Combe Printing Company, 1893.

Campbell, Douglas, A.M. LLB. *The Puritans in Holland, England and America, Volumes I. & II.* New York and London: Harper and Brothers, 1902.

Carbaugh, Marsha Wilson. *The Barbour Collection of Connecticut Vital Records*. Genealogical Publications Company, 1708-1850.

Chernow, Ron. *Alexander Hamilton*. New York: The Penguin Group, 2004.

Clark, Sir George. *English History, A Survey*. Oxford University Press, 1971.

Cook, David L. *Seven Days at the Links of Utopia*. Utopia, Texas: 2006.

Coleman, R.V. *The First Frontier*. New York: Castle Books, 2005.

Davidson, Levette Jay. *The Literature of the Rocky Mountain West. 1803-1903*. Caldwell, Idaho: Caxton Printers, 1939.

Dickens, Charles. *A Child's History of England*. New York: Peter Fenclon, Collier & Son, 1950.

Earle, Alice Morse. *Customs and Fashions in Old New England*. New York: Charles Scribner's Sons, 1894.

Emerson, Frederick. *North American Arithmetic*. Boston: Boylston School, 1854.

Faris, John T. *Real Stories from Our History*. Boston: Grimes and Company, 1916.

Gordon, Dan. *Path of the Puritan*. Boston: Xulon Press, 2004.

Gordy, Wilbur F. *American Beginnings in Europe*. New York: Charles Scribner's Sons, 1922.

Green, John R. M.A. *History of the English People, Volumes 1-4*. Chicago: Donohue Henneberry & Co., No Date.

Guilliam, Barry. *King's Lynn, The First Thousand Years*. King's Lynn, Norfolk, England: The King's Lynn Town Guides, 1977.

Hall, W.P. *A History of England and the Empire Commonwealth*. Toronto: Hall, Albion & Pope, 1997.

Harris, John. *Saga of the Pilgrims*. Chester, Connecticut: The Globe Pequot Press, 1989.

Higgins, David. *The Antiquities of King's Lynn*. King's Lynn, Norfolk, England: Phoenix Publications, 2001.

Hillen, Henry James. *History of King's Lynn*. West Yorkshire, England: E.P. Publishing, Ltd., 1907.

Holcomb, Robert N. *Story of Connecticut*. New York: The Hartford Times, 1936.

Hubbard, William. *A Narrative of the Indian Wars in New England*. Boston: William Fessenden, 1814.

Huntley, Dana L. "British Heritage." *History Magazine Group*. Volume 29, No 1. "Hands Across the Sea" Series, pages 17-19. March, 2008.

James, Russell H. *The Making of a Connecticut Town – Voluntown*. Voluntown, Connecticut: Adkins Printing Company, 1996.

Jeremiah, Josephine. *The River Great Ouse and the River Cam*. West Sussex, England: Phillmore & Co. Ltd., 2006.

Kagan, Neil: Kinney, Karin and other contributing authors. *Concise History of the World*. Washington, D.C.: National Geographic Society, 2005

Larned, J.N. *History of England*. London: Houghton, Mifflin & Co., 1900.

Lewis, Jon E. *The Birth of Freedom*. New York: Gramercy Books, 2003.

Martins, Susan Wade. *History of Norfolk*. West Sussex, England: Butler & Tanner, Phillimore & Co. Ltd., 2003.

McWhirter, Norris. *Book of Millennium Records*. Toronto: Sterling Publications, 1999.

Mills, Lewis Sprague. *The Story of Connecticut*. New York: Charles Scribner's Sons, 1935.

Morrison, Dane Anthony and Schultz, Nancy. *Salem*. Boston: Northeastern University Press, 2004.

Neale, J.E. *Elizabeth I. and Her Parliaments, 1559-1581*. Oxford: Alden Press, 1953.

Noel, Thomas J. *Denver's Larimer Street*. Denver: Historic Denver, Inc., 1981.

Owen, Dorothy. *The Museums of King's Lynn*. London: Oxford University Press, 1984.

Paine, Thomas. *Common Sense*. New York: Barnes and Noble, 1995.

Perley, Sidney. *This History of Salem, Massachusetts*. Haverhill, Mass.: S. Perley, 1987.

Peterson, Charles J. *A History of the Wars of the United States*. New York: J.B. Smith, T. Lynch, 1859.

Philbrick, Nathaniel. *Mayflower*. New York: The Penguin Group, 2006.

Richards, Paul. *King's Lynn*. West Sussex, England: Butler and Tanner Ltd., Phillimore & Co. Ltd., 1997.

Richards, William. *History of King's Lynn, Volumes 1 and 2*. London: Balderson Paternoster and Row, 1812.

Roach, Marilynn. *The Salem Witchcraft Trials*. Boston: Houghton, Mifflin Company, 1996.

Roberts, Cokie. *Founding Mothers, The Women Who Raised Our Nation*. New York: Harper Collins Publishers, 2004.

Saul, Nigel. *Medieval England*. New York: Oxford University Press, 1997.

Summers, D. *The Great Ouse – History of a River Navigator*. West Sussex, England: Newton Abbot, 1973.

Thompson, John M. *The Revolutionary War*. National Geographic Society, 2004.

Upham, Charles W. *Salem Witchcraft*. New York: Dover Publications, 2000.

Wish, Harvey. *Society and Thought in Early America*. New York: Longman, Green and Company, 1958.

Woodward, W.E. *A New American History*. New York: The Literary Guild, 1937.

Kinneykinnook Home in Estes Park, Colorado

Moving On
Will, Colby, and Blake

Printed in the United States
135721LV00002B/3/P